An Illustrated Encyclopaedia

WONDERS *of* ANIMAL LIFE

also available by the same editor

An Illustrated World Gazetteer

Peoples of all Nations

Their Life Today and Story of Their Past

In 14 Volumes

Volume One
Abyssinia **to** Azerbaijan
Volume Two
Belgium **to** British Empire in America
Volume Three
British Empire in Asia **to** Canada
Volume Four
Ceylon **to** Dahomey
Volume Five
Danzig **to** England
Volume Six
Esthonia **to** France
Volume Seven
Georgia **to** Iceland

Volume Eight
India **to** Italy
Volume Nine
Japan **to** Mexico
Volume Ten
Monaco **to** Oman
Volume Eleven
Palestine **to** Rumania
Volume Twelve
Russia **to** Sin-kiang
Volume Thirteen
South Africa **to** The Ukraine
Volume Fourteen
The United States **to** Wales
with General Index

About the Editor

Sir John Alexander Hammerton (1871-1949) was an English statesman and author, best-known for his editorship of popular encyclopaedias published in the first half of the 20th century, such as the 10-volume New Book of Knowledge.

From 1914 to 1919, Hammerton was joint editor with HW Wilson of the periodical "The Great War: The Standard History of the All-Europe Conflict", published by the Amalgamated Press. It was lavishly illustrated with photographs and with realistic drawings which were sometimes hardly distinguishable from photographs.

He was also a contemporary and friend of Arthur Mee, about whom he wrote a biography.

An Illustrated Encyclopaedia

WONDERS *of* ANIMAL LIFE

by Famous Writers on Natural History

Volume Seven

Edited by

J.A. Hammerton

Over Three Thousand Illustrations from Photographs and Thirty-three Colour Plates

LOGOS PRESS, NEW DELHI

ISBN -13: 978-81-7268-175-3 (Set)
ISBN -10: 81-7268-175-5 (Set)

ISBN -13: 978-81-7268-176-0 (Vol. I)
ISBN -13: 978-81-7268-177-7 (Vol. II)
ISBN -13: 978-81-7268-178-4 (Vol. III)
ISBN -13: 978-81-7268-179-1 (Vol. IV)
ISBN -13: 978-81-7268-180-7 (Vol. V)
ISBN -13: 978-81-7268-181-4 (Vol. VI)
ISBN -13: 978-81-7268-182-1 (Vol. VII)
ISBN -13: 978-81-7268-183-8 (Vol. VIII)

ISBN -10: 81-7268-176-3 (Vol. I)
ISBN -10: 81-7268-177-1 (Vol. II)
ISBN -10: 81-7268-178-X (Vol. III)
ISBN -10: 81-7268-179-8 (Vol. IV)
ISBN -10: 81-7268-180-1 (Vol. V)
ISBN -10: 81-7268-181-X (Vol. VI)
ISBN -10: 81-7268-182-8 (Vol. VII)
ISBN -10: 81-7268-183-6 (Vol. VIII)

Edition : 2008

Printed & Published by

LOGOS PRESS

Building No. 4788-90, Street No. 23, Ansari Road, Darya Ganj, New Delhi-110 002 (India)

Phone : 23272187

Foreword

Here is not a 'natural history' in the accepted meaning of that description. There exist many and excellent natural histories and more than fifteen years ago the present editor was associated with the publication of one which, in its authoritative letter-press and profuse illustration, had wide acceptance. But it is undeniable that the general reader finds large and exhaustive treatises on animal life, encumbered with Latin names, somewhat hard reading, however fine their illustrations, if they are arranged on the approved scientific divisions—order, family, genus, species—into which naturalists split up animated nature. A proper natural history, however, must follow this method of treatment if it is to form the basis of a scientific knowledge of the subject.

Does the ordinary reader desire such knowledge? Does he require it?

The answer to both questions is a negative: emphatic in the first and modified in the second case. No matter how slightly youth is drawn to the conventional study of zoology, not even the forbidding scientific approach to natural history can rob it of its inherent fascination.

A boundless curiosity about the infinite diversity of creatures that share the life of the globe with him is a deep and abiding and a most natural trait in man. The stories of a Adam naming the beasts, and of the animals, two by two, going into the ark are ancient evidence of man's interest in his fellow-creatures of the so-called lower orders. A study of the life-histories of many animals and birds, fishes and reptiles, or of the astounding social systems of certain insects, is calculated to limit man's pride in himself as the incarnation of the highest intelligence or the finest physical product of the animal world. Especially is it likely to extend his sympathy to all lowly things that are living out their little days with him upon this planet. It lies at the root of humanitarianism. Interest in animal life is never an idle curiosity, and it may prove more absorbing than any other interest that could be named.

Not, then, to add a new natural history to a list already adequate, but to meet this universal and most healthy interest in the astonishing realities and the mysterious ways of the animal kingdom is the purpose of WONDERS OF ANIMAL LIFE. Its title adequately suggests its scope: to enquire into and to illustrate all that is of uncommon interest in the life of the animal kingdo n.

While the reader will find in our pages a constantly changing panorama of animal life, with no more apparent order than the naturalist finds in the Brazilian jungle, he can hardly fail to be interested and he is certain to be instructed, for though the only method that is observed throughout our chapters is a rough alternation of interest, now in mammals, next in reptiles, then in birds, fishes, insects, each chapter of this work is written either by one of the leading specialists on his subject or—where expert knowledge is less needed than vividness of descriptive style—by a popular author.

A glance at the list of contributors, their scientific and literary credentials, and the subjects allotted to them in our scheme, will indicate to the reader that though WONDERS OF ANIMAL LIFE is designedly popular in its appeal, it is not the less authoritative in being more entertaining than the conventional sort of natural history.

Never before has there been brought together so representative and so varied a collection of photographic documents covering the whole range of animated nature. In the last decade, and particularly within the latter part of it, naturalists have acquired an immense amount of new knowledge, and marked progress has been made in recording the wild life of the world by means of direct photography.

The exploits of the camera experts employed by the organizers of some of the great 'nature and adventure' films—'Simba' is a fine example—that have fascinated millions throughout the world in these years have produced so rich a body of material for illustrating such a work as this that editorially we are in a more favoured position than any of our predecessors in the same field and we hope the reader will agree with us in thinking that we have taken advantage of that fortunate circumstance for his entertainment and instruction.

J.A. HAMMERTON

Publisher's Note

We are happy to present the illustrated encyclopaedia—Wonders of Animal Life—to the learned readers. As its title suggests, it attempts to enquire into the astonishing realities and the mysterious ways of life of the animal kingdom—mammals, reptiles, birds, fishes and insects.

Presented in eight volumes, each chapter of this work is written either by one of the leading specialists on the subject or—where expert knowledge is less needed than vividness of descriptive style—by a popular author. The text is enriched with a representative and varied collection of photographic documents covering the whole range of animated nature. Our other notable illustrated encyclopaedias include *The Living Animals of the World* (4 volumes), *The Wonders of the World* (4 volumes), *Peoples of All Nations* (14 volumes), and *The Earth and Its Inhabitants* (8 volumes).

TABLE OF CONTENTS

Volume One

List of Colour Plates

Volume Two

List of Colour Plates

Volume Three

List of Colour Plates

Volume Four

List of Colour Plates

Volume Five

List of Colour Plates

Volume Six

List of Colour Plates

Volume Seven

List of Colour Plates

Volume Eight

List of Colour Plates

Chapter CXVII

The Animal Life of Deserts

By Dr. Marion Newbigin

Author of "Animal Geography"

A DESERT, the dictionary tells us, is a desolate, barren region which is treeless and waterless. A more precise definition could be given; but from the point of view of animal life it is true that all deserts are characterised by their scanty growth of plants and the scarcity of free water. Now all animals require water in some form, and all depend ultimately on the plant world for food. Thus it would not appear that the desert habitat is a favourable one; in point of fact, however, the deserts of the world carry faunas at once more diversified and richer in individuals than might be expected.

In trying to explain these facts we must begin with the broad features of the desert plants. Two of these are outstanding. True desert plants tend to have short, stunted stems, with small leaves, or no leaves, while spines are frequent. All these are obvious results of the limited water supply. Even more important is the fact that they do not—in the desert proper—form a close cover over the surface. In the forests of the world the branches of the trees touch or overlap, producing what foresters call a closed canopy. In the grasslands the herbs and grasses form, in the upper layers of the soil, a felted mass of underground stems or roots—the characteristic turf. But in deserts bare surfaces of sand or stones intervene between the scattered plants, which may stand at considerable distances from each other.

It might be supposed that the plants are occupying ground where some subterranean water is present, while the intervening bare patches overlie drier areas. But this is by no means necessarily the case. It has been shown that a stunted desert plant may have roots which, in proportion to the height of the plant above the surface, can only be described as of enormous length, and branch and spread in all directions. In other words, desert plants show a development of the underground parts which is in striking contrast to the restricted growth of the aerial shoots. The bare patch surrounding each plant is thus not really empty, but is the zone tributary to the plant which occupies the centre. The deep layers of the soil may contain only very limited quantities of water, and the size of the zone occupied by the roots, that is the horizontal spacing of the plants, depends both on the amount of available water present in the soil and the needs of the plants.

Again, many shrubby desert plants store a greater or less amount of water in their aerial tissues, and the amount so stored, as in some cactuses, may be large. So far as the plants are concerned the object of the storage is to provide for the strain of flowering and fruiting; but it means that they form reservoirs which can be tapped by animals, or on occasion even by man, as with the candelabra cactuses of the Arizona deserts. Dry as desert areas may seem, therefore, we have to remember the existence of this miniature drainage system. The wide-spreading roots of the plants collect diffused ground-water over a large area, and this water is passed up into the aerial shoots whose compact form ensures bulk storage.

Such perennial shrubby plants are not, however, the only ones found in deserts. Few if any deserts are completely rainless, even if rain only falls in small amounts and at irregular intervals. Almost all, in consequence, carry at certain seasons, or even only in certain years, some short-lived plants. These may be true ephemerals, running through their life history from seed to seed with great rapidity; or they may be forms able to exist for long periods underground as resting buds, throwing up leaves and flowers when the rains come, and dying down again as the surface dries out. Such plants, because water is plentiful during their short period of activity, often produce succulent leaves and sometimes fruits containing considerable amounts of water, such as water melons. Because they depend upon the water contained in the upper layers of the soil, derived directly from the rains, they do not show

W. S. Berridge

JACKAL OF THE NORTH AFRICAN DESERTS

Found both well within the desert region and also on its fringe, the jackal is rather like a dog in appearance and is, like a dog, related to the wolf, though a much smaller animal. Its prevailing tint is a yellow grey to harmonise with a desert background.

"SHIPS OF THE DESERT" DEALING WITH BIG LOADS IN THE WASTES OF AUSTRALIA

Not only is the camel's celebrated ability to endure for a long period without drinking responsible for its suitability to desert travel. As important as this quality is its possession of pad-like hoofs especially adapted for treading on sand. These pads spread out and rest on a large surface each time they are put to the ground and in this way a good speed can be kept up on the loose surface. The above photographs show camels successfully used for transport work in the sandy scrub of Australia's desert interior.

to the same extent the open spacing of the more permanent desert plants.

These two kinds of plants constitute both the basal food supply and an important element in the water supply of the desert animals. Some desert forms indeed seem never to drink at all, but to depend on the fluid taken in with their food, or the dew which covers it. This is probably true of gazelles and various small rodents among mammals, and is undoubtedly true of many insects and other invertebrates.

Few deserts are, however, so completely arid as to be entirely devoid of springs or water-holes, and the rare and local rains may give rise to temporary streams, flowing for a few hours or days. In many cases also the great deserts of the world are ringed round or margined by lofty mountain chains; these feed streams able to penetrate a certain distance into the arid area, before sinking into the desert sands, where their water ceases to be available till once more brought to the surface by the roots of plants, or by man in wells. Such localised supplies of free water make it possible for the desert to carry animals which do require to drink, and even demand considerable quantities of water.

Since, however, these supplies are obtainable only at considerable intervals—of space or time—the water-demanding animals must display special adaptations. Many of them are able to store water within their bodies, so that while they drink deeply when occasion offers, they can do without further drinking for a considerable time. The camel, with water-storing cells within its stomach, is of course the outstanding example of this; but there are others.

Many reptiles, animals as a rule tolerant of desert conditions, are able to store water in various organs and cavities of the body, and primitive peoples in various parts of the world have found by experience that in certain of the large tortoises, some lizards, and so on, these body fluids are quite drinkable, and form a valuable source of supply in arid regions. As contrasted with reptiles, frogs and toads as a rule avoid deserts, for the adults require generally a moist atmosphere, and the eggs are usually laid in water in which the tadpole larvae undergo development. But some striking exceptions occur. An Australian frog, living in the arid central area, is regularly sought by the aborigines for the water which it stores within its body-cavity. This frog (*Chiroleptes*) makes a burrow in which it lies, and it has been remarked that the inner walls of the burrow were moist, even when it was excavated in hard, sun-baked clay. The moisture presumably escaped from the skin of the animal, which is swollen up with the water absorbed, and we seem to have here an ingenious device by which the creature can produce for itself a moist atmosphere, even under highly arid conditions.

Apart from special adaptations of such kinds, most desert animals economise water by seeking to diminish natural loss. One method of doing this in

H. Shepstone

E.N.A

QUICK TRANSIT AND FOOD FROM THE SAME BEAST : CAMELS TO RIDE OR MILK

The so-called dromedary is really not a special race of camel, distinguished by the formation of its hump, as is often supposed, but an animal bred for speed. The name means a " runner " and the animal so referred to is always of the Arabian and thus of the one-humped kind. Below we see three Arabs with their fast mounts in the desert. Notice the queer saddles contrived for the camels peculiarly awkward gait. Above is a camel being milked. As supplying both food and transport the camel's importance to the desert folk may be well understood.

E.N.A.

BACTRIAN CAMELS NEGOTIATE SNOW AND SAND IN THE ASIAN DESERTS

Bactrian camels are more stoutly built and considerably shorter in the leg than the Arabian camels which break their legs very easily on uneven ground. Indeed these last are only fitted for travelling on sand, whereas the Bactrian can cope with snow and rock as well as the sandy wastes of Central Asia which are its home. Here we see (bottom) a caravan starting for Mongolia through the snow and (top) a caravan in the sands of the great Gobi Desert, where dust storms are sometimes formidable obstacles in the way of travel.

E.N.A.

ANIMALS OF THE ASIATIC WILDS: TIBETAN YAK AND WILD ASSES OF THE GOBI

In the desolation of Tibet the yak picks up a living and survives the rigours of great altitude, great cold and country which is, in many places, rocky and unfertile. The lower photograph shows a domesticated yak with its Tibetan master. These animals are very useful for transport over the dangerous mountain tracks. The upper illustration is of a herd of wild asses galloping in alarm from the photographer in the grim desert called Gobi. These animals live in small herds and, as a rule, keep to the open where their swiftness can keep them safe.

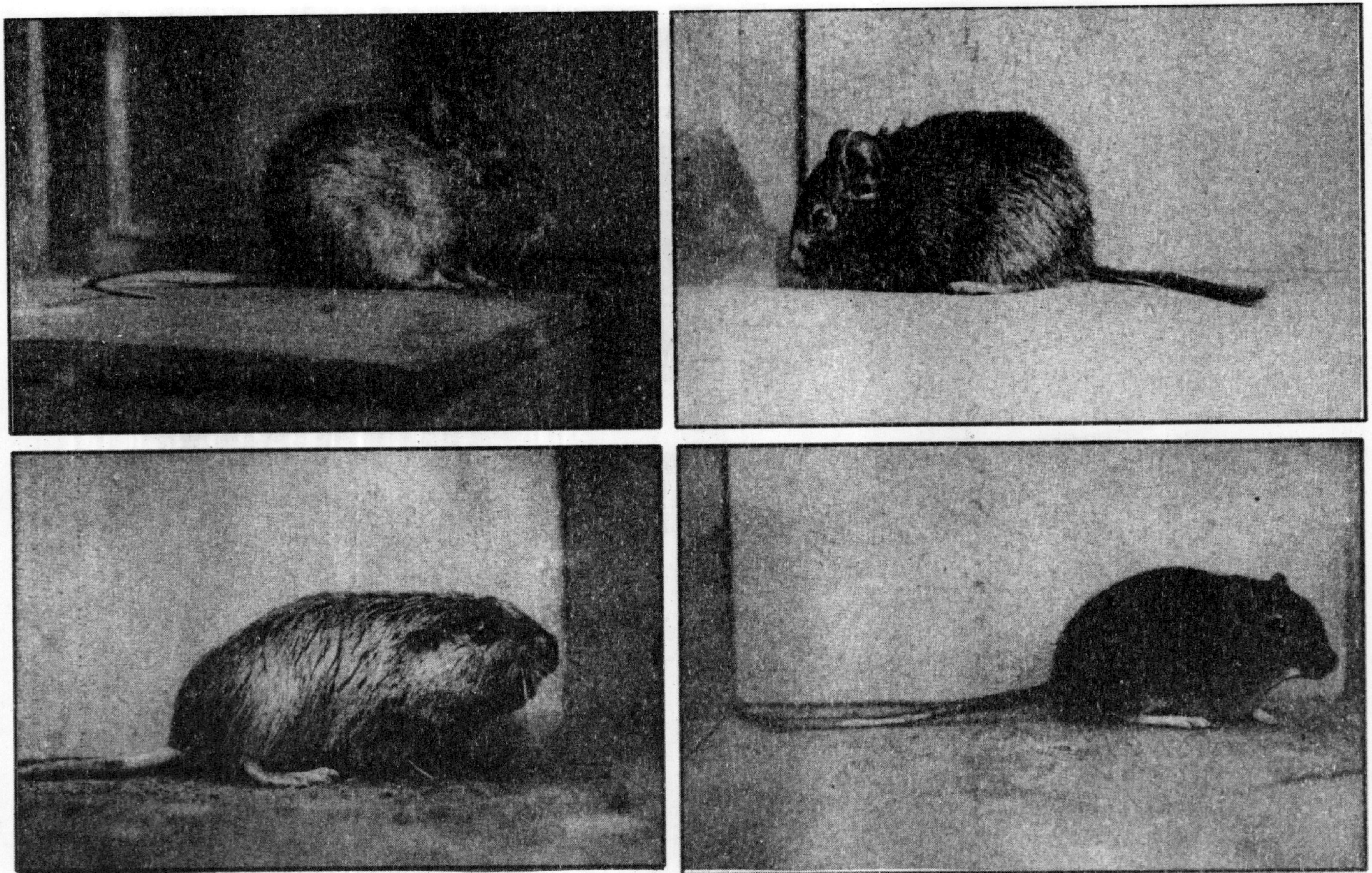

W. S. Berridge

LITTLE FURRED DWELLERS IN WASTE PLACES: THE TUCO-TUCO, THE GERBIL AND THE OCTODONT

In the more barren territory of South America there is a little rat-like, burrowing animal (bottom left). From its strange cry, uttered under the ground, it is called the tuco-tuco. The colour is neutral. The Cape gerbil (bottom right) is also a dweller in desert places, burrowing in sandy plains. But if cultivation reaches the fringe of its domain farmers have found to their cost that it will soon change its habitat and become a serious nuisance to their agriculture. Above is (top left) another breed of gerbil. It belongs to a large family found in both Africa and Asia. The top right-hand photograph shows an octodont, one of a strange race of desert creatures inhabiting the mountains of the Sahara.

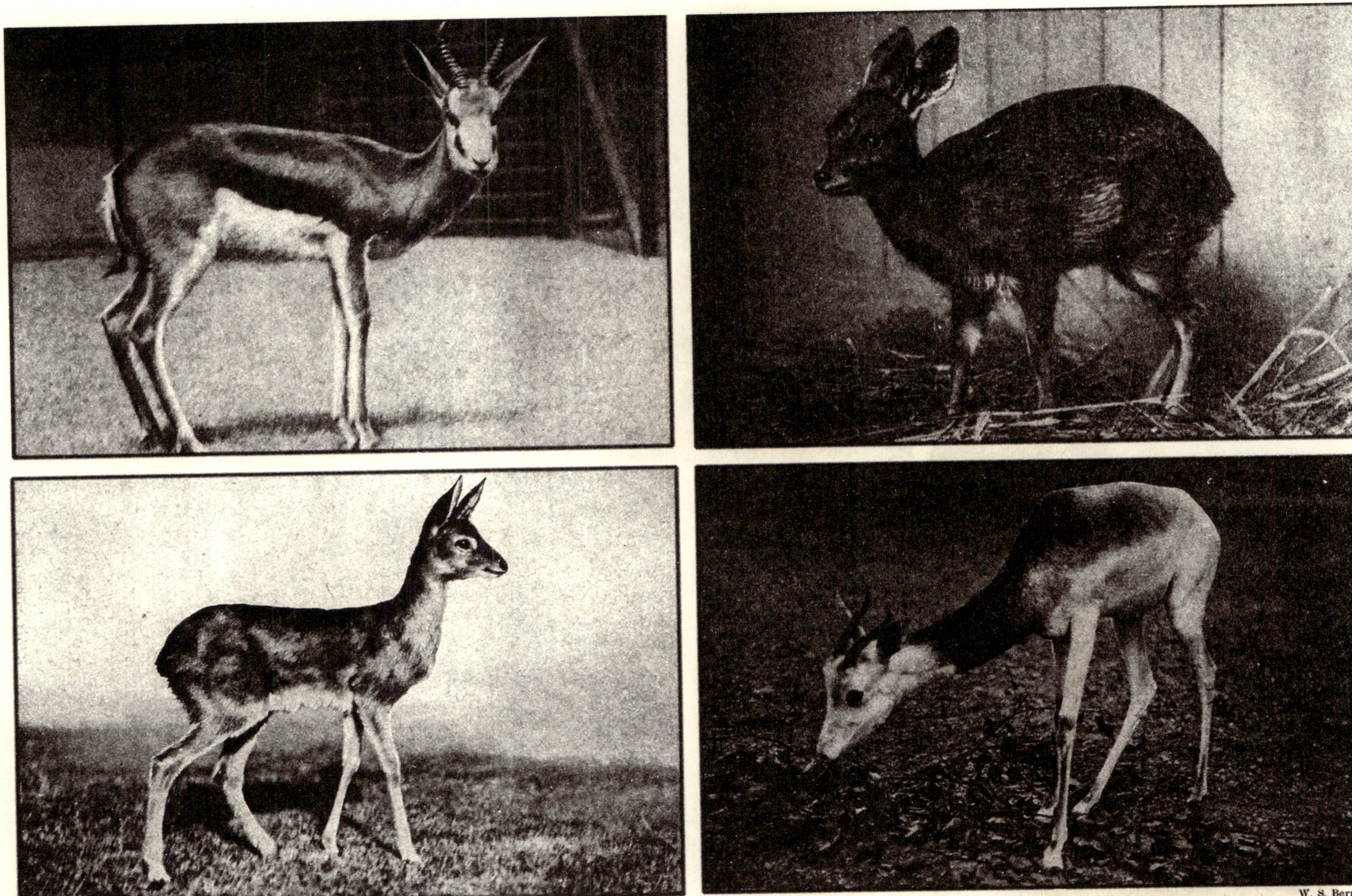

W. S. Berridge

STERNBOK, RED-NECKED GAZELLE, SPRINGBOK AND GRYSBOK OF THE GREAT WASTES OF CENTRAL AFRICA

A desert, in the usual meaning of the word, is a waterless district. But no desert is always entirely free from water, and in many places that are regarded as deserts, rain falls heavily—though irregularly. The various animals that live in barren districts are adapted for taking water either at long intervals or from the specialised desert plants that act as natural reservoirs. It is to be remembered that there are often isolated water holes well known to the local fauna if little known to man. Our four photographs show (bottom left) a sternbok, a red-necked gazelle (bottom right), a springbok (top left) and a grysbok (top right).

the hot deserts of the world is by the acquisition of the nocturnal habit. Because of the rapid radiation, desert temperatures fall quickly after sundown, and many desert animals, such as the lion, hyaena, desert fox, most insects, scorpions and spiders, and so on, seek shelter during the heat of the day when evaporation is at a maximum, and become active when the cooler night air acts as a check, and the dew gives sufficient moisture for small creatures. On the other hand animals with thickened skins, or some form of protective covering, often show as much indifference to sun heat as do plants like cactuses, which have also a much thickened cuticle. Thus desert beetles run about in the full glare of the sun, being apparently sufficiently protected against loss of water by the hard wing-covers which form a sheath over the greater part of the body

THE thickened and tubercular scales of many desert lizards are possibly an analogous adaptation, the agamas of the North African and Asiatic deserts having keeled and spiny scales, almost like a coat of armour On the other hand, in the curious moloch lizard of Australia the spines which cover the body are said to be hydroscopic, sucking up water like blotting-paper. They would seem, therefore, rather to be a means of enabling the creature to absorb rain-water, than a device for preventing loss of water.

A more thorough-going adaptation than the nocturnal habit, or the acquisition of a protective coat, is the power of aestivation, that is of passing into the resting state during periods of exceptional drought We have seen that many of the desert plants, either as seeds or as resting buds, can pass months or even years in the passive state, awakening at once if rain falls The desert snails have in many cases acquired a similar power of becoming quiescent as their host-plants die down, remaining in this state till awakened by a moistening of the atmosphere. Curators of museums have sometimes been astonished to find that what they thought were neatly-mounted specimens of snail-shells have started to creep over their mounts, the snail within, though shrunken and deeply withdrawn into the shell, having retained, even after the lapse of years, the power of reviving. One Australian snail plugs the mouth of its shell with a morsel of clay before beginning its dry season sleep, much as Indian fakirs are said to be able to pass into a state of suspended animation after carefully plugging the nostrils.

This power, as indeed one would expect, is particularly marked in aquatic forms.

W. S. Berridge

BANDICOOT AND CAVIES

The little rabbit-eared bandicoot (bottom) of Australia seems to retreat before the march of cultivation so much is it a creature of the untamed wild. The Patagonian cavy (top) inhabits very dry country but is also disappearing as cultivation advances.

Pools and patches of water form from time to time in desert areas, to disappear sooner or later under the influence of evaporation. Such temporary accumulations of water often display a wealth of small and simple animals, such as crustacea, molluscs, and others. All these, again, show certain analogies to the short-lived rain plants of the desert. Thus the resting forms may be eggs, comparable to the seeds of the ephemeral plants ; or the adults may bury themselves deeply in the clay or baked mud, when they may be compared to the underground resting buds of the perennial herbs. The great rapidity with which growth takes place when water is supplied is another feature common to both plants and animals. Some simple aquatic crustacea found in the Australian desert have been observed to grow to their full length of over 2½ inches within a fortnight of the time when the rain led to the hatching of the eggs.

Accelerated development of this kind is a common feature of the simpler animals of the desert, both terrestrial and aquatic, and is, of course, a response to the uncertainty of the rainfall. It means that the

W. S. Berridge

CREEPING CREATURES OF THE BURNING SANDS: ZONURE AND SAND SKINK

From some of the hottest parts of Africa and also from Madagascar come the zonures or girdle-tailed lizards of which we have a specimen in the lower photograph. Above is an ocellated sand skink found in North Africa. It is wonderfully adapted to a life on burning sands and, though not a quick mover above ground can bury itself with such astonishing celerity that it has the appearance of swimming through the sand. On occasion it will burrow several feet below the surface in an extraordinarily short time.

Thorny-tailed mastigure

Blue-tongued lizard

Common skink

Heloderm

Grey monitor

Stump-tailed lizard

QUEERLY FORMED ANIMALS THAT CAN LIVE IN CONDITIONS OF GREAT HEAT AND DRYNESS

Many of the desert creatures seek the shelter of rock or burrow during the heat of the day and come out during the comparatively cool night which very rapid radiation causes in desert regions. But others do not seem to mind the heat or the intense glare of the day-time at all. Many of the monitors and lizards are in this category, and we find their skins are peculiarly adapted for standing the effects of very strong sunshine. Notice particularly the stump-tailed lizard (bottom right) which has a skin rather like a pineapple. Photos by W. S. Berridge.

E.N.A.

H. Shepstone

DESERT TORTOISE FOUND SIXTY MILES FROM WATER AND AN IGUANA

Living in the Colorado Desert and sometimes found as much as sixty miles from any known source of surface water this desert tortoise (bottom) is a wonderful example of adaptation to special circumstances. It lives and thrives where it would seem that animal life was impossible. The upper photograph is of two land iguanas, desert dwellers whose mouths can deal with cactus leaves which are not only leathery but covered with sharp spines. But nevertheless these plants yield life-giving moisture to animals that can eat them.

W. S. Berridge

LLAMAS IN THE DESERTS OF PERU AND THEIR WILD RELATIVE THE GUANACO

In South America, and peculiar to that continent, the llama (bottom) represents the camel family. It has no hump and its teeth are rather different from those of the camel. The llama is really a breed, domesticated for centuries, of the guanaco (top) which is about the same size as the llama, but usually has darker hair. It is found in bleak mountainous districts where large herds congregate together. Like the camel, the domesticated guanaco, or llama, is used both as a beast of burden and for milking.

reproductive stage is reached rapidly, so that if the normal condition of aridity once more supervenes, and food ceases to be available for the adults, eggs at least are left to continue the species. If, however, in any particular part of a desert area the rains are unusually long-continued and heavy, some of the terrestrial animals may reproduce to such an extent that there is not room for all, and mass migration to surrounding areas may take place. This at once raises the question why desert animals remain in surroundings which seem so unfavourable, when they might move out to lands where life is easier.

But even the mere putting of the question gives us a hint of the fallacy which it involves. So far from it being true that life would be easier for most desert animals in lands of greater rainfall, we find that the more closely they are suited to desert life, the more difficult it is for them to live elsewhere. We have already noted some of the characteristics of the desert plants, particularly the scattered—or open—distribution of those not directly dependent on rain. In addition to this bareness, the desert surface, because of the general absence of running water, is of remarkably uniform relief. Wind may pile up sand-dunes against obstructions, open valleys mark the site of the wadis or temporary streams. But that dissection of the surface which is so marked in lands possessing high rainfall and permanent streams is absent, and with it the variety of vegetation possible on a diversified surface.

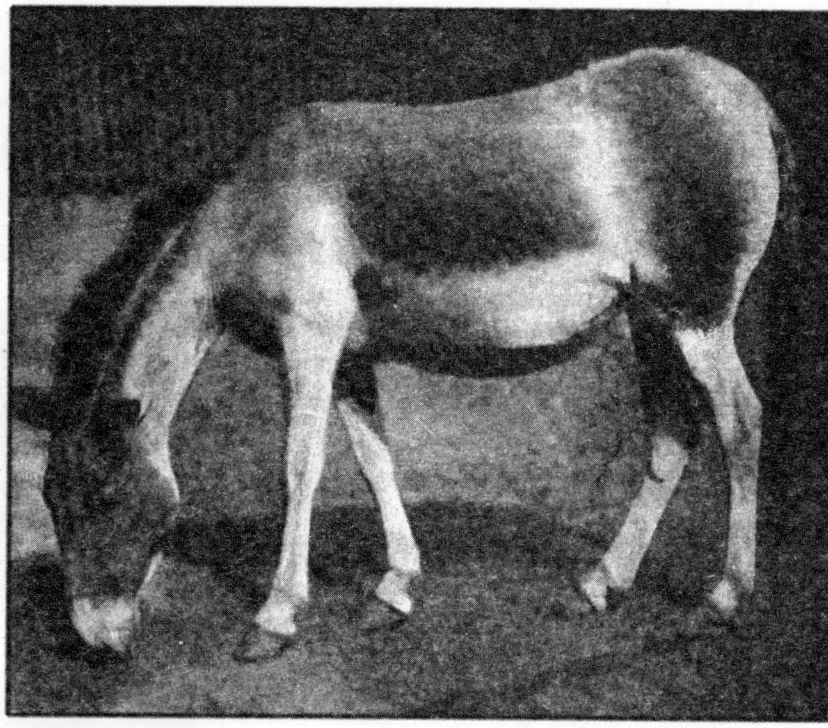

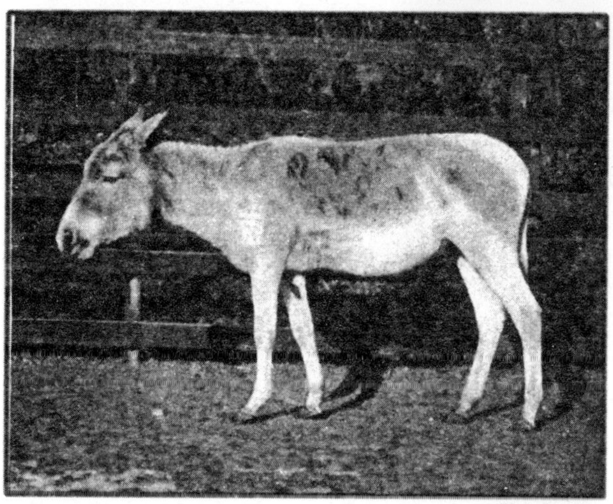

W. S. Berridge

ONAGER OF THE BLEAK STEPPES AND THE KIANG

Over the barren steppes of Asia roam the wild asses called onagers which are smaller than the wild asses of Africa. They are of a light sand colour which harmonises with their rather arid surroundings. The upper photograph shows the kiang of Tibet.

The more highly organized desert animals are structurally adapted for swift movement over its vast, uniform surfaces. Even those birds which have well-developed wings, like the desert larks and the sand grouse, habitually run more than they fly. The true running birds, those with aborted wings, are mainly inhabitants of arid areas, the African ostrich being an outstanding example Many kinds of desert insects, again, especially beetles, have lost the power of flight, but run swiftly over the sand. Where the animals are incapable of sustained running movements they are usually burrowers, with limbs fitted for shovelling away the loose sand. The North African skink lizards, for example, are so beautifully fitted for life in loose sand that they are described as "swimming" through it.

All such adaptations, of great value in the desert, are often a handicap in damper country, carrying richer vegetation and having more varied relief. The camel, with its padded toes, walks easily over the desert sands, and its long legs, less closely tied to the body than in many others of the great ungulates, enable it to take long strides, and on occasion to move swiftly. But on wet ground it is very helpless, apt to slip and break its long legs. A damp atmosphere also seems to cause it great discomfort.

THE most typical rodents of deserts are jerboas, small burrowing animals with long hind legs by means of which they take flying leaps. They are very defenceless, but find safety in the desert, where they remain in their burrows during the day, emerging at night to feed. Like most desert animals they have very acute sight and hearing, and habitually feed in a semi-erect position, carrying their food to the mouth with their short fore-paws. This attitude gives them a wider range of vision. Life in an area of dense vegetation would be difficult for such animals, for they could not perceive an enemy approaching, nor take the characteristic leaps which carry them to safety in the burrows. The Egyptian jerboa, indeed, is said to be so closely adapted to dry conditions that rain or a damp atmosphere causes it to pass into a torpid condition—a very striking reversal of the aestivating process already described as common with many of the desert animals.

Another adaptation common among desert animals which must diminish their power of spreading into adjacent regions is found in their coloration. This is very often yellowish or sandy, which makes the animals inconspicuous in their natural habitat, but would betray them elsewhere.

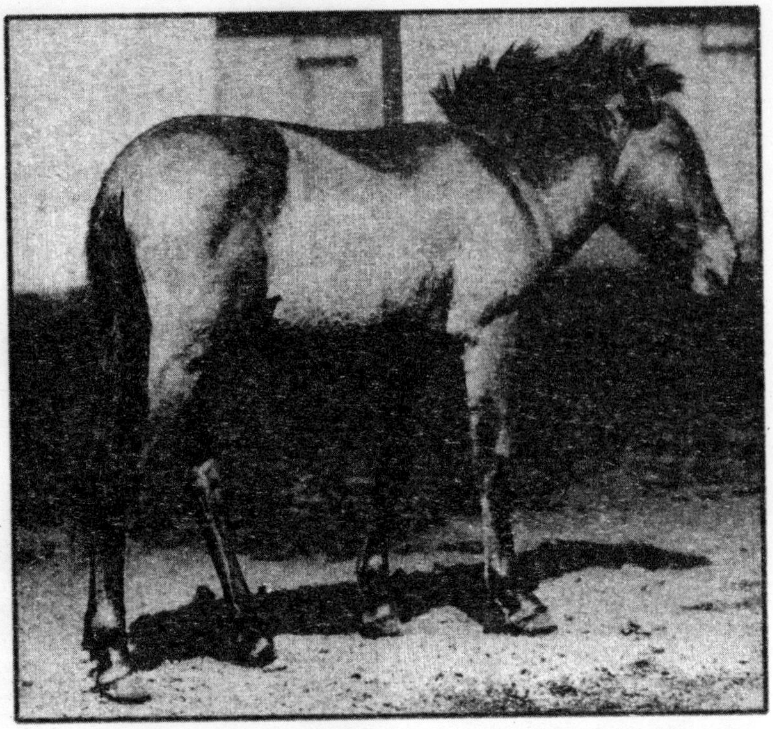

E.N.A.

CAMEL TRANSPORT AND THE WILD HORSE OF MONGOLIA

About three miles an hour is a fair pace for a baggage camel when loaded. Loaded is certainly the term to use about the animal in the lower photograph which is carrying Arab girls across the North African desert. The upper photograph shows a specimen of Przevalsky's wild horse. This strain, though thought to be impure, probably comprises the last really wild horses left.

There are, however, cases where the adaptations to desert life are much less marked, and the limitation to a single type of habitat correspondingly less striking. We have mentioned the lion as a desert mammal; but at the present time it is not restricted to arid areas, either in Asia or Africa. But the lion is an animal perfectly adapted to the predatory life, and possessed of such strength and intelligence that it is not limited to a particular kind of prey. It is apparently an example of a successful form which has been able to colonise areas other than the arid tracts in which its main characteristics were first fixed.

Certain small herbivorous forms afford examples of another condition. Desert snails, and some kinds of locusts which seem to have their home in the desert, at times, or even periodically, swarm outwards to the more productive lands on the desert margin. It is possible that some of these are forms in the act of increasing their range. In other cases

Chas. Barrett

W. S Berridge

DORCAS GAZELLE AND ANTS' NESTS IN THE AUSTRALIAN BUSH

The Dorcas gazelle (bottom) is a desert dwelling animal of North Africa and Arabia, and remarkable for the speed with which it covers the ground when frightened. The upper photograph was taken in a hot, barren part of the Australian bush and shows the strange crater-like nests built by the ants there.

the invaders seem to disappear as suddenly as they made their appearance.

In trying to explain such cases we have to recall what has been already said in regard to the power which the rain-plants of deserts have of lying dormant in times of drought, and of the way in which some plant-eating animals share this power. As a rule, however, the predatory animals which feed upon the plant-eaters do not display this characteristic. Thus a prolonged period of drought, followed by exceptionally heavy rains, leads to a rapid growth of plants, and a correspondingly rapid multiplication of plant-eating animals; but there may be a marked lag before the predatory forms, which have been thinned by the years of famine, make their appearance in any numbers. Now the normal rate of reproduction of the plant-eaters is such as to allow for, as it were, a certain percentage loss; if snails and locusts did not reproduce faster than the birds which fed upon them, both groups would cease to exist. Thus the numbers of the herbivorous forms may show a very marked increase, and migration takes place.

In some such fashion we may explain the appearance from time to time, often at a fairly regular interval of years, of swarms of locusts in cultivated lands. These lands have had both their flora and fauna greatly altered by human effort, and the locusts, and, if to a far less-marked extent, the migrating desert snails, may become a veritable plague. But one point of interest is that there is no very satisfactory evidence to show that the invaders can maintain themselves. Such lands contain a larger number of predatory animals than the deserts, and these, if man had not reduced their numbers, would probably exterminate the immigrants. In such cases it is not the fact that the desert animals are structurally unfitted for life in better-watered lands but rather that there is a smaller number of enemies to be feared there.

H. Shepstone

SWARM OF LOCUSTS DARKENING THE AIR AND HUNGRILY PURSUED BY A SQUADRON OF STORKS

This is such a terrible swarm of locusts as is often mentioned in the Old Testament, and both these photographs were taken in Palestine. Swarms of locusts comprising millions of individuals—in some cases hundreds of millions—come up like rain clouds, with a favouring wind. The whole sky may be darkened with their passing. In fact, it is plain that the old Hebrew writers regarded locusts as one of the most horrible things upon the earth, for these insects are constantly used as a standard of comparison for the loathly or the dreadful. The right-hand photograph shows that the insects do not have it all their own way. A company of storks is in hot pursuit of the swarm.

Chapter CXVIII

Creatures that Change the Landscape

By F. Martin Duncan

Librarian to the London Zoological Society

We are, I think, as a rule, too apt to take this world and all that it implies for granted. We know, of course, that countless ages have gone to its making; that marvellous changes in its structure have taken place since, some time and somehow, in the dim and distant past it started on its course, and that all the forces of Nature have been employed to shape and mould it into the fruitful earth we inherit to-day. Yet we do not always remember, perhaps, that the process of evolution is still going on; that Nature is still at work, here building up, there breaking down, using as her tools the wind and the rain, the beating waves and the flowing streams, the frost, the snow and the heat of the sun's rays; even living creatures are pressed into service and have their part to play in the ever-changing, ever-shifting scene.

Most of the changes brought about by Nature's living agents are the result of the activity of numbers of the lesser and humbler creatures of the earth; for although a large herd of African elephants in their periodical treks across country will leave their mark upon the landscape by breaking down and destroying the trees in mimosa plantations, and a migrating herd of springbok will lay waste large tracts of land over which they have passed, the effects produced by these quadrupeds upon vegetation are as nothing compared to the devastating achievements of a swarm of Oriental locusts or the disastrous operations of vast armies of North American cicadas.

Fortunately the visitations of these terrible insects are not of annual occurrence. Migratory locusts, in overwhelming numbers, make their appearance in Eastern countries only at fairly long intervals, though when one of their occasional invasions takes place the havoc they create is appalling. A huge, dark cloud, composed of incalculable numbers of insects, will suddenly appear and settle down upon the land, and in the space of a few hours the raiding hordes will have completely cleared the ground of every living green thing. When we learn that in 1889 a swarm of locusts estimated to be some two thousand square miles in extent passed over the Red Sea, and twenty-four hours later another, even larger, swarm was observed flying in the same direction, we realize how the face of the earth can be revolutionised by the combined forces of small, insignificant creatures that individually are comparatively powerless.

Myriads of young locusts, before they have acquired their wings, will often migrate on foot, moving over the land like a living flood, destroying every scrap of vegetation in their victorious march, leaving ruin and desolation in their wake—"the land is as a Garden of Eden before them, and behind them a desolate wilderness."

The American cicadas almost equal the migratory locusts in their power of turning fertile land into a howling waste. These remarkable insects (which are allied to the *Hemiptera*, or bugs, and are not locusts, as they are often erroneously called) are noted both for their musical talents and for being, as far as is known, the longest lived of all insects. The male insects alone, by the way, are provided with the drum-like instruments that produce the peculiar "song" that has been likened to the whistle of a locomotive and a noise resembling the sound of a distant threshing machine combined with the croaking of frogs! The females of the species are completely dumb—a fact that inspired the famous couplet perpetrated by a cynical poet:

> "Happy the cicadas' lives
> Since they all have voiceless wives."

The most notorious of these musical insects is the North American *Cicada septemdecim* that appears in its millions in certain districts once, approximately, in every seventeen years—and "that once too often," as a victimised Kentucky farmer said.

The life-history of the cicada is a most remarkable one. The adults are stout, heavy-bodied insects with strongly developed beaks, large, bulging eyes

H. Shepstone

BEETLES FEEDING ON A PEACH

One of the finest fruits in the world is endangered in the United States by a kind of beetle. In three years the number increased so enormously that a gallon and a third of them could be taken from each of 156 trees in a New Jersey orchard.

Natural History, N.Y.

FLIGHT OF LOCUSTS IN THE PHILIPPINES

One of the many safeguards against the annihilation of life by the locusts is the sea. A sudden change of wind may mean the safe drowning of an entire swarm, especially when islands are being attacked. This remarkable photograph was taken in the Philippine Islands and shows how the whole sky is covered. The landscape will very shortly be covered too.

and wings that fold over the back, tentwise, like the wings of a moth. The females possess stout, horny-cased ovipositors, or egg layers, complete with saw-like cutting instruments, with which they drill neat holes in the buds and twigs of convenient trees; and in these incisions they proceed forthwith to deposit their eggs to the tune of some four or five hundred apiece. The cicada grubs, on hatching, promptly drop to the ground and disappear from view, having burrowed their way beneath the soil, where they remain for the next seventeen years sucking the juices of the roots of trees and field crops, and although the pests are stated to do but little harm at this period of their existence, the plants on which they feed must be impoverished to a certain degree by the constant drain on their vitality.

But the small amount of damage the cicadas may do while still in the larval stage is as nothing compared to the depredations they commit when at last, their metamorphosis completed, they emerge from their hidden retreats. When, in the eventful seventeenth year of their life, the insects are ready to undergo their final transformation they come up to the surface and construct for themselves chimneys or flues, two or three inches in height. Whole acres are often covered with these strange erections, which are massed side by side as thick as blades of grass in a meadow, and when the moment of emergence finally arrives the earth appears absolutely to teem with cicadas; they pour forth in myriads and within the space of a few days in the infected area all the crops are completely demolished and every tree and shrub laid bare. The musical males do not eat now they have attained the adult stage, but their wives make up for this with their insatiably ravenous appetites.

Naturally these despoilers of the earth do not have things quite all their own way. Thousands of larvae are devoured by birds, frogs, and even by pigs, who root them out of the ground with their snouts, without, however, effecting any considerable diminution in their numbers. Nevertheless, the triumphant day of the cicadas is now almost at an end. Extensive cultivation and building and the introduction of the English sparrow to America are all helping towards the extinction of this terrible pest; and as years roll on the unwelcome voice of the cicadas will in all probability be heard less and less in the "land of the free."

The curious processionary caterpillar of Southern Europe is another insect that enjoys an unenviable reputation as a ruthless destroyer of vegetation. One species (*Bombyx processionea*) causes serious damage to oak trees in many of the forests in France by stripping them of their foliage. Being of a sociable disposition these caterpillars live together in hundreds in a kind of cobwebby nest which they spin for their mutual protection during the hours of daylight. Thousands of these bag-like nests may be seen upon the trees in the springtime; and although quantities are cut down and burned by the foresters, it is an impossible task to destroy them all.

Packed closely together in their nests the caterpillars remain quiescent until the sun goes down, then with one accord they sally forth to feed. When their own particular tree has been completely stripped of its leaves they descend to the ground and march in a regular, orderly procession to another one, often quite a long distance away. They proceed in single file, forming a long, sinuous line, each caterpillar apparently holding on to the tail of the one in front of him. It is said that the leader of the procession spins a thread as he goes and that all the parading insects are attached one to another by a fine silken rope. When the army reaches its objective rank is broken and the caterpillars swarm over the tree voraciously devouring the foliage, then once more they form up, in precisely the same order, and march home again. If by some mischance the procession is broken the caterpillars become hopelessly confused and disorganized and, unless they are able to join up again, wander helplessly about in small gangs or roll themselves up into tangled balls, few, if any, succeeding in finding their way home.

H. Shepstone

ANY GREEN THING IS LOCUST FOOD, EVEN THISTLES

What one might consider most tough and stringy food, namely a palm leaf, is being devoured in the lower photograph. But any green vegetation is food for the locust. It is this fact that gives the insect, in its myriads such power to turn fertility into desolation. In the upper photograph it is a thistle that is being dealt with.

Fortunately, all the changes in the landscape wrought by Nature's living agents are not so destructive in character. Much valuable work is performed unconsciously by many humble, unconsidered creatures. Without the ministrations of the despised earthworm, for example, many a fertile plain would be a barren waste ; for the proper drainage and aeration of the soil depends largely upon the burrowing activities of these unattractive animals. Earthworms are Nature's chief "ploughmen," constantly at work tilling the ground, turning the soil, slowly but thoroughly, bringing the lower, exhausted layers up to the surface to be submitted to the purifying and regenerative influence of the sun and air. Long before the coming of man, these lowly creatures were hard at work, doing their bit, in preparing the earth for his occupation by their indefatigable labours in past ages. Through their agency ground has been levelled, bare rocks covered, and rich, dark layers of vegetable mould formed in which seeds are able to germinate and tender plants flourish. Indeed, to quote Darwin, to whom we are

H. Shepstone

SWARMING PESTS BUSY IN DESTRUCTION WITH A MILLION LEGS AND THOUSANDS OF HUNGRY MOUTHS

As thick as the foliage was before cling the insatiable, ravening hordes of the locusts. In the left-hand illustration they are eating an olive tree and their bodies look at a distance almost like the leaves themselves, so close do they cluster. On the right is a view of a fig tree which is being attacked by crawling locusts. They are swarming on the trunk and branches and ever more and more thousands are advancing over the ground to share in the remains of the meal. One can imagine the feelings of despair in the mind of some hard-working cultivator who must stand and watch the results of, perhaps, many years of patient work disappear in an hour, and be helpless to do anything at all.

H. Shepstone

FIG TREE IN FULL LEAF AND HOW THE VISITATION OF A SWARM OF LOCUSTS LEAVES IT BLASTED

If lightning had struck this fig tree it would not have left it more barren. Indeed it is a skeleton picked clean rather than a tree at all. The photograph was taken in Palestine where the locust is a scourge just as it was in Bible times. The power of these flying and crawling hosts to alter the whole look of a landscape is as remarkable as it is appalling. Areas of cultivation, of course, only favour the multiplication of these insects more than ever by providing great quantities of food concentrated in a comparatively small space. The chief way of salvation lies in trapping them while they are yet in the crawling stage. Once winged, the situation is well-nigh hopeless.

H. Shepstone

LOCUSTS ENCOUNTERED CROSSING A WALL AND IN THE DESERT

Obstacles of a seemingly insuperable kind are crossed by locusts while in the crawling stage. In the lower photograph we see them negotiating a wall. But they can cross rivers, the living walking on the floating bodies of the dead. Above we have an idea of what it is like to encounter a swarm in a desert. The horseman has had to dismount and hold his horse.

indebted for our knowledge of the ways of the earthworm, " it may be doubted whether there are many animals which have played so important a part in the history of the world as these lowly organized creatures."

A worm has neither jaws nor teeth, but takes in its food by the muscular action of the pharynx, which operates very much in the manner of a suction pump. It may be said literally to eat its way through the ground, as in burrowing it swallows the earth for the sake of the organic matter it contains. Worms also help to enrich the soil by pulling down bits of leaves and other vegetable refuse into their burrows, and their castings, brought constantly to the surface and blown away by the winds, are spread in successive fine layers over the ground.

Although earthworms pursue their activities in various parts

H. Shepstone

LOCUSTS ROB THE WILDERNESS OF EVEN SUCH GREEN AS IT HAS

Despite the hard, sharp spines, the cactus leaves suffer from the appetites of a locust swarm just as every other green, growing thing does. It seems that, though the insects crawl unconcernedly between the spines, yet most of the locusts are concentrated on the edges of the thick, fleshy leaves. Thus the dry desert is robbed even of such scanty plant life as its barren soil can support, and, in the case of the cactus, despite the efforts of Nature to protect it. This photograph came from the " wilderness " of Palestine.

H. Bastin

MINUTE CREATURES THAT CAN DESTROY FORESTS: DEALING WITH THE SCALE INSECT AT BURNHAM BEECHES

Scale insects do damage out of all proportion to their size. Many different trees and shrubs are attacked by them, our photograph being of beech trees at Burnham Beeches, the celebrated Buckinghamshire beauty spot, which have been attacked by a species of scale insect. The left-hand illustration shows a man at work clearing one of the mighty trees of these quickly breeding pests while, on the right, is a section of the trunk which has been attacked. The scale insects do the damage by fastening themselves to the bark by means of their strong, sucking beaks, and imbibing the moisture from the tree. If unchecked these insects would soon destroy whole plantations, so rapidly do they multiply.

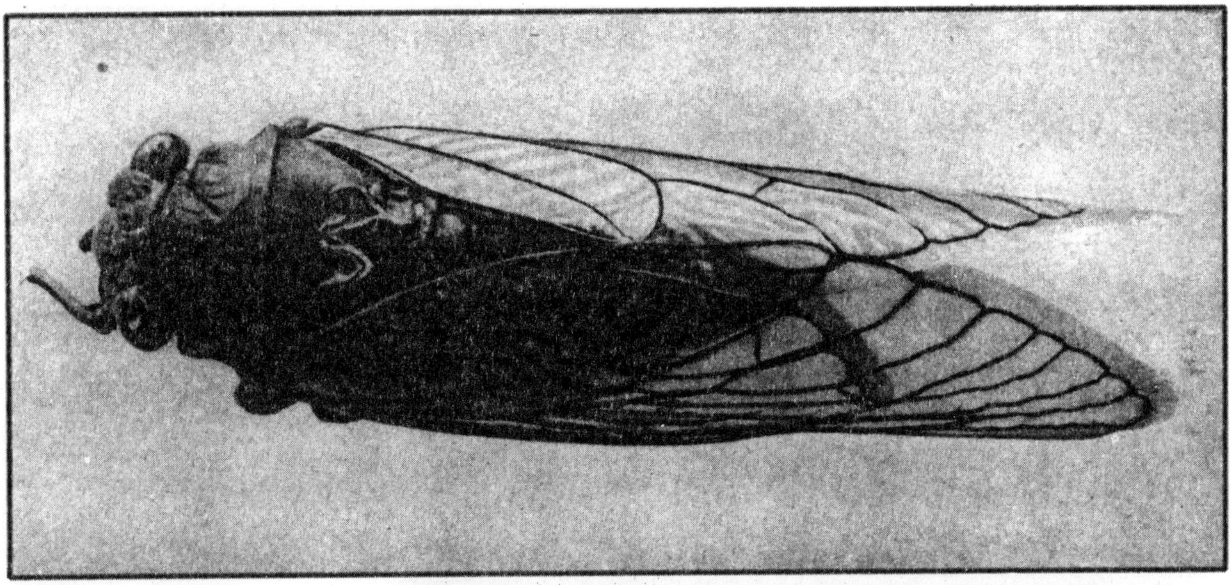

CICADA THAT MAY LIVE FOR SEVENTEEN YEARS BY SUCKING TREE ROOTS

When it is realized that some cicadas take seventeen years to mature, and that all this time they may be busily engaged in sucking the life juices of a tree from its roots, it will be readily seen how cicadas, in their thousands, may transform a fine wood into so many acres of dying trees. The specimen seen here—there are four or five hundred different kinds of the insect—is considerably enlarged. In Europe the cicadas, during their long larval stage, are very fond of attacking ash trees.

of the globe, being found in such widely separated places as Iceland and Madagascar, India and the United States, it is only in those countries that enjoy a temperate and humid climate that they are able to carry on their labours on an extensive scale. In hot, dry, sunbaked regions they can only exert themselves during the short rainy seasons that occur periodically in tropical zones. In Africa the necessary turning and loosening of the soil is carried on to a large degree by the termites, or "white ants" as they are popularly called. The workers of these termite communities are small, unpleasant-looking insects with soft, bloated bodies; but they are provided with strong, serviceable jaws with which they excavate numberless underground chambers, connected by a regular network of galleries whose ramifications often extend over a considerable area, and mine the ground to a depth of several feet.

In the construction of these subterranean towns the excavated soil must necessarily be thrown out upon the surface, and in this way the huge ant-hills that form such a striking feature of the landscape in the elevated regions of Central Africa are built up. Some of the mounds are ten or even fifteen feet high, the larger ones measuring thirty or forty feet in diameter (see photographs in pages 19 to 23). They may rise singly, standing out against the sky as tall towers, or be grouped together in clusters of low hillocks, while their bare sides are worn and sculptured by the action of the wind and the rain into all sorts of fantastic shapes and patterns. The peculiar insects responsible for these erections live almost exclusively on dead wood; living wood is never touched, but a fallen tree trunk is immediately attacked by armies of termites, and within an incredibly short time the whole of the interior will be entirely consumed, nothing remaining but the outer shell that crumbles away at a touch.

One of the most extraordinary things about these white ants is that although the ground may be teeming with their legions, they are seldom or never seen in the flesh, so to speak. Even when they ascend tall trees in order to reach a decayed branch at the top, they never appear in the open. They march from their subterranean dwellings over the ground, and up the tree trunks, under a covered way which they build up as they go, formed of tiny pellets or earth. By this proceeding the soft, tempting bodies of the termites are not exposed to the sharp eyes of birds and beasts who would be only too ready to make a meal of them.

Termites do not, unluckily, confine their attention solely to decaying forest trees; for should there be any human habitation within their field of operations they will attack the doorposts, beams and rafters, working secretly from within the wood in their approved fashion, eating it away, so that it is speedily reduced to so much matchwood and suddenly falls about the ears of the unfortunate owner of the house with a crash. Even tables and chairs are often riddled through and through by termites, so that they crumble away in the most disconcerting manner at inopportune moments. So quickly do the rascals work that in some parts of Africa it is said that if a man with a wooden leg lay down to sleep in the open he would wake to find it a mere heap of sawdust in the morning!

Nevertheless, in spite of their exasperating ways, termites do much valuable work not only by breaking up and destroying decaying vegetation but by acting as denuding and transporting agents. Their earth-

W. S. Berridge

CANADIAN BEAVER AND ITS DEVASTATING WORK

Very soon a colony of beavers can change the landscape round a river on which they have decided to build a dam. With sharp, specially adapted teeth they gnaw round and round a tree trunk (bottom), cutting it so that it falls towards the stream. Thus a vista of short stumps quickly replaces the spectacle of standing timber.

tubes, or covered ways, crumble away and are scattered as fine dust over the land. The great ant-hills are gradually broken down and the debris washed away by the fury of tropical storms. Much of the fine earth is washed into streams and rivulets and carried away to fertilise with fresh alluvium distant plains and valleys—thus the "white ant" helps to "sow the dust of continents to be," and plays its humble part in the vast economy of Nature.

Among the four-footed diggers and delvers of the soil the retiring mole stands out prominently from his inveterate habit of covering large areas of gently rolling pasture land with an ever-increasing number of miniature mountain ranges. Although his method of changing the landscape by throwing up heaps of mould in all directions are not approved by agriculturists, the mole actually does a useful amount of spade-work in the fields, in addition to destroying quantities of noxious grubs that lie buried in the soil. Unfortunately, however, in the ardent pursuit of his labours he is apt seriously to disturb the roots of growing crops, so on the whole the energetic little "gentleman in velvet" does as much harm as good. Below the surface of the ground the mole carries on his mining operations at

a furious rate. Driving his pointed snout into the soft earth and flinging the loose soil to right and left with his spade-like hands as he goes, he seems almost to swim through the ground, and in the course of a few hours will excavate a tunnel right across a fair-sized field. The industrious little animal is most wonderfully adapted in every particular to the subterranean life he leads.

In his natural haunts, the banks of well-timbered streams, the beaver, measuring but 25 inches or so from nose to tail, is responsible for a considerable number of minor alterations in the scenery. In some parts of North America generation after generation of beavers has been at work burrowing, felling trees, cutting canals, erecting " lodges " and constructing dams ; with the result that streams and rivulets have been diverted from their course, lakes and pools have been formed, and large tracts of forest entirely cleared of timber. In some districts low-lying land has been flooded ; in others, marshy ground has been raised above high-water mark and converted into fertile meadows.

In bygone days beavers were much more numerous than they are now.

W. S. Berridge

MARMOTS THAT ALTER THE LOOK OF SQUARE MILES OF GROUND

Marmots are found distributed over a large part of the earth's surface. The Alpine marmot (bottom) is found in the Alps and the Carpathian mountains, while the prairie marmot (top) or prairie-dog is peculiar to North America. These animals tunnel huge areas of territory, and make little mounds for watch-towers beside the burrows.

H. Shepstone

TREES DESTROYED BY GOATS AND A CANAL CLEARED BY BUFFALOES

The scene of desolation in the lower photograph is laid in Guadalupe. Goats attacked the bark of the cypress trees in this forest and utterly destroyed them. The upper photograph is of a very different but very interesting change in the landscape. A herd of buffaloes is being driven through a canal, draining the Pontine Marshes near Rome, in order to clear it of weeds. The drainage of this district has to be carefully looked after, as the soil is among the most fertile soils in the world.

They have been so mercilessly hunted and trapped for their beautiful fur coats that in many of their former haunts they are almost, or quite, extinct. Once widely distributed in the Northern regions of both the Old and the New Worlds, in America beavers are now practically confined to the slopes of the Rockies, while in Europe, with the exception of a few isolated colonies in Scandinavia and on some of the branches of the Rhone, these interesting rodents have been almost exterminated. At one time beavers must have been common throughout Great Britain; such place-names as Beverstone, Beverbrook, Beverley Brook and so on bear witness to the presence of these little craftsmen in various localities in olden days, and it is believed that we owe some of the striking features of our English landscape to their industry. In East Anglia, for example, the inception of the Fens may have originated in the destruction of primitive woodland by colonies of beavers and the obstruction of the natural drainage of the land by beaver dams. The formation of the peat-moors in Lancashire may have been brought about in the same way.

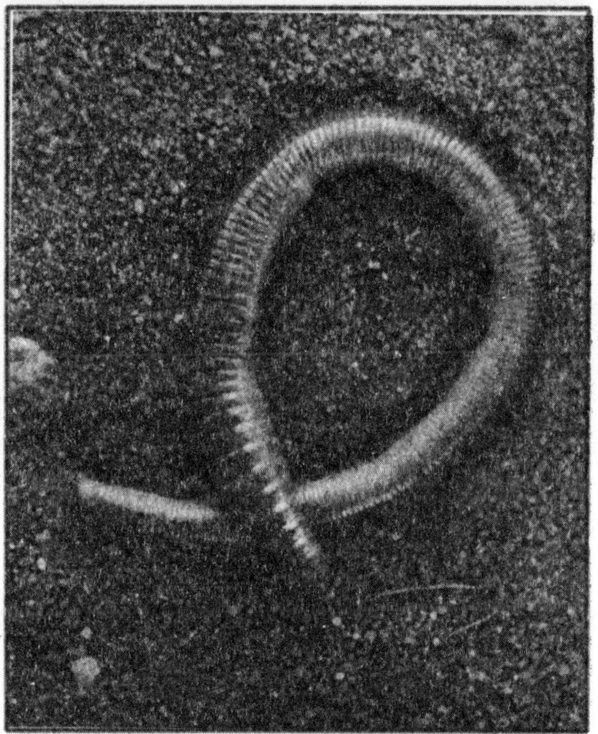

W. S. Berridge

EARTHWORMS, REFRESHERS OF THE LAND

Darwin spent years in observing earthworms. He calculated that the soil is continually being changed by their action. Notice, in the upper example, the swollen ring which secretes a substance to form the horny cocoon in which the eggs are laid.

The only tools the beaver has to work with are his strong fore-paws, armed with powerful claws, and his strong chisel-teeth, which are bright orange in colour and, like those of all rodents, grow continuously throughout the animal's life. The hind feet, which are webbed, and the broad, flat, scaly tail are only used in swimming.

With his sharp teeth the beaver gnaws all round the stem of slender trees growing by the waterside until they fall; then, after stripping off the bark, which is used for food, he cuts up the stems into logs of convenient size for transportation. The lodge, or house, of the beaver is built with sticks and grass and moss well plastered with mud, and is entered by inclined shafts which lead down from the lodge and open beneath the surface of the water. The dam, which is the masterpiece of the little craftsmen, is made of logs and brushwood piled up to form a barrier right across the stream, the crevices being carefully filled in with sods and stones. Some of the dams in America are one hundred yards or more in length, and have been in existence for hundreds of years—lasting memorials to the skill and industry of colonies of these wonderful little animals in by gone days.

E. W. Bond

BABOONS, HAPPY IN THEIR NATURALISED SURROUNDINGS AT THE LONDON ZOO

It was a happy thought, the idea of exhibiting those very interesting animals, baboons, in a colony on a hill, as they live in their wild state. The advantage is manifold. The animals are happier and therefore healthier, and we can watch them as though we had actually been transported to their own country, which makes the exhibit far more interesting and instructive. Notice, in the lower photograph, how the animals sit about in pairs and are, obviously, very much at home despite the English climate.

Chapter CXIX

The Rights of the Animals

By Sir William Beach Thomas

Author of "The English Year"

THERE is not a great difference between the words "human" and "humane"; but the human race has been a long time in coming to feel the strength of its duty to be humane to other animals. Even in the best of the old books very little is found about the subject.

One of the most beautiful stories about the Founder of Christianity—handed down by word of mouth but not in the Bible—concerns a dead dog left lying in the street. One after the other the passers-by who noticed the body made comments on its ugliness and repulsiveness, till Jesus came and, looking at the poor dead thing with eyes full of pity, said: "Pearls are not equal to the whiteness of the teeth."

As the years go on we see and, what is more, we feel more than before how many are the beauties of all life, of all living creatures and in some ways how like they are to ourselves. Among other great men Darwin did much to give us an intellectual reason for being more humane. Man is very different from all other animals, but he is also very like in structure and to some extent in the more common emotions. Though all that Darwin believed is not true there must be much that is true in evolution. As we realize this, we tend to have a closer fellow-feeling with the rest of animal life.

St. Francis may be said to be the founder of the general society for the spread of greater kindness to animals, and when he called the birds and mammals "our little brothers," he said very much what Darwin said in a different way. St. Francis, who loved nothing more than feeding birds, *felt* our kinship and Darwin *proved* it intellectually when he wrote his "Descent of Man." Both men preached sermons from the same text, however different their ways of thought and expression were. Perhaps Darwin himself did not guess what influence his theory of the evolution of men's minds would exert.

During the past few years in Britain the teachings of St. Francis have been advanced much more than at any time in history. It is not only that separate groups of people, labelled humanitarians, have multiplied and extended their power; but that the general population thinks more of consideration for all animals, human or not human. Proved cruelty to, say, a dog or a horse is an offence against the law just as truly as cruelty to a child. Indeed, this feeling for animals has advanced so much that it is sometimes complained that domestic animals are better protected than people.

AT present a very sharp distinction is drawn between wild animals and tame. It is curious that there is no law against being cruel to, say, a rabbit or a fox; but the general feeling is progressing rapidly towards further protection in very many directions. Sanctuaries for birds and mammals and indeed some insects, such as butterflies, multiply. More and more people feed the birds, very like St. Francis. More societies and associations of people spring up for preventing or regulating the trapping and killing and hunting of wild animals, so that the pain may be as little as possible. When any act or system of cruelty is made public, as recently in the wholesale slaying of penguins, or in the murder of sea-birds by waste oil, or in the trapping of rabbits, flames of indignation burst out from the general public; and we must believe that the reign of kindliness and common sympathy is being steadily and progressively established.

It is indeed very remarkable that the prime movers in all the three special cases I have mentioned have been, not, as you would expect, people known as humanitarians, or sympathetic or sentimental women, but men proud to be known as sportsmen. In one case the most effective preacher was a Master of Fox-hounds, in another a famous shooter of big

F. W. Bond

ARTIFICIAL SUN FOR IGUANAS

If animals are to supply the benefits of interest and wide knowledge to men, then it is only fair that the animals should share in the things which benefit human life. Electricity, for instance, can supply the effects of the tropic sunlight which captive reptiles so sadly miss.

affectionate master or mistress. We have certainly added to the mental power of some animals by talking to them and making them companions. Every dog-lover is struck, not only by the intelligence of his dog, but by the almost continuous effort of the dog to understand. It wrestles mentally to discover what the words, tones, movements, gestures, and even moods of his master or mistress may mean; and this perpetual and humble effort to penetrate the wishes of a being possessed of gifts denied to him has unquestionably developed the mind of the dog, as it will develop the mind of almost every animal capable of domestication in any degree, for instance of the otter and mongoose. It is probable that the tamed animal has a much greater capacity than the wild for pain if not for pleasure; and this is due partly to its association with man, partly to a certain softness incident to its more artificial condition of life.

All this implies that we have a greater responsibility to mere creatures; and we are morally

E.N.A.

RIGHTS AND WRONGS

It is universally admitted that the best way to lift heavy animals is by means of a sling passing under the body so that the weight is distributed (bottom). Above we see a cow suspended painfully by its horns, a method followed in some South American countries.

game. It may be difficult or impossible to be humane and a sportsman at one and the same time. It does not appear to be logical to be fond of animals, and to enjoy killing them. But however bad the logic, even a professor of logic may rejoice that the sportsmen fight with zeal and effect for the reduction of cruelty in this direction and that.

It is right and proper that the law should have begun its compaign with special care for the domestic animals, for several very good reasons. Now one of the standard marvels of the world is the domestication of animals. It is a real addition to the life of man that he has taught certain animals to enjoy a mutual companionship with him; and we may say generally that such domestication is at least as real an addition to the happiness of the animal's life as to man's. It is certainly true of all the dogs and cats that have a good home, and of the horse which has an

LOOKING AFTER THE RIGHTS OF ANIMALS AT MARKET AND RAILWAY STATION

In England at markets and railway stations and all centres where livestock are dealt with in large quantities, supervision is carried out to see that no unnecessary suffering is caused to the animals. In the lower photograph an inspector of the Royal Society for the Prevention of Cruelty to Animals is watching calves being put into a motor lorry. Calves are lively creatures, and when scared at the bustle and strange surroundings are apt to hurt themselves unless carefully handled. Above, we see cattle being inspected in a truck on the railway.

THE POULTRY EXPRESS: A HUNDRED THOUSAND BIRDS CARRIED IN COMFORT

Many people must have noticed large crates of live fowls being handled at a railway station. Too often the birds look miserable and as though suffering from cramped quarters and thirst. In the United States, whence this photograph comes, tremendous amounts of poultry are continually being moved. Thus, special poultry freight cars have been devised, each holding about 4,500 birds, and with a compartment for an attendant. Water, food, and leg room are all provided. Loss of weight in transit is greatly reduced under these conditions.

compelled to see to it that we do them good and not harm. In the past very many animals have suffered all sorts of pain and hardship because of this unworthy captivity. While some creatures live much longer in captivity (especially birds) some die miserably soon. Quite a few years ago consumption, which is one of the especial maladies of civilization, carried off monkeys wholesale in the Zoological Gardens. Or again, to give an example that came within my special knowledge, vast quantities of beautiful birds caught for exhibition and sale perished annually in Australia.

But apart from what may be called the wholesale capture and exhibition of animals, we are all of us under an obligation to know how far we are justified in training animals or caging animals for the diversion of the human race: dogs, monkeys, elephants, lions, with every creature that appears in a circus or even in a zoo. It certainly may be said of some animals that they rejoice in captivity as a dog rejoices in its home; and if released might feel like Byron's "Prisoner of Chillon":

Even I
Regained my freedom with a sigh.

But their content depends on their treatment. We ought all to be very sure that we are not inflicting pain or perverting instincts unworthily when we deal with our pets or captives or domestic companions. When we consider how very much dogs and cats rejoice in domestication it is a little surprising that other sorts of animals are not commoner in our houses. A good many animals have a sort of gift for understanding the ways and intentions of man; and they are of very different sorts. A list would include, among birds, almost all the crow tribes, especially ravens, magpies and jackdaws; a number of starlings, especially the Nepal minah; a number of parrots, cockatoos and parakeets; several owls and hawks; the robin and the wagtail; swans and ducks of many varieties; and birds related to domestic hens. Among mammals, dog, cat, horse, donkey, elephant, monkey; otter and mongoose, seal, and brown and black bear. In the list of animals either utterly untamable or rebellious against captivity, even when used to it, come the hyaena, the Tasmanian 'devil,' and less markedly, wolf, fox, badger and stoat.

Many people begin to feel that some of these animals which especially rebel against captivity should be excluded from our zoos. No one can enjoy seeing a wolf going half mad as he patrols to and fro in utter restlessness behind the iron bars of his narrow cage. It would be enough to satisfy curiosity if the very small group of animals which are by nature miserable in captivity were represented by stuffed effigies or even pictures.

Some animals in zoos look miserable, though they are in reality happy enough. The vultures and eagles, for example, in the London Zoo are marvellously

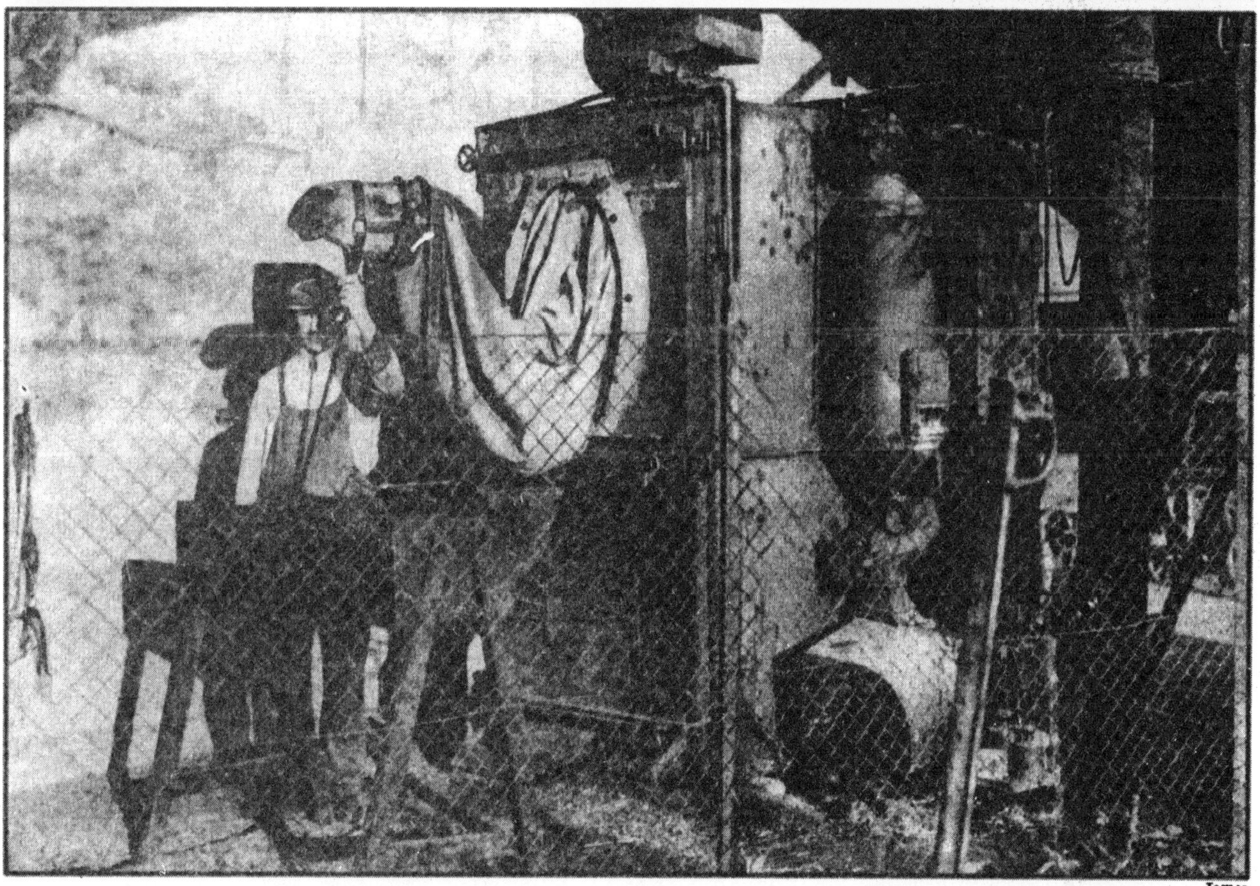

James

PROVISION FOR SKIN TREATMENT AND THE WATERING OF CITY DRAUGHT HORSES

Below we witness a most unusual sight—a camel in a gas container. The animal is suffering from a form of skin disease, and is being treated with a special gas. Notice how the problem of the camel's neck is cleverly dealt with by means of a special gas-proof material fastened at the throat so that the animal breathes in comfort. Above is one of the drinking troughs for London draught horses erected by the Metropolitan Drinking Fountain and Cattle Trough Association. It stands in the Strand.

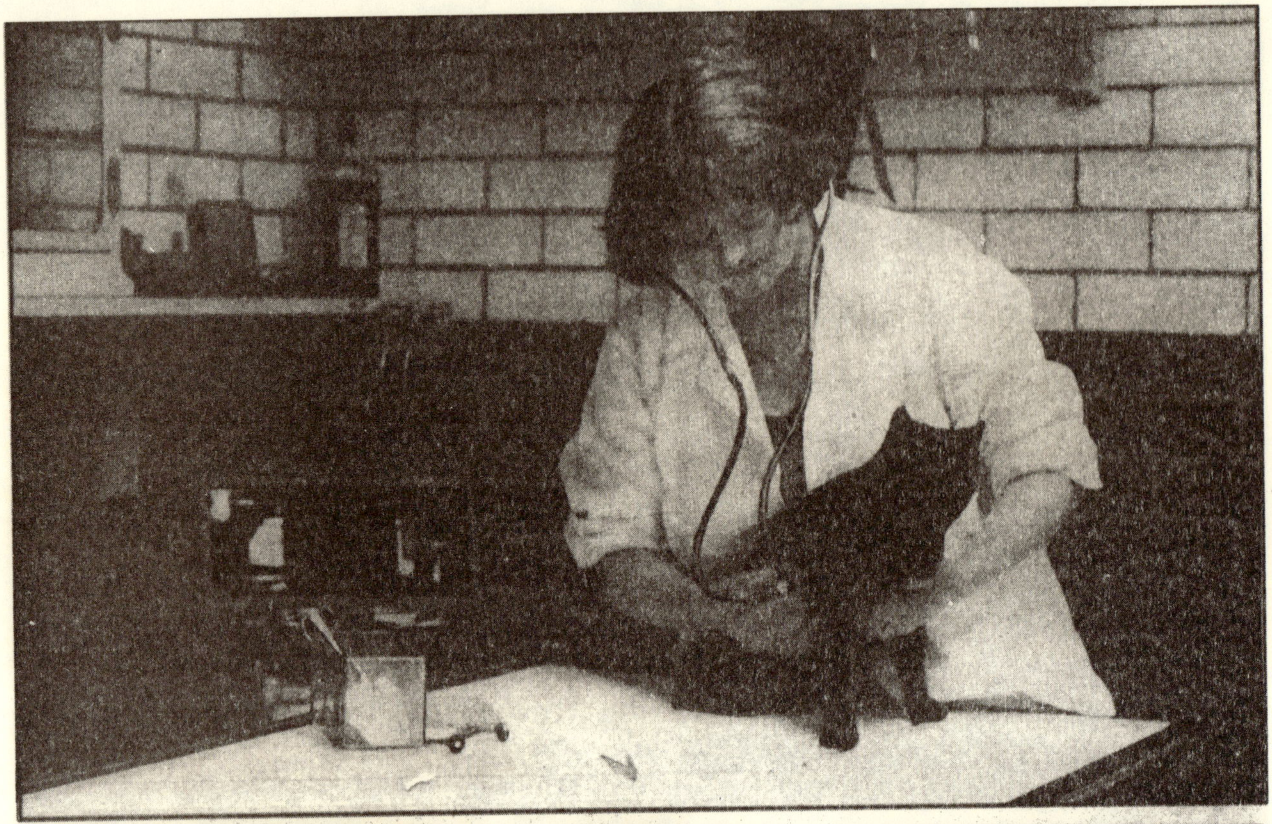

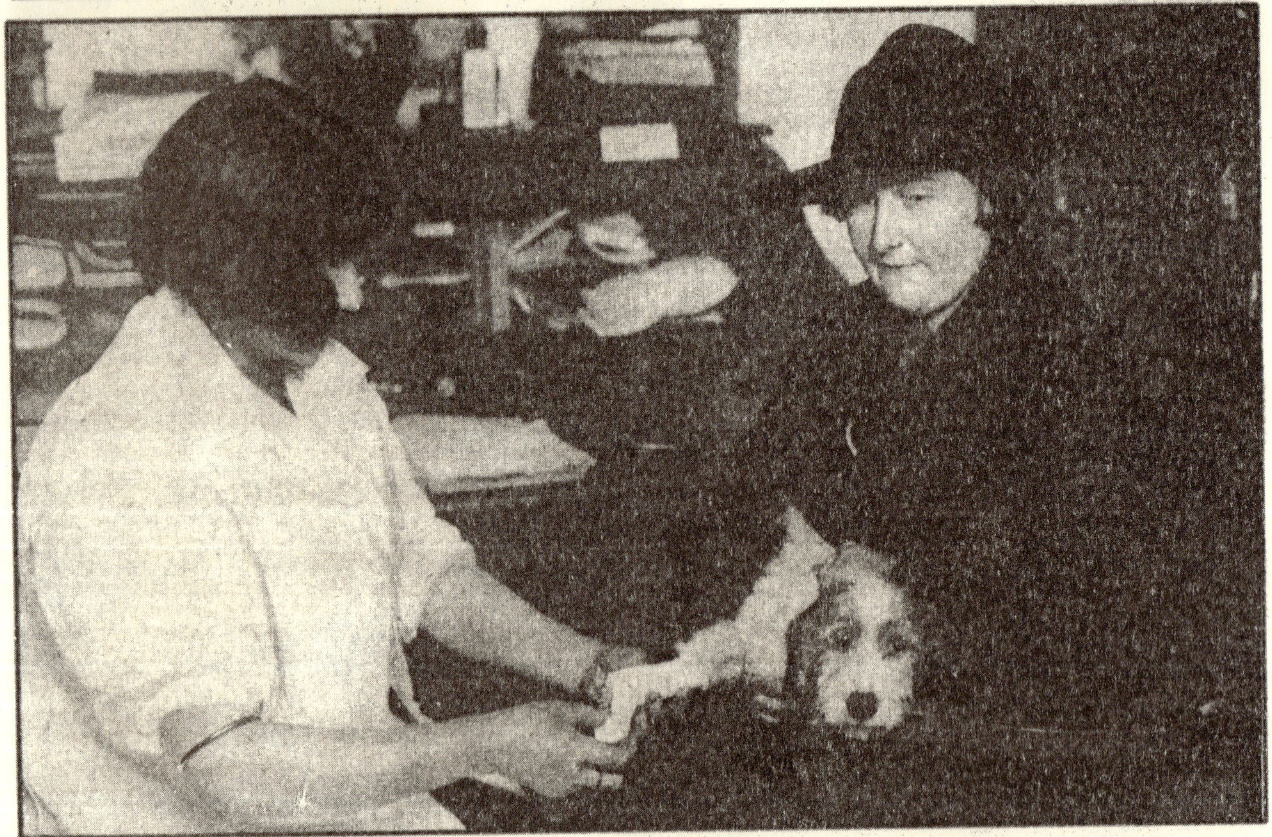

BANDAGE AND STETHOSCOPE FOR OUR SILENT FRIENDS WHEN THEY ARE IN TROUBLE

The problem of the multitude of dogs and cats kept by an animal-loving city like London grows more acute as the human population increases. Special institutions now deal with this problem, and casualties and disease can be scientifically treated by experts. Your dog has damaged its paw—and you can have the wound carefully bandaged and sterilised (bottom). Your cat may have a little touch of bronchitis—and you can take it where the stethoscope will diagnose the trouble (top) without frightening the patient.

QUARANTINE FOR DOG IMMIGRANTS AND A HOLIDAY HOME FOR TIRED HORSES

When dogs come into England from abroad they have to spend an allotted time in quarantine for the sake of the rest of the canine population. Our photograph shows an Irish wolfhound arriving at a quarantine station on the outskirts of London. It has just come from the docks, whither it has landed from a ship from Port Said. Above we have nine inmates of the home for tired horses at Cricklewood. Here rest and quiet recuperate those animals suffering from the turmoil of London traffic.

Royal Society for the Protection of Birds

EGRETS AND THEIR SLAUGHTER FOR MILLINERY

In these more enlightened days, enactments have been made against the import of egret plumes in most civilized countries. When it was realized what disgusting brutality was connected with the collection of the plumes, public opinion was able to check if not to stop the "industry." We see here a bird, dead and mutilated, and above in undisturbed conditions.

playful on occasions. It is true, though surprising, that there are one or two visitors and keepers who regularly take part with these birds in games and romps that suggest a children's Christmas party.

The growing feeling of kinship with animals is stirring inquiry into the treatment of all sorts of animals used for the amusement of man. It is remarkable that the cries for reform come chiefly from Anglo-Saxon countries. Few well educated English people, sportsmen included, now take any pleasure in a bullfight, which still excites to the utmost the public in some of the Latin countries. Their admiration for the skill of the man blinds some people to the feelings of the victim, the intentional killing of the bull and less intentional killing of the horses.

Of the two the bull suffers the less, especially if it is a fine animal. The reason is this: If an animal is full of the rage of battle, as sometimes the bulls are, but not always, it is singularly careless of wounds or pain of any kind ; all is lost in the rage of battle. But the horses, which are often poor and miserable to start with, have no battle rage. They suffer from fears at the sight of the bull and they suffer from the pain of wounds. The sight of them coming into the ring is definitely painful to humane eyes, and when they are gored, as often happens, the spectacle is scarcely endurable to those who love horses. Besides that, it can scarcely be doubted that the experience of seeing and encouraging the spectacle has a definitely bad effect on the mood and character of the spectators.

A very few years ago even in England spectacles of no better sort were common and popular enough. Badger-baiting was a disgraceful performance. The animal has the toughest hide of any of our wild mammals, and this meant that the worrying of a badger was very long drawn out. This pastime was only less popular than cock-fighting, which certainly encouraged some of the worse instincts of its supporters. But the cocks suffered less than the badgers. The methods of fighting employed by the game-cock is for one bird to attempt to leap over the other and strike backwards at the other's head with the sharp spur at the back of its foot. This was often artificially armed with metal so that the blow might be more deadly, and it was argued that so far from being inhumane, the metal spurs tended to shorten the fight by killing one of the feathered combatants outright.

Royal Society for the Protection of Birds

YOUNG EGRETS STARVING FOR THE SAKE OF A HAT

Egrets were killed wholesale just at the time when they were attending their young in the nest. These photographs were taken in an egret colony in New South Wales after a visit by the plume hunters. We see them (top) crying for food to the mother who lies mangled and dead (see opposite page) and (bottom) at the point of death, too weak to stand.

But in Nature the result of a fight either between two cock pheasants or between two stags is much more often than not simply to drive the weaker from the field. The narrow confines and the artificial stimulus totally alter conditions and make the duels unlovely in detail, even if the fighting animals are too sharply enraged to be very conscious of the infliction of the pain or the prospect of death.

In the past certain wholesale cruelties have been committed which shocked the feelings of a great part of the civilized world. One of these was the destruction of so-called ospreys in their breeding plumage. The feathers of these lovely birds are much prized for the adornment of hats, and prices ruled very high. Now the birds, which have a certain resemblance to the

THE MONKEY ON THE ORGAN HELPS TO EARN A LIVING
At one time a monkey on an organ was just a curiosity. Few people wondered how the monkey felt at having to trail about in a town. Nowadays the owner has to treat his living advertisement properly, for it has been realized that even an ape dressed up in a travesty of human clothes has its rights like other animals.

British heron, nest in large companies at the top of high trees, like the herons, and are rarely approached at the nesting season. The simplest way to get the feathers was to shoot the birds. It happens that the osprey is one of the most affectionate of birds. The courtship is one of the most romantic spectacles in all bird life, and the parents are devoted to their young. It often happened in the course of this grim commerce that one of a pair was left lamenting and the young were often left to starve in the nest.

Every observer of nature and humane person must feel that a sanctity belongs to the animal creation at any rate at the breeding season. It is what was called in effect by Plato a " sin in the soul " to murder so highly-strung an animal as the heron at this season merely for the sake of money and unnecessary adornment. Happily we may begin to expect with some confidence that such outrage will no longer be permitted by any country of the civilized world on either side of the Atlantic.

Some people think that the world is growing too humanitarian, that more is now thought of " lower animals " than of mankind, that many begin to exclaim against all sorts of treatment that is not cruel at all, or even in any degree unkind. Is it an unhappy fate for a bear to be dragged round the country and forced to dance for the amusement of people and the livelihood of his master ? Is the organ-grinder's monkey a proper object of pity ? Is the dog who drags the barrows or little carts about in Belgian towns undergoing a labour that he hates ? Who shall say ? Yet we begin to know enough about the minds and temperaments of animals to be able to feel confident on certain points. A dog certainly delights in the act of pulling. I have known a favourite dog ask to be put on his lead solely in order to tug at it. He would walk quietly to heel without the lead, but directly he was attached he would pull hard throughout a long walk.

The actual pulling of the carts is certainly not distasteful to the dogs ; at the worst not so distasteful as the pushing of the barrow is to the man. The bear, the monkey and the dog all acquire a real sense of comradeship with their master. They regard him, one would say, not as a slave driver or hard master, even if he is a little harder than need be, but as a creature sharing both the pleasure and pain of a common life. Plenty of food fills so very large a part of the animal's demands on life (though they all need play and leisure and what the Greeks called " the free-play of life ") that, if the master is generous in this respect and of a moderately kindly nature, the animal is perhaps as happy in his way as the man. The bear is probably happier than the monkey, for it is an animal not ill-suited to our climate, whereas the monkey is a lover of warmth ; and not all the jackets in the world can make up to it for the sun of its native clime. The Zoo, incidentally, has been very successful in supplying it with a sort of artificial tropics. Its intense and skilful activity, too, is so very real a part of its nature that the wandering life of an organ-grinder can hardly satisfy it at least to the full. Some of us, therefore, feel much more sorry for the monkey than for the bear, but neither can be said to live a miserable life.

PART of one's pity for such animals as these comes from the same source as our pity for circus animals. It is not pleasant, at least so a great many people feel, to see animals going through a number of unnatural and ridiculous performances: monkeys

ORANG-UTAN, "MAN OF THE WOODS," THE MOST HUMAN OF THE APES

Emotionally the orang-utan is perhaps nearer the human being than any of the other anthropoids. Its behaviour in captivity had not a little to do with the reformation in the treatment of caged animals. Under old conditions it so plainly fretted. Other animals suffered less obviously. Now we realize that if an animal is caged for our pleasure, at least it has the right to as much happiness as we can give it.

W. F. Bond

REGAL TREATMENT FOR THE KING PENGUIN AT THE LONDON ZOO

Compared with the old days, the conditions under which many animals are now kept in zoological gardens are positively magnificent. Here we have a King Penguin with a fine swimming pool, bordered by plants and grasses and with rocks to dive from. There are no enemies to fear, and as much food as a penguin's heart might desire. These are not indifferent compensations for a life which, at the best, is one of very dangerous liberty, and the bird seems happy enough, as visitors may see for themselves.

pedalling round on bicycles with their feet attached to the pedals; horses put to bed; dogs and cats walking foolishly on their front paws or turning back-somersaults out of a window; lions imitating the domestic cat, or roaring in pretended savagery under orders. It is, of course, tolerably certain that the animal does not feel the indignity, the unworthiness of these fantastic tricks as we do. It would be a mistake to attribute our own feelings to animals who are without the gift of speech and partly without the gift of reason, in our usual sense of the word. The circus performance itself does not occupy a very long time; it is likely enough that the animals (so far as they look forward) think more of the small reward that follows than of the unpleasantness of the performance.

What matters most is the training and the life of the animals off the stage. Not very many animals can be finely trained except by kindness. It is for example quite impossible to do anything with any member of the cat tribe except by wheedling. Any touch of cruelty breeds rebellion, and destroys any docility they may have. Dogs have a very different temperament. Almost everyone who owns a dog finds that some punishment is a help in training, whether it is in house manners or in keeping to heel. But when he comes to teach him what are called parlour tricks, such as begging or "dying for his country" or shutting the door, he finds that punishment is very much less effective than what may be called bribery. All the best retrieving dogs are taught by kindness only. Indeed, the prime secret of training all animals is infinite patience, accompanied by a quiet manner.

A GOOD many of us would rather not see a number of stage performances that are nevertheless sufficiently popular and wonderful, but we have no well proved reason for feeling sorry for the animal on the ground of indignity. What we should insist on is that the animal should have a comfortable and healthy life off the stage, should not suffer in transport, should not live in too small a cage, and should be well fed and well looked after.

It must always be a sad moment when a pet or indeed a farm animal comes near its end. We all use the phrase about putting an animal "out of its misery." If a horse—and horses' bones are of such a nature that they cannot be set—breaks its leg, the most humane act is to kill it. Any wounded animal is quite certainly desirous to be "out of its misery" one way or another. In nature animals show no sign of fearing natural death. Birds retire to an obscure spot and slip easily out of life; but domestic animals often suffer in old age, and are a pitiable sight. In the East it was forbidden by the founder of the Buddhist religion to kill any live thing, and throughout the world there are found sacred animals which may not be slaughtered. The Hindoo may not kill his sacred cow, however it may suffer from age or

E.N.A.

WONDERFUL LANDSCAPE PLANNING FOR ANIMALS IN THE HAGENBECK ZOO

At Stellingen, near Hamburg, is the most wonderful zoological garden in Germany, if not in the world. It was planned by Carl Hagenbeck, the famous man who did so much for the welfare of caged and performing animals. There is a miniature mountain range on which lions roam, and where they can take refuge in concrete caves (bottom). No bars spoil the animals' or the spectators' view, deep trenches, too wide to jump, making all safe. Above is a kind of reconstruction of the African veldt, complete with ostriches, zebras, and antelopes.

E.N.A.

TOO MUCH DOG POWER OR TOO LITTLE: MILK CARTS IN BELGIUM

Harnessing dogs to vehicles is a practice forbidden in England, but in Belgium, wherever the motor has not ousted animal traction entirely, dogs may be seen drawing small carts. These photographs, from the last-named country, present a little puzzle. If five dogs are put to pull the cart in the lower photograph, how is one enough for a very similar equipage seen in the upper photograph? The official in the lower view is a milk inspector. Dogs seem to like pulling, as anyone who has a dog on a lead may discover.

E.N.A

COCK-FIGHTING STILL GOES ON OPENLY IN SOME PARTS OF THE WORLD

It is probable that cock-fighting was put down in England rather because of what was deemed to be the damage to the minds and morals of the people who watched it than because of an abhorrence of animal suffering. In other parts of the world cock-fighting still goes on, and they are particularly fond of it in the Dutch East Indies. Below we see a couple of cocks matched in a village in Sumbawa Island, between Lombok and Flores, while above is a scene in Mexico of two owners setting on their rival birds.

E.N.A.

PORTUGUESE AND SPANISH BULLS ON THE FARMS WHERE THEY ARE BRED

Breeding bulls for the bull-fighting is a regular industry in Spain and Portugal, where large farms are kept up and likely beasts picked out. In the lower photograph we have a Portuguese herd and above a scene on a Spanish farm, with mounted herdsmen carrying long poles seen in the background. The chief cruelty at a bull-fight is not to the bull at all, but to the wretched horses which are used by the mounted men in the preliminary attacks. These are frequently ripped open by the infuriated bull.

W. F. Bond

NATURAL SURROUNDINGS FOR INMATES OF THE LONDON ZOO

Antelopes, we may be sure, enjoy their new style of paddock at the London Zoological Gardens far better than the old. A tree affords grateful shade, while there are rocks, such as the animals might know in their wild state, where they can retreat or over which they can scamper. Above is an egret in surroundings copying those to which a wild egret is used.

disease. Its sufferings may be lighter than they seem, but so far as we can tell it is often kindest and best to put our old and diseased animals out of what seems their misery.

There is one form of cruelty still prevalent against which the whole world should rebel. Most trapping involves brutal cruelty, especially if the traps are of the nature of toothed steel traps. In the West of England these traps kill or maim foxes, badgers, cats, dogs, and birds, as well as the rabbits for which they are purposely set. In other countries the men, most of them of a very fine hardy type, whose profession it is to trap ermine, foxes, lynxes, skunks, sables, in the northern countries, are by the circumstances quite unable to visit their traps at close intervals, and this means that the captured creatures must undergo hours, perhaps days, of agony. The sooner the fashion for such furs, or for such feathers as the osprey's, dies out, the better for our common humanity.

Chapter CXX

Animal Wonders Revealed by the Microscope

By W. H. S. Cheavin

Corresponding Member of the Manchester Microscopical Society

To describe all the wonders to be found in the various forms of animal life would require many volumes, and the time occupied in doing so would take many years. Every animal in its structure presents marvels which when examined by means of a microscope become more and more wonderful as they are magnified in detail. In the many forms of insect life, for instance, we fine interesting examples unseen by the human eye but revealed as objects of great wonder under the powerful lenses of the modern microscope.

The antennae, or feelers, of an insect, situated on the front of the head or projecting from the sides, consist of two filament-like outgrowths which vary considerably in length, not only in the same species but also in the male and female forms. These antennae are used as sense organs, tactile, olfactory or auditory in purpose. Each antenna has a central thick nerve, and connected with this nerve are fibrous filaments passing to sensitive cells at the extremity. Distributed throughout the surface of the antenna will be found pit-like markings of various shapes, and the whole of this sensory apparatus is connected directly with the brain of the insect.

These pits, or surface markings, can be seen clearly in the antennae of ants and ichneumon flies; that of the ant is devoid of hairy outgrowths, while that of the ichneumon fly is covered with very fine hairs and S-shaped markings throughout its length; it is believed that the pits act in a stethoscopic manner on account of their thinner structure and so render the antennae very sensitive.

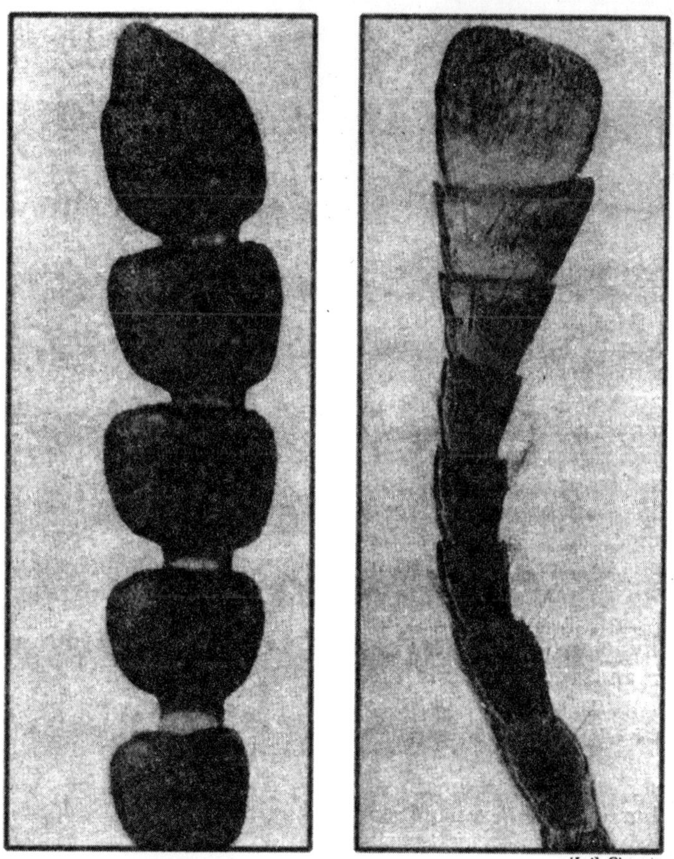

H. S. Cheavin

GLOW-WORM AND LADYBIRD ANTENNAE

On the left we see the construction of the antennae of a female glow-worm and on the right that of a ladybird. (Both photographs mag. x 137.) The glow-worm (left) has a series of swollen-looking nodes covered with stumpy processes. The ladybird has antennae made of flat plates.

As a contrast we have in the male gnat a pair of large antennae covered with a large number of long hairs radiating from peculiar thickened joints placed at regular intervals throughout their length; while in the female gnat we have quite a different structure with a few stout hairs from each joint and smaller hairs at the tip, the thickening of the joint as seen in the male not being present.

The antennae of the gnat family show the same features, and in the plumed Corethra we have a very marked example in the male insect.

The provision of the hairy antennae in the male of a species has been shown by experiment to be sensitive to the hum of the female species when in flight, and by this means the males are guided to the females for mating purposes. The hum produced by the female vibrates the male antennae, which can then sense in what direction to fly.

The snipe fly shows these marked differences in another way. The male antennae are each made of two large joints, the lower being much thicker than the upper, whereas in the female we have a thin, short upper joint and a thicker very long second joint, both types being covered with a series of very short hairs. The marsh fly antennae consist of delicate projections with fine hairs alternating with each other; while in the dung fly we have a similar pair of delicate antennae, but the hair-like projections occupy only about one half of the whole length, also the upper half is covered with fine rib-like markings.

In the crane fly we have another peculiar feature in the antennae; they are not

depression which probably makes the insect sensitive to smell or sound.

The antennae of the flea are very peculiar, because they can be hidden away in a groove at the side of the head and protruded when desired. This tucking away of the antennae enables the insect to creep quickly through the hairs of the host. The antennae are probably of more importance than the eyes and act as auditory, tactile and olfactory organs. They enable the fleas to find each other, for when the male and female meet, the antennae are raised from their groove. These appendages are also used for removing dirt, and the operation is carried out by a series of short hairs. found at the base which act as a comb for cleaning the tips. The antennae of the male flea are longer than those of the female.

A greater contrast is seen in the antennae of the spider family. The female has a pair of powerful two-jointed projections adjoining the powerful jaws, each antenna being covered with a series of stout hairs and armed at the tip with a short claw which is often used in conjunction with the jaws

only covered with fine hairs over the whole surface, but in addition there are thickened joints, each bearing a series of stout, short projections.

As a contrast to the insects belonging to the Diptera family we find in the Coleoptera (beetles) family that the antennae are very large and heavy in appearance. A good example of this type is seen in the female glow-worm, which shows antennae consisting of enlarged divisions covered with a great number of fine pit-like markings with a series of very minute hairs hardly distinguishable. In the male glow-worm we have similar thickened joints, but a large number of short hairs is also present.

The antennae of the ladybird, another member of the beetle family, are many-jointed and plate-like, the joints becoming wider and wider towards the extremities and covered with a series of fine hair-like projections on their surface.

A DRAGON-FLY antenna consists of a short unjointed hairless projection, but on close examination shows rib-like markings, which structure suggests that this insect relies on vision rather than on hearing.

In the green-fly (rose aphis) the antennae show an irregular thin jointed structure covered with blunt projections. In each joint can be seen a small

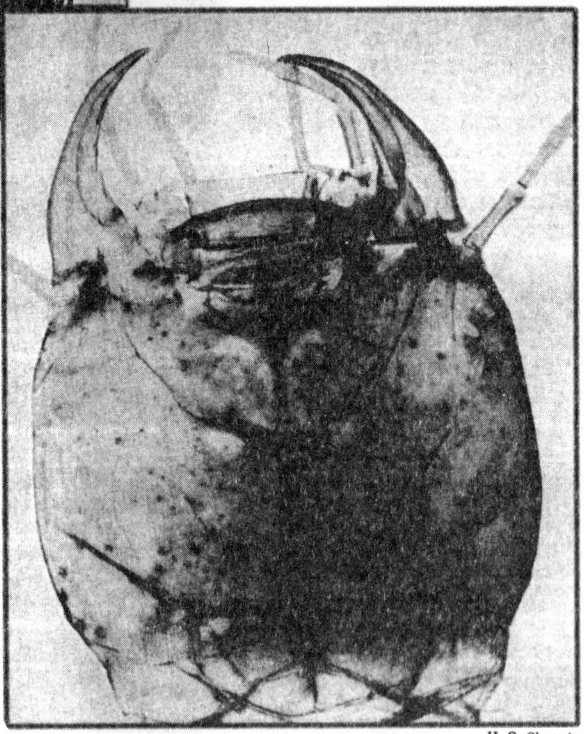

H. S. Cheavin

WATER BEETLE AND ANT-LION LARVAE

Two types of jaws are seen here. Those of the water beetle larvae (bottom) are for sucking, while those of the larva of the ant-lion (top) are deadly cutting instruments with saw edges for slicing through the bodies of the insects on which the larva preys.

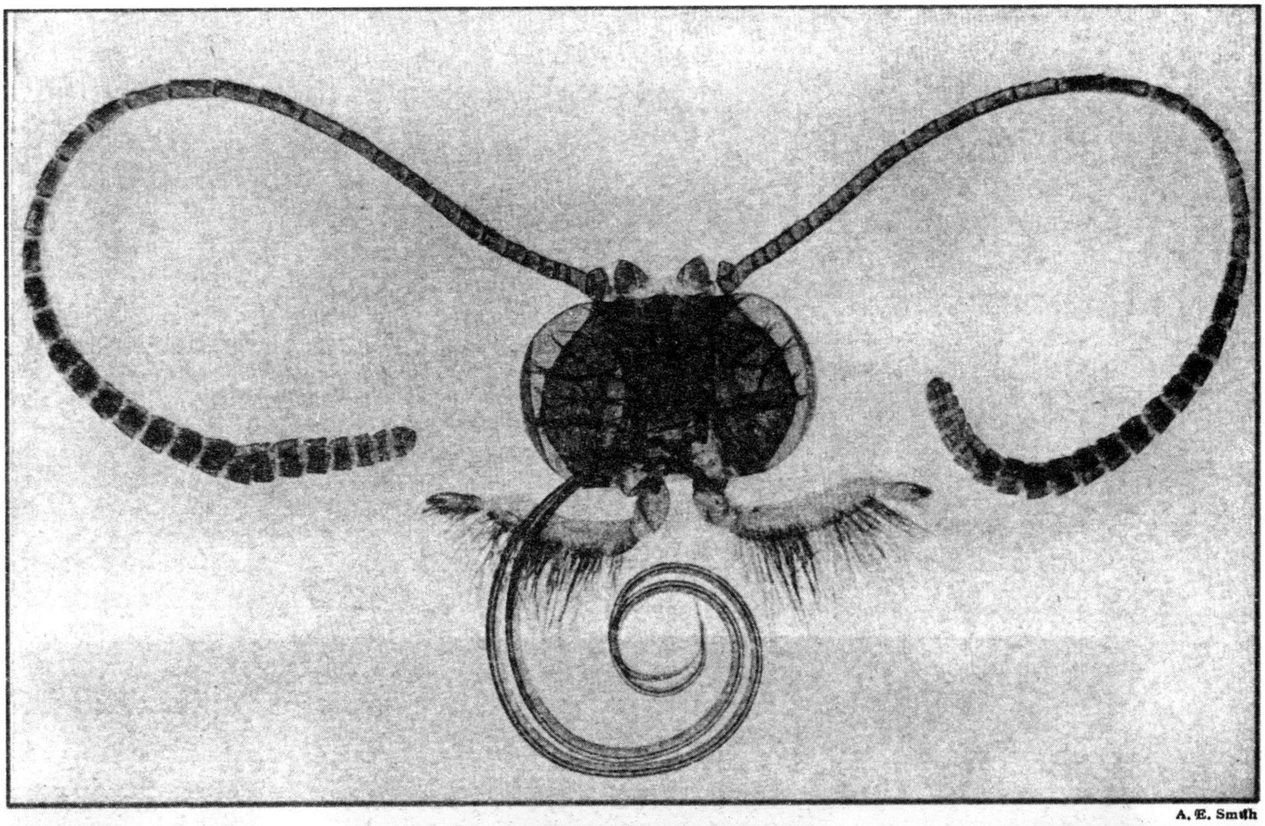

A. E. Smith

H. S. Cheavin

INTRICATELY MADE FEELERS OF GNAT AND MEADOW BROWN BUTTERFLY

Antennae or feelers take many strange forms in different insects. They are ringed in the plumed gnat (bottom) and covered with a system of very fine, hair-like growths. In the case of the meadow brown butterfly (top) the antennae are segmented. These details would, of course, pass unnoticed by the naked eye but a powerful magnifying lens reveals marvels of construction whose varied purposes we can only guess at. The upper photograph shows also the long, curled proboscis of this butterfly, which is found commonly in English hay fields.

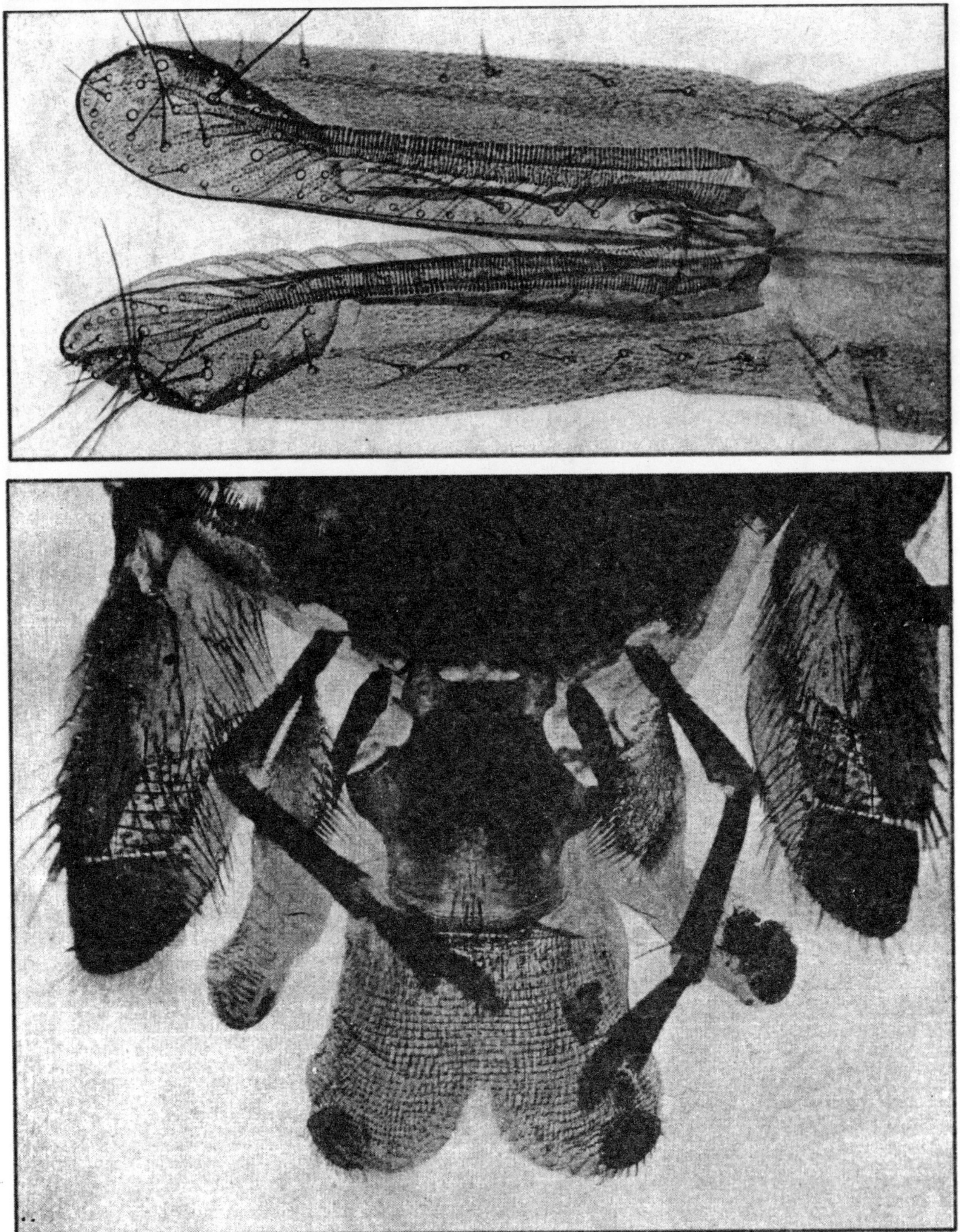

MICROPHOTOGRAPHS OF A WASP'S MOUTH AND THE PROBOSCIS OF A HOVERING FLY

Compared with the higher types of animal life the mouths of insects are very complicated pieces of mechanism. Our lower photograph shows the mouth parts of a common wasp, the culprit responsible for so much damaged fruit in our orchards. Above we see the detail of the end of the proboscis owned by a large, dull-red fly whose name is *Rhingia rostrata*. Notice the complex surface and the large hairs. This insect is a pollen-eater and may be seen hovering, apparently motionless, in the air, during the summer.

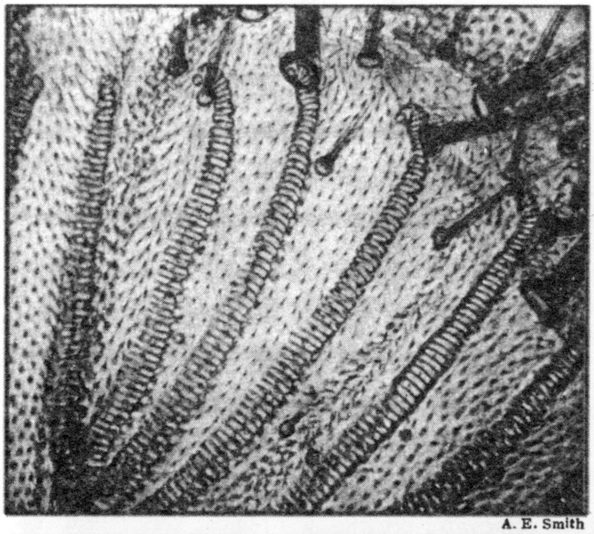

A. E. Smith

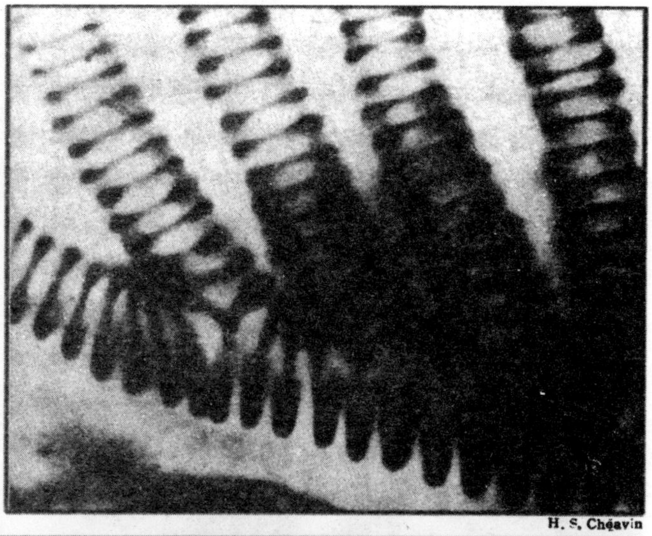

H. S. Chéavin

E. A Botting

WONDROUS MECHANISMS POSSESSED BY GRASSHOPPER, BLOWFLY AND HOUSEFLY

The common grasshopper has a kind of gizzard equipped with so-called gastric or stomach teeth. These (bottom) consist of a number of plates provided with serrated edges. The upper left-hand photograph (mag. x 300) shows part of a blowfly's proboscis. This is a kind of trunk and used for sucking up food previously dissolved by the application of saliva. In taking up food the proboscis of the housefly (top right) makes a rubbing movement with the flat part at the extremity in the way that paint is taken up on to a brush from a palette.

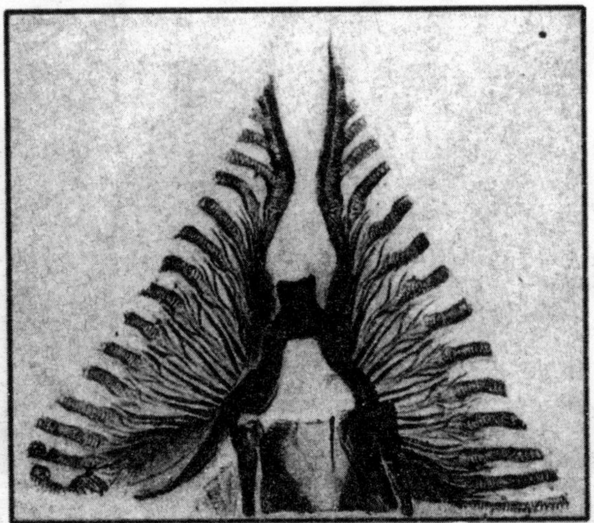

H. S. Cheavin

DETAIL OF A BLOWFLY'S PROBOSCIS

This is a highly magnified photograph of a blowfly's proboscis—the sucking tube with which it feeds—showing the teeth at the base of the pseudo-tracheae. The latter have been cut away to show the teeth better.

or feet in the capture of prey. The antennae of the male spider are very much modified and very elaborate. Here the appendage has become a pedipalp organ and serves in the transference of spermatozoa from the hinder end of the body and later to the female in mating. This differentiation of the male and female antennae in the spider family is a constant factor and makes it possible to distinguish between the sexes.

The jaws of lions and tigers are looked upon with a feeling of fear and horror on account of their strength and power when used against prey. But the minute jaws of insects are just as mighty and powerful, proportionately, as those of the large carnivores.

The mouth parts in many insects are modified for seizing and biting the solid bodies of their prey. In other insects the food can be cut up ready for passing through the mouth; while still other insects have mouth parts designed for suction only, as in many flies. The plant bugs have still more modified mouth parts for suction and cause great damage to the stems of plants.

NOTWITHSTANDING the great diversity of structure in the mouth parts of insects, the fundamental design is the same. They are all identical in performing the same function of supplying food for the appetite of the insect.

Each insect has its mouth parts specially constructed for taking in the kind of food upon which it subsists, and the diversity of structure in the mouth parts assigned to each species in the economy of Nature provides entomologists with important features which are used in the classification of the various families. In those insects endowed with the power of biting we have the labium, or upper lip, and adjacent to this the main part, consisting of a pair of mandibles or horny jaws, each of which moves on a powerful joint.

These mandibles are very strong, curved and pointed, and on the inner edge have serrations, or teeth. At the apex is a large powerful claw used for holding the prey, and it is by means of these mandibles that the insect is able to bite so fiercely and make its way through wood.

Insects which feed upon hard substances have their mandibles flattened to produce a large cutting surface. The teeth on the inner edge are very blunt and can be well compared with the molar teeth in quadrupeds used for grinding their food.

As if the mandibles were not sufficient, insects have another pair of jaws moving on powerful joints and situated immediately behind the mandibles; these secondary jaws are the maxillae, and they also have teeth on the inner surfaces.

One of the fiercest insects is the hornet, which is very voracious, preying on almost any form of animal substance as well as on honey and fruit. This insect hawks after wasps, conveys them to some plant and proceeds to cut off the head, then the waist, finally crushing the body with powerful mandibles and sometimes devouring the prey piece-meal.

It is interesting to note that the wasp preys on the common house-fly in a similar manner, and often enters the rooms of dwellings to capture its prey.

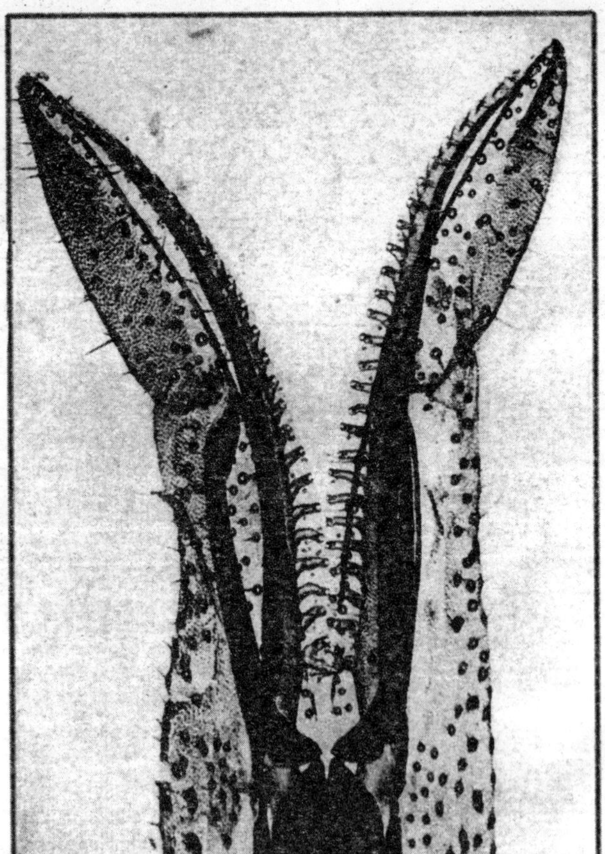

H. S. Cheavin

SUCTION FEEDING APPARATUS

A large sucking surface with tubes on the inner edge for carrying fluid food to the gullet are seen to be features of the proboscis of the snout fly when magnified. The larvae of this fly do good service to man by feeding on aphides.

A. E. Smith

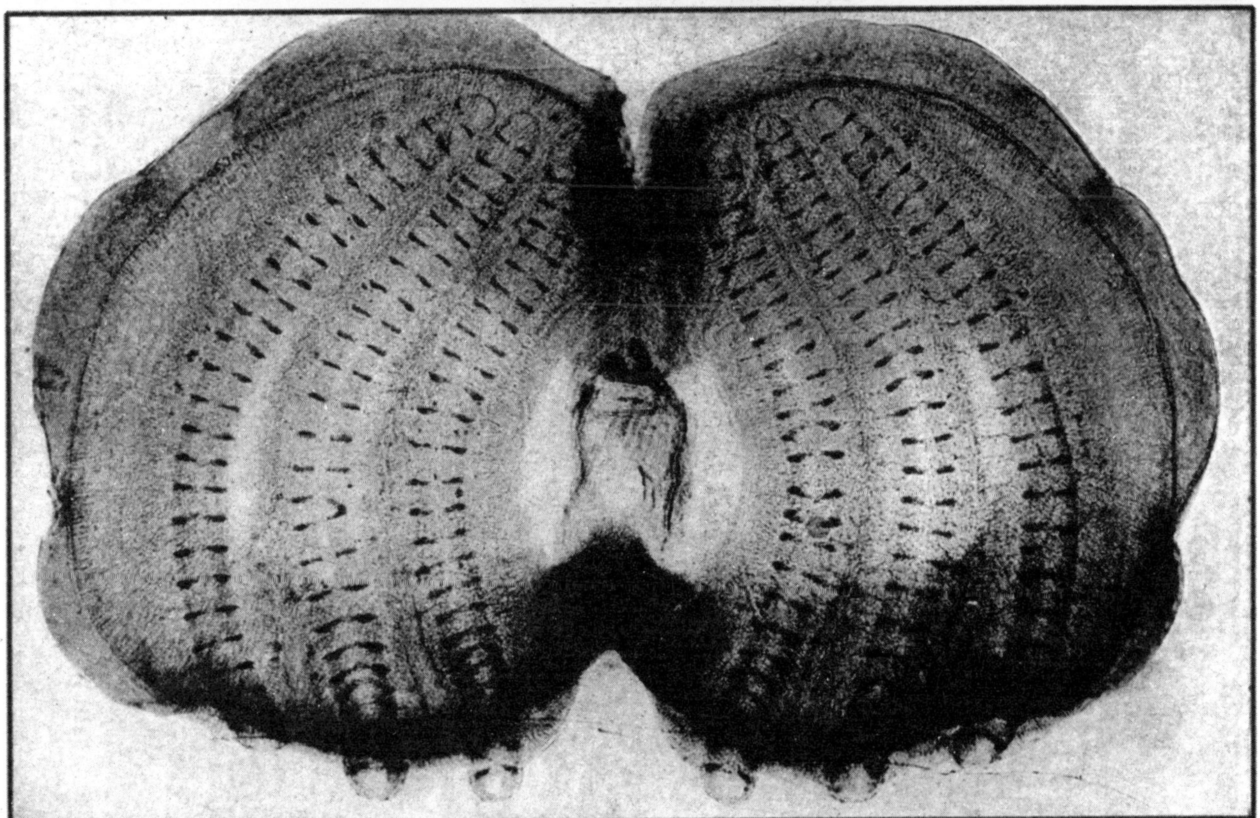

E. A. Botting

MAGNIFIED MOUTH PARTS OF BOT-FLY LARVA AND SAWFLY

Bot-flies do enormous harm to their host, the horse. Their eggs are swallowed inadvertently by the animal and hatch into larvae within the stomach. Here they suck nourishment, weakening their host. Our lower photograph shows a highly magnified view of one of these larvae, head on to the camera. Above are some of the cruelly-edged saws used by the sawfly. They have as complicated a cutting edge as any saw devised by man and are reproduced here as no unaided human eye would view them, from a micro-photograph (mag. × 200).

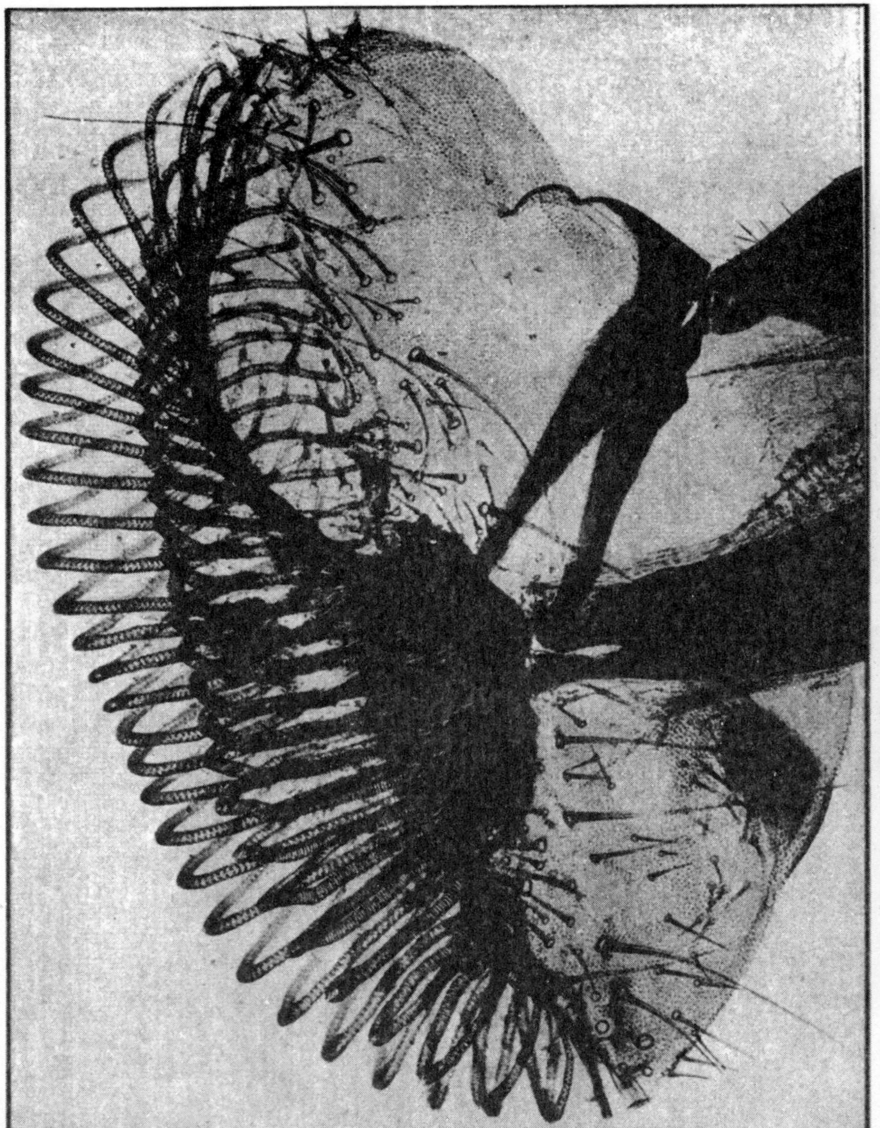

E. A. Botting

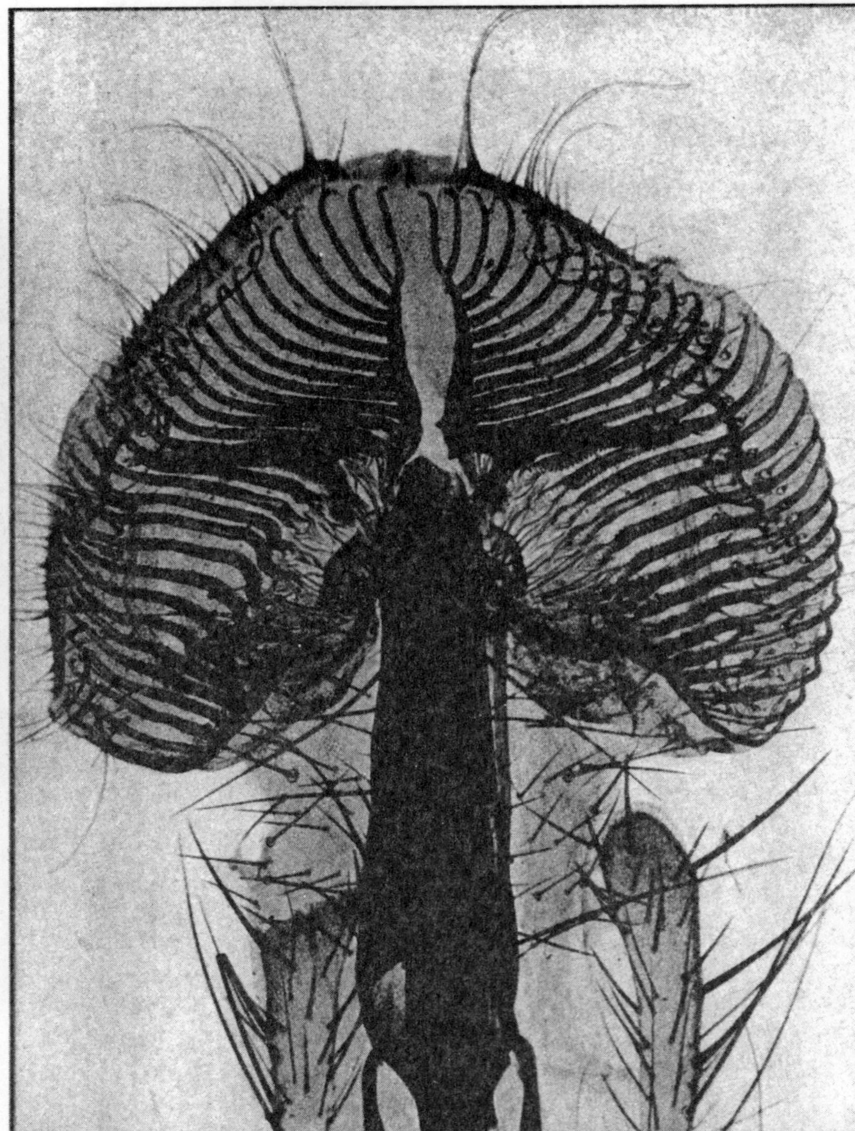

Martin Duncan

HIGHLY MAGNIFIED VIEWS OF A BLOWFLY'S TONGUE SPECIALLY CONSTRUCTED TO SUCK MEAT JUICES

What corresponds to the tongue in a blowfly is really a hollow trunk whose proper name is proboscis. At the lower end of the tongue, the end which is placed upon the food, there is situated a pair of cushion-like lobes. Inside is a series of tubes or pseudo-tracheae. These tubes connect with a main food canal which communicates directly with the mouth proper and here a special pump carries the food, always taken in liquid form, into the stomach. This is the process we see going on when we notice a blowfly dabbing at a piece of meat with its trunk-like proboscis.

In the left-hand micro-photograph we have a side view of this wonderful tongue (magnification × 150). On the right is the front aspect. The trunk is quite visible to the naked eye

E. A. Botting

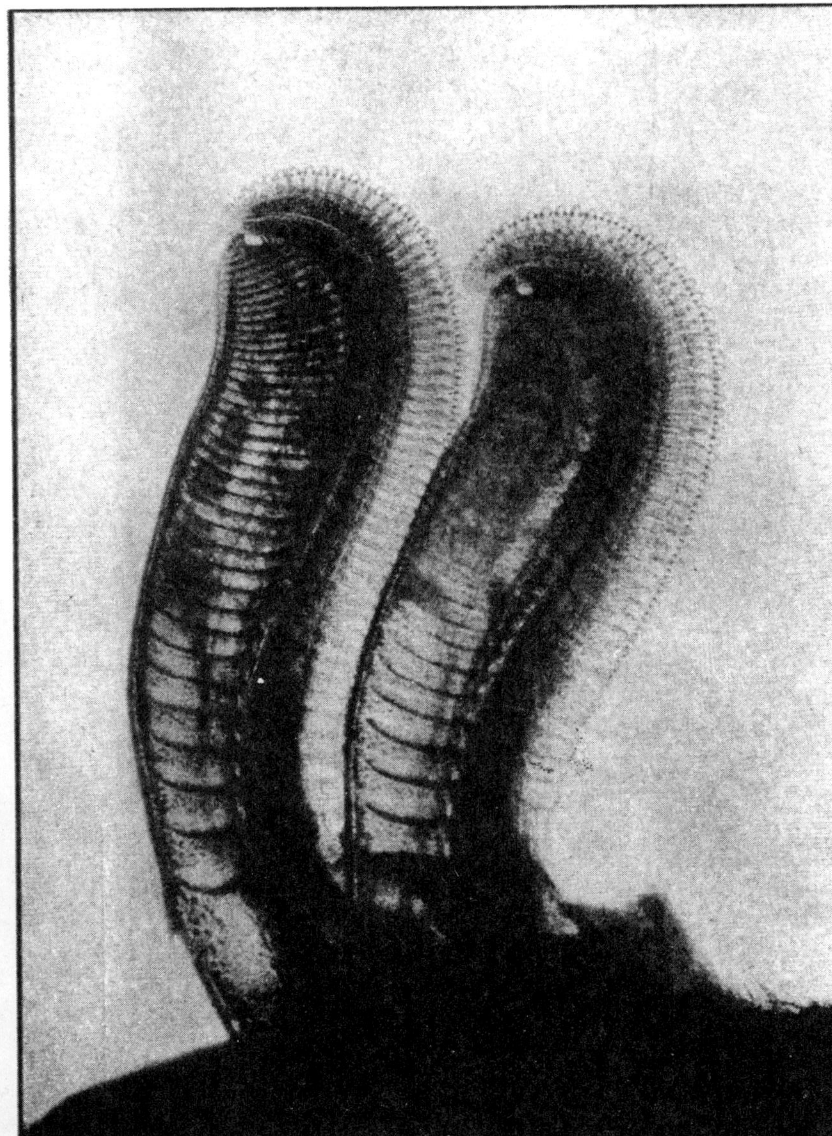

A. E. Smith

WASP-FLY'S TONGUE PROTRUDED FOR THE COMPLICATED ACT OF FEEDING AND A SAWFLY'S "JAWS"

When feeding, an insect passes the food through its mouth parts into a receptacle which fulfils rather the same function as a bird's crop—that of a kind of preliminary digestive chamber. Here the food is mingled with digestive juices and, when thoroughly steeped in them, and, thereby, partly digested, passes into the gizzard where it is masticated and strained. Lastly, the food enters the stomach proper where nutritive parts are absorbed into the blood which flows outside the alimentary tract. Our left-hand photograph shows a magnification of the sucking tongue of a wasp-fly fully protruded for the beginning of the act of feeding, and (right) the reflexed jaws of a sawfly.

H. S. Cheavin

ANTENNAE OF MALE AND FEMALE SPIDER SERVING SEVERAL PURPOSES

In the lower photograph we have the antennae of a female spider. These are jointed and covered with very sensitive hairs. At the top of each is a sharply pointed claw, for these antennae are used in conjunction with the jaws. In fact, they are also used, if occasion demand, as extra legs. Above we have the male spider's antennae. These are specially modified for purposes of mating and carrying the fertilising agent. The more we study the uses of the antennae of insects the more wonderful do they appear.

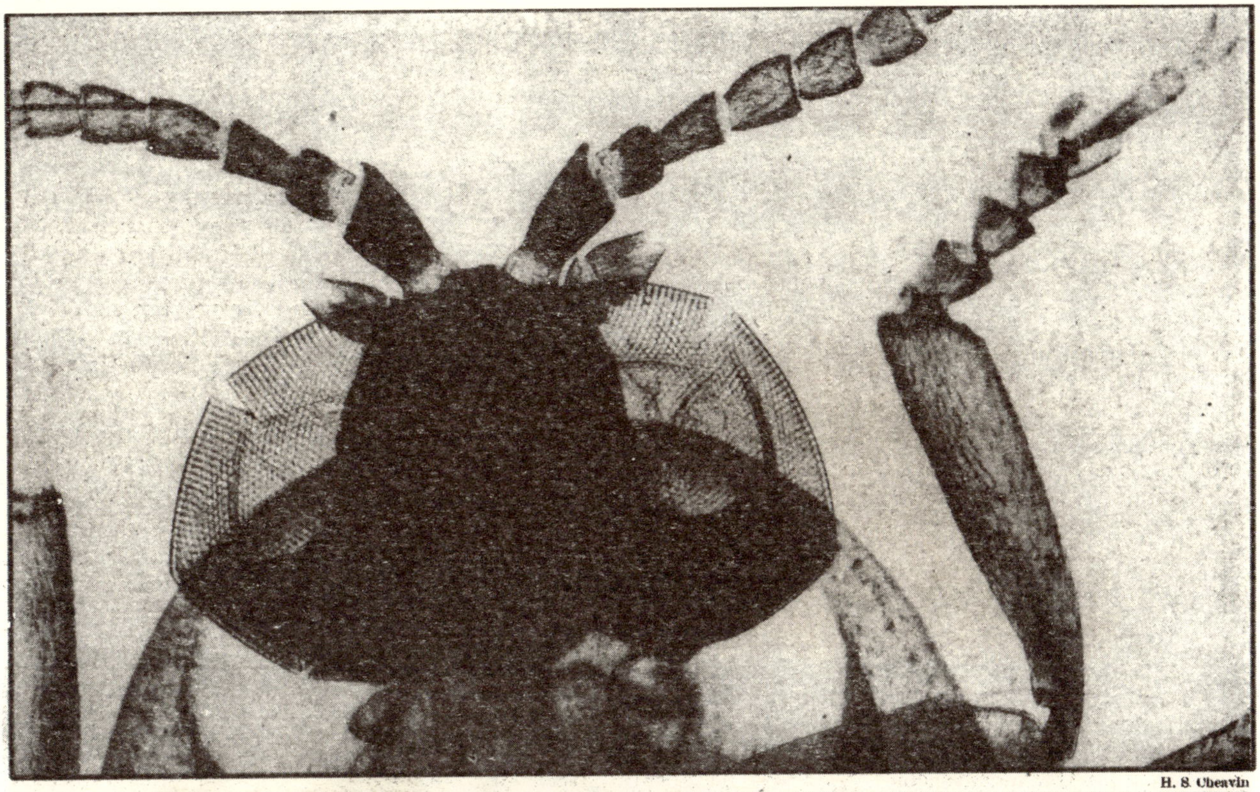

H. S. Cheavin

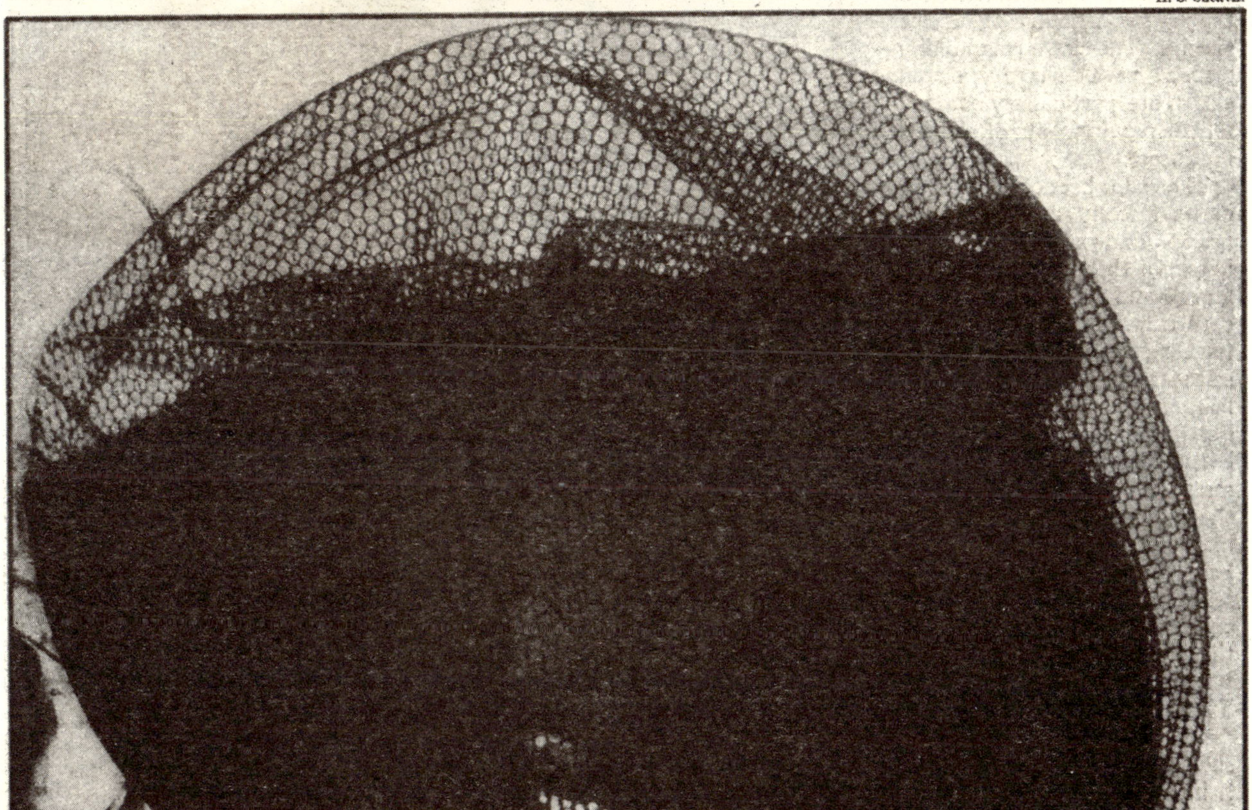

H. S. Cheavin

EYES WITH WHICH THE DOWNHILL FLY AND THE GLOW-WORM SEE

Supported by a strong and wonderful frame of chitin—the horny skeletal substance which forms the exterior covering of the great division of the animal kingdom, the arthropods which include insects and crustaceans—the compound eye of the male downhill fly (bottom) is thus kept in a spherical shape. The upper photograph, also taken at a high magnification, shows the eyes of a male glow-worm. Each of these is divided into an upper and a lower part, the latter having the larger area, as we can see in this microphotograph.

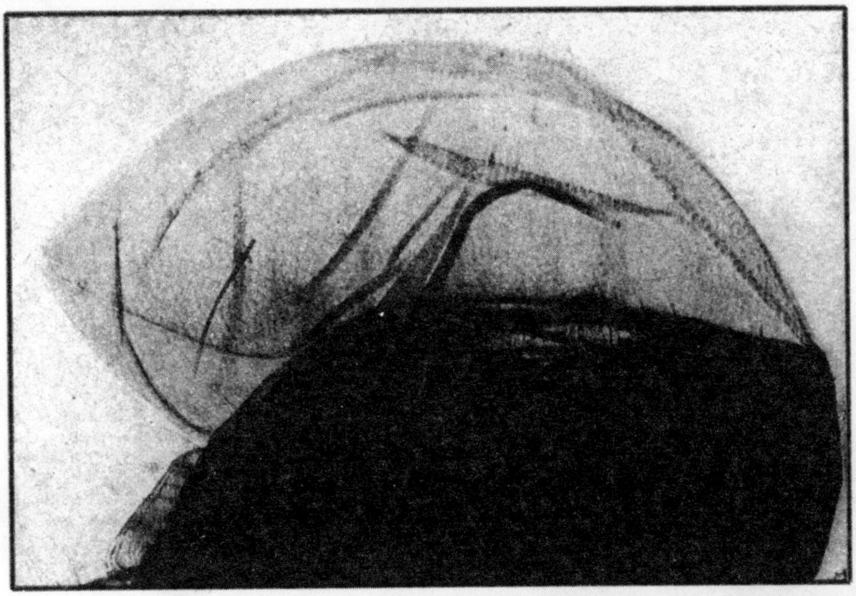

account of the larger size of the mouth parts. The mandibles have become much modified; they are no longer slender and perforated as in the larva; also they are much wider, and in addition have a row of double teeth particularly adapted for preying on other forms of insect life.

A companion of the larva of the water beetle in ferocity is the larva of the dragon fly, which is sluggish in habit and lurks for its prey at the bottom of the pool. It captures slow animals by pursuit and stalks its prey, using for this purpose a large hinged arm-like appendage, which is a modification of the second pair of maxillae forming the labium in other insects. This appendage is provided at the tip with a pair of lobes and also a pair of powerful, hinged, sharp-pointed claws or fangs.

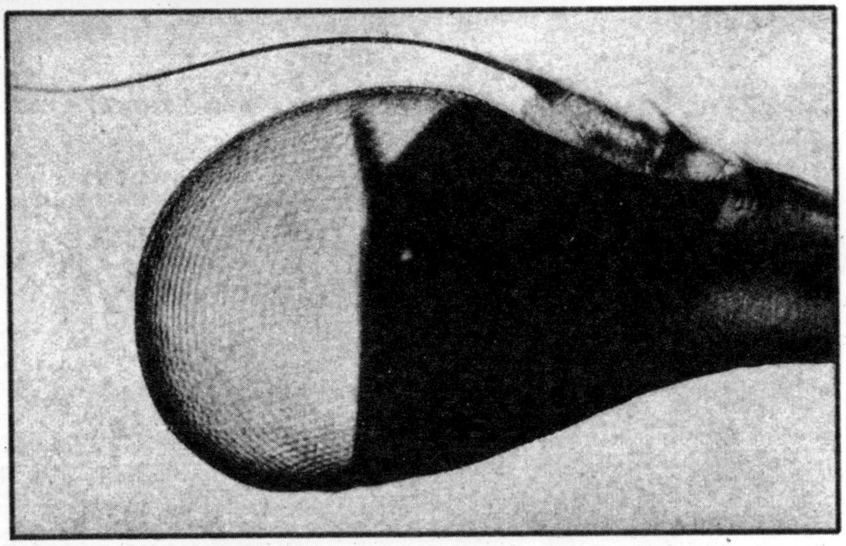

SIGHT AS IT IS PROVIDED FOR THE STALK-EYED AND DRAGON FLIES

Composed of many small facets, each eye of the strange stalk-eyed fly of Natal (bottom) is set at the end of a club-like projection from the head. One of the antennae is also shown in this photograph. A view of the whole insect appears in p. 790 (top left illustration). Above is a dragon-fly's eye, specially constructed for an insect which captures its prey on the wing.

Another type of formidable jaws is found in the soldier beetle, which feeds voraciously on other insects and even on the weaker members of its own species. The curved mandibles, armed with sharp pointed claws, are particularly adapted for the requirements of a fighting insect.

The water beetle, on account of its ferocity and voraciousness, is known as " the savage beetle of the pool." Both the larva and adult forms are carnivorous, and when in the former stage the creature will seize tadpoles, or even young fish, and its own species, are not immune from attack.

In the larval form the mandibles are very large, sharp, conical-shaped, claw-like organs, controlled at the base by means of powerful muscles. The prey is seized by the mandibles and pierced by the sharp ends, which make small punctures in the body of the victim.

EACH mandible is hollow, and at the tip is a small hole through which the blood of the victim is sucked by means of a powerful pharyngeal pump. It is interesting to note that while this operation is proceeding the mouth proper is completely closed, the mouth being used only for devouring solid pieces of its victim which have been previously torn up by the mandibles.

In the adult forms of this beetle we have practically the same story. The ferocity and voracity of the larva still persist with greater intensity on

The appendage can be folded under the head when not in use, as when the larva is lurking in its hiding-place. On the approach of a victim it is suddenly projected to seize the prey within reach, generally an unwary tadpole or insect, and it is bent over the victim, which is held near the real jaws. These are armed with powerful teeth at the upper extremity, and with them the prey is consumed.

Another type of ferocious jaws is found in the ant lion, which in its larval form lies concealed in a pit made in sand, and here it traps unwary insects that fall over the edge of this pit. They are at once seized in

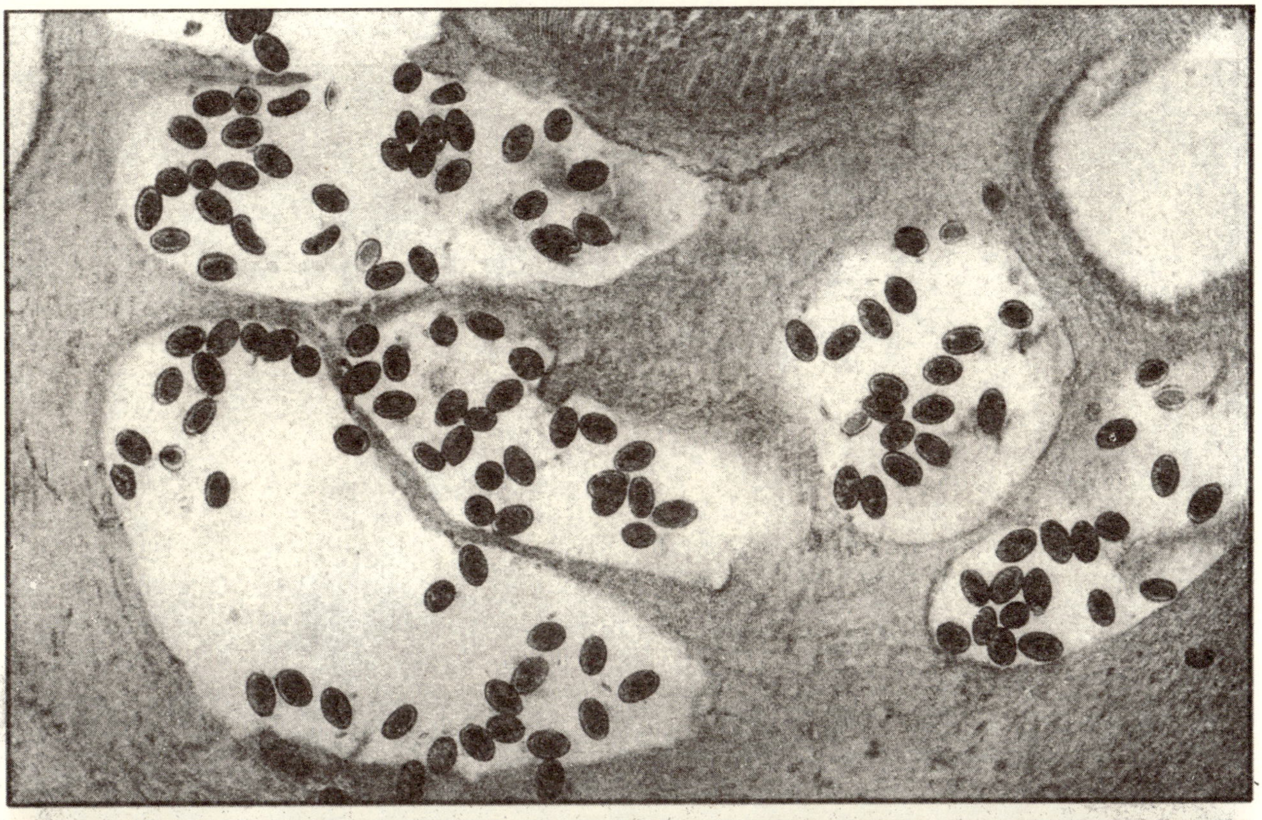

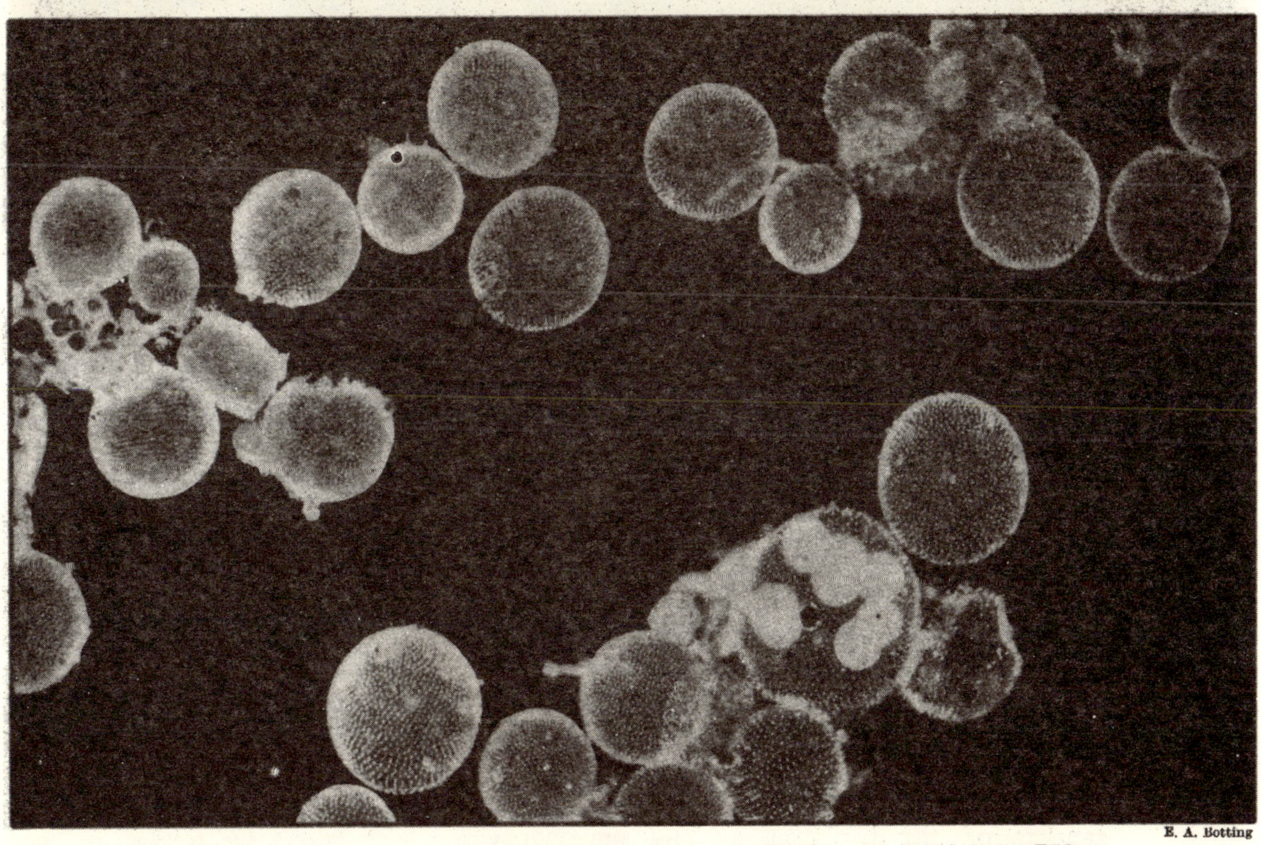

E. A. Botting

WHAT A POWERFUL LENS REVEALS IN A SPOONFUL OF DITCH WATER

One of the most beautiful of the minute animalcules inhabiting fresh water is *Volvox globator* (bottom). This tiny lump of life is spherical and rolls slowly through the water by agitating the numerous whip-like or flagellate appendages which protrude from its surface. *Volvox* swims about in colonies. Above we have a section through a liver fluke, magnified so as to show the ova or eggs developing. The liver fluke, which infests the livers of sheep, has a wonderful life history, first in water, then inside a water-snail, then on a grass stem and finally inside a sheep.

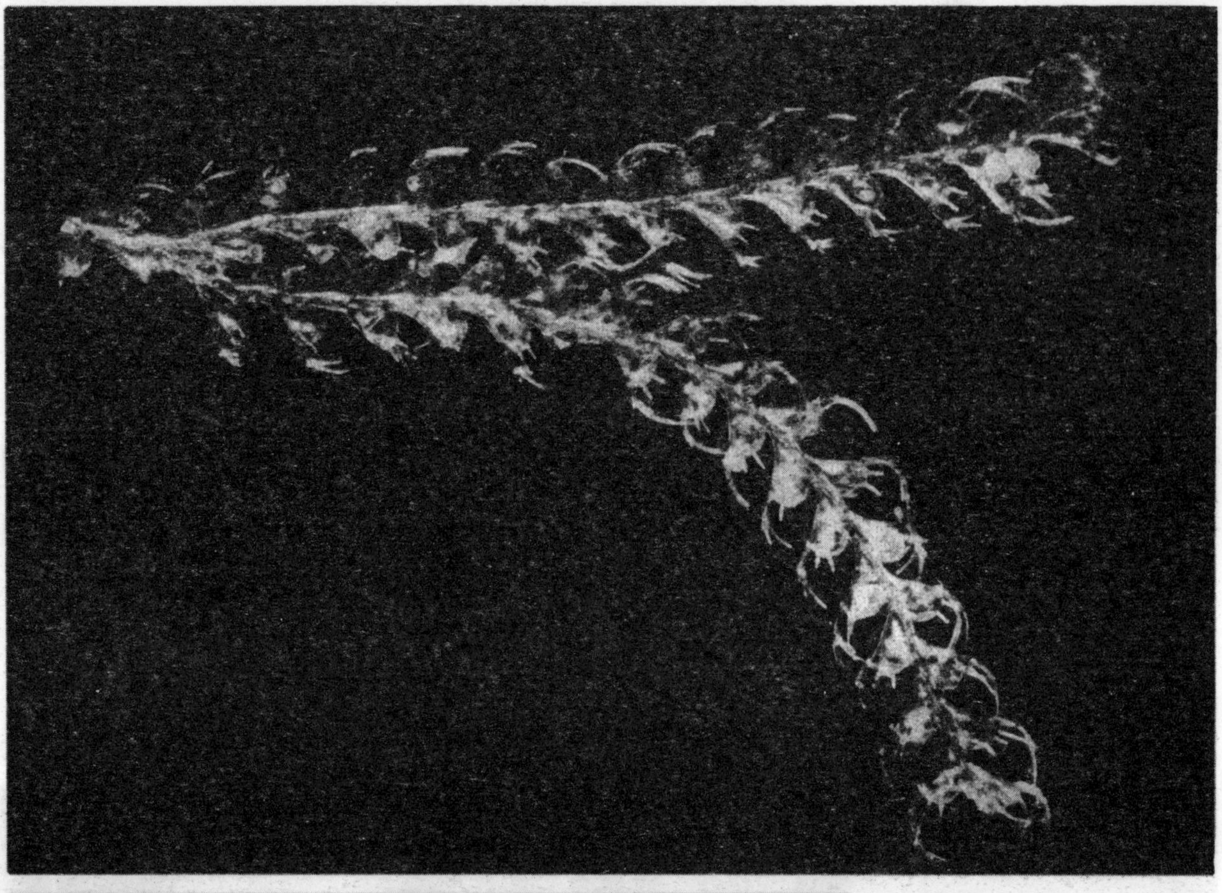

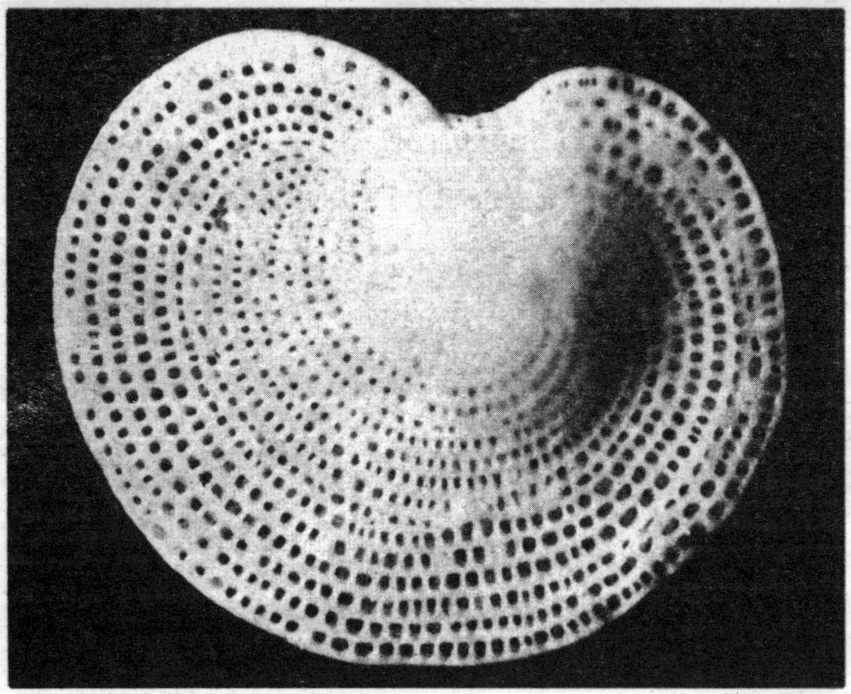

E. A. Botting

SECRETS OF THE SEA TOLD BY THE MICROSCOPE

The full wonder of the little creatures called foraminifera can only be appreciated as seen here (bottom) through a magnifying lens. These minute organisms secrete a limy shell which is perforated with many little holes (Lat. *foramen*, an opening) through which grow thread-like processes for supplying movement. In the upper photograph is a species of polyzoa.

the powerful tubular jaws, the remains of the victim being later thrown out to a considerable distance, when the ant lion prepares to receive the next unfortunate insect.

For its size the ant lion is very powerful, and it can remove small stones, jerking them out by means of its powerful legs. Some stones are carried out on its back, and those a little heavier than usual are only removed by great persistence. In this way the pit is prepared to receive its prey.

Many other insects have their mouth parts modified to take in food material by the dissolving action of a fluid secreted by a large tongue-shaped projection sometimes termed the proboscis. In these insects the mouth parts such as mandibles and maxillae used in other insects for tearing up their food are completely absent. The biting parts may be present in the form of lancets, and these

Ronald Rigby

MICROPHOTOGRAPHY SHOWS A CAT'S TONGUE TO BE A WONDERFUL RASP

Anyone who has had his hand licked by a cat will know how rough the surface of its tongue feels. This roughness is due to a large number of spike-like projections called papillae. It can be seen from the above photograph how these papillae convert the tongue into a very efficient rasp. The cat tribe use the tongue for rubbing from the bones they devour such meat as they cannot conveniently tear off. The papillae also act like the teeth of a comb between the hairs when the fur is being washed.

H. S. Cheavin

E. A. Botting

AUSTRALIAN SPINY SPIDER AND A DESTRUCTIVE TICK PEST THAT DEVELOPS IN THE NOSES OF SHEEP

It needs the microscope to show all the wonder of this minute spider from Australia (left). The spiders, as a family, are found in every part of the world where there is any supply of insect life. This example comes from Australia and demonstrates that adaptation of form for protective purposes for which the arachnids are famous. Our right-hand illustration is of a sheep tick. This is very destructive, the adult female laying her eggs in the nostrils of the sheep. After hatching, the larvae make their way up the nasal passage into the forehead, causing great irritation. Eventually, when mature, they once more enter the nose and are sneezed out, when they bury themselves in the ground, to emerge eventually as flies to lay more eggs.

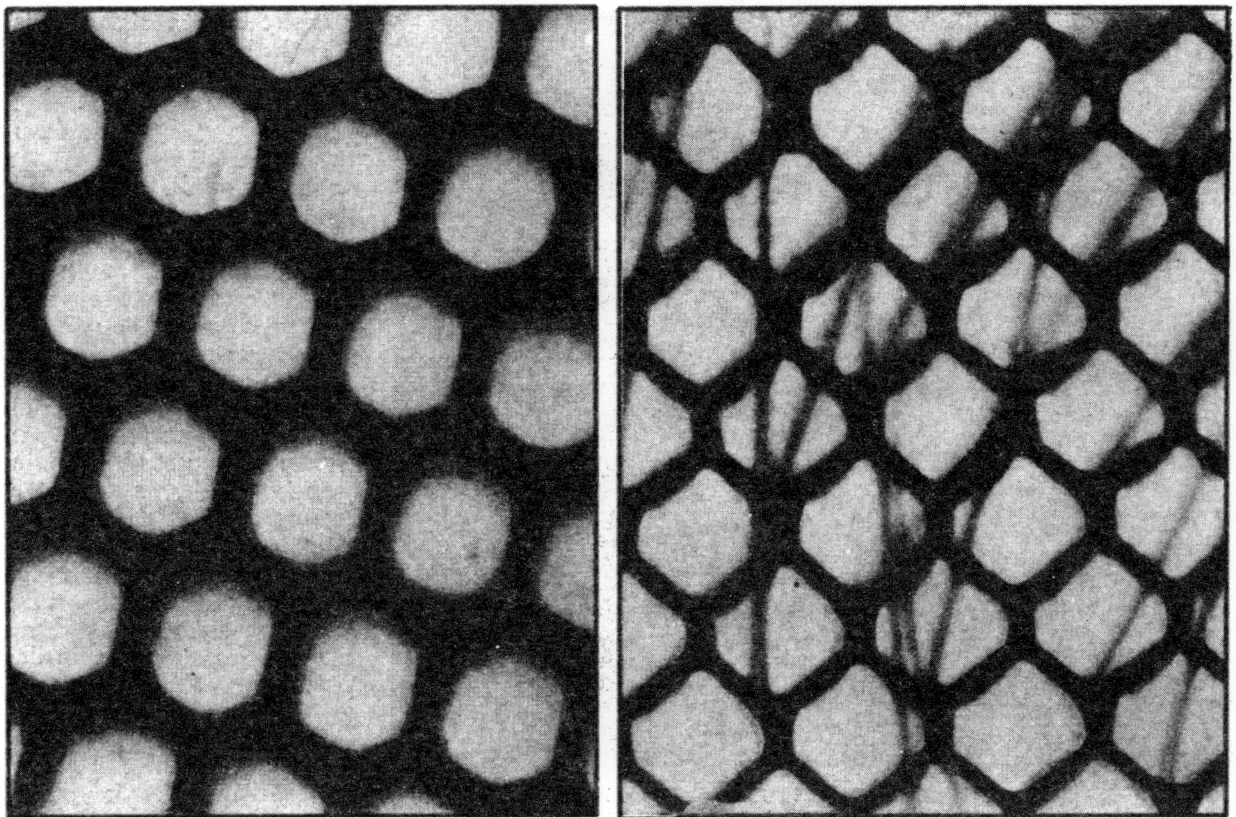

H. S. Chesvin

COMPOUND EYES OF THE GADFLY AND THE DRONE-FLY AS SEEN WHEN MAGNIFIED

The facets of the compound eye possessed by the gadfly (left) are small and very numerous, the arrangement giving increased powers of vision as against fewer facets each of larger area. It is very necessary to the gadfly, or at least the female, that it should be able to see very well, since the animals which it stabs with its proboscis for the sake of drinking their blood are apt to retort with a death-dealing whisk of the tail. The right-hand photograph shows the thin-walled facets fringed by hair-like growths of the drone-fly's eye.

are used for piercing a hole to which the proboscis, or tongue, is then applied and the liquid sucked up into the body. This proboscis, or tongue, consists of a pair of cushion-like lobes having on their inner sides a series of open channels known as pseudo-tracheae.

The inner channels are connected to a large main channel which opens directly into the mouth, where a powerful pharyngeal pump carries the liquid food into the crop and from there into the stomach.

The proboscis, when not in use, is carried bent under the lower part of the head. When the insect alights on suitable food it is extended, saliva is allowed to flow, which is then spread over the surface of the food and dissolves this ready for pumping up into the body. The house-fly in taking up food uses the flat parts of the proboscis to produce a rubbing action in the same manner as a painter uses a brush on a palette, and this action has been misinterpreted by some people as "biting," but in no case is the skin pierced. It is interesting to note that the blow-fly has at the base of its pseudo-tracheae a series of sharp-pointed projections which probably function as teeth and are used to scrape the surface of food material to help the tongue to absorb a larger amount of food in a short time.

The mouth parts of the hive bee show further modification. The smooth mandibles are devoid of teeth, but the straight inner edge is very sharp and is used for biting purposes, as in autumn when the wings of the drones have to be cut off preliminary to turning them out of the hive so as to economise food for the winter.

The maxillary palpi are present also and are seen as rudimentary projections at the base of the mandibles. These maxillae are four-jointed thin appendages and the tips are used as organs of touch. The main feature is the long hairy tongue, used for sucking purposes, with a special spoon-shaped lobe not unlike that found at the tip of an elephant's trunk. The tongue is fully extended when exploring a deep flower tube, but when not in use it can be folded into a cavity behind the head, where it becomes completely hidden from view.

THE mouth parts of the flea consist of a very much complicated apparatus for piercing and sucking. The maxillae consist of a pair of horny triangular plates seen behind the other mouth parts and well away from the mouth opening. They have no real function in feeding and are used to make a way through the hairs of the host so that the flea can reach the bare skin and thus facilitate piercing and sucking up the food. The maxillary palpi were once looked upon as antennae, because of their resemblance to those

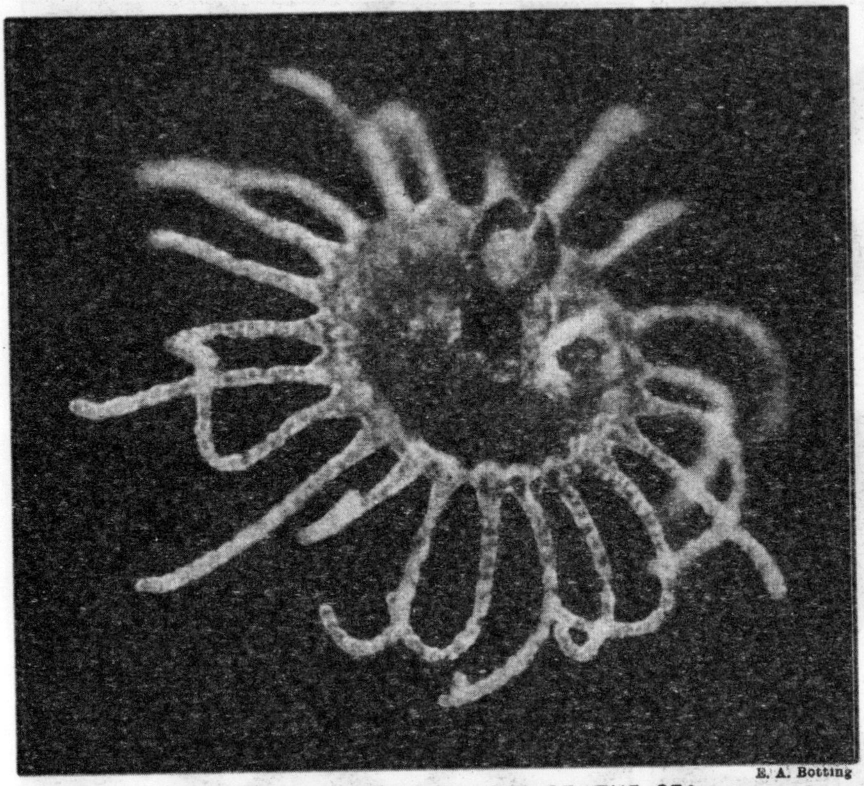

E. A. Botting

ONE OF THE TINY MEDUSAE OF THE SEA

Many species of jellyfish are included in the family whose name is Medusa, and while some members, especially those living in the Tropic seas, attain large proportions, some having a diameter of more than six feet, many others are microscopic in dimensions. Above we have an example of one of these minute species as seen on the slide of a microscope.

of other insects, and because they bear a number of stiff bristle-like sensitive hairs used as feelers or organs of touch. The piercing parts consist of two labial palpi seen to be segmented, the segments varying from two to seventeen in different flea species. At the base and tip of each segment are a number of fine hairs used also as sensory organs.

The mandibles consist of a sharp pair of lancets with serrated edges, used for making punctures in the skin of the host. In conjunction with the mandibles is the labrum, a hard, sharp-pointed structure, the edges being toothed and the whole in the shape of a trough which serves as a channel for the blood of the host to be passed through into the body of the flea.

In the common gnat, another complicated system of mouth parts has been further modified, these consisting of a case of slender lancets used for piercing the skin of the animal attacked, whose blood is drawn up by means of a long flexible sucking tube divided at the tip into a tongue-like organ.

In the act of biting, the female gnat applies the lancets to make a puncture, the divided tongue-like tip is placed on each side of the lancet over the puncture, the sucking process commences, and from time to time the lancets are plunged into the puncture, making a deeper and deeper hole. The tongue becomes bent in the shape of an S, and in the final stages the head almost rests over the hole with tongue bent double, the body of the gnat becoming visibly distended with the gorge of blood from the victim.

The mandibles of the gad fly, sometimes known as the cattle fly, because it attacks cattle, draw blood by piercing the skin with the lancets and causing considerable pain to the animal under attention. We find on the edge of these mandibles the most wonderful saw in the world; there are from 10,000 to 16,000 teeth in each inch of its length on the one edge, whilst on the other edge is the keenest blade in existence. These teeth are coarser at the tip, where there are 10,000 per inch, and become much finer at the base of the mandible, where there are 16,000 per inch.

An insect in feeding passes its food through the mouth into the crop, where it is mixed with the salivary fluid, undergoing partial maceration and digestion. The food then passes into the gizzard, which acts as the masticatory organ and strainer to detain coarse particles. It next enters the stomach and there takes place the absorption of dissolved matter, the nutritive fluids entering the blood which bathes the exterior of the alimentary canal.

The gizzard is generally muscular and well developed. Examples are found in the members of the beetle and cockroach families, the interior of the gizzard bearing chitinous teeth and bristles which act as a strainer. In the cockroach we have six stout teeth formed by a thickening of the chitinous lining and between are folds of chitin, whilst at the centre is the hairy patch which acts as a strainer. The gizzard of the water beetle shows thinner curved teeth with a larger area of hairy patches at the centre. The gizzard of the flea is found as a bulbous expansion in front of the stomach. It is made up of thin muscular folds which taper towards the extremities. The folds have a valvular action and prevent the return of fluids from the stomach and also force the blood of the victim from the gullet into the stomach.

Another wonder of insect life is to be found in the powers of vision which are particularly adapted for the habitat of the individual. In most types the large protruding eyes are very prominent features of the head.

Rounded horny structures resembling a net stretched over a frame constitute the cornea of the compound eye of the fly, and are made up of a large

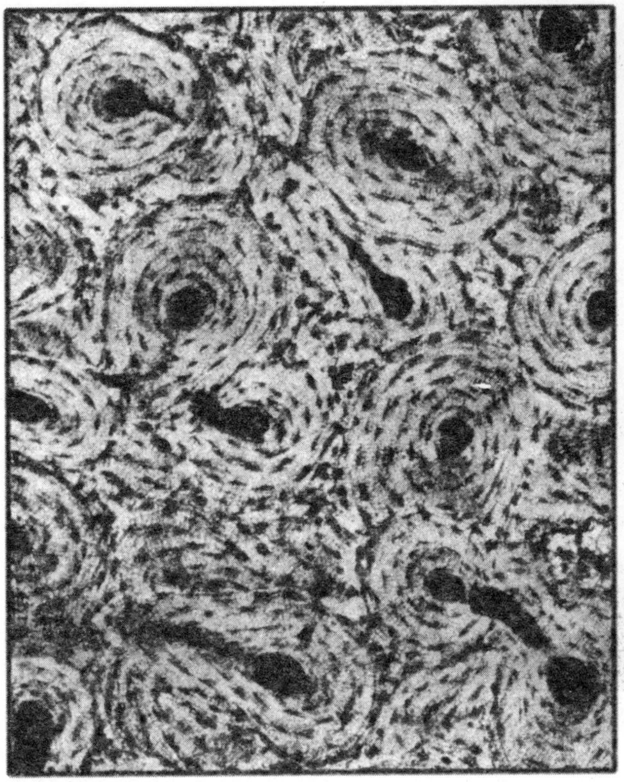

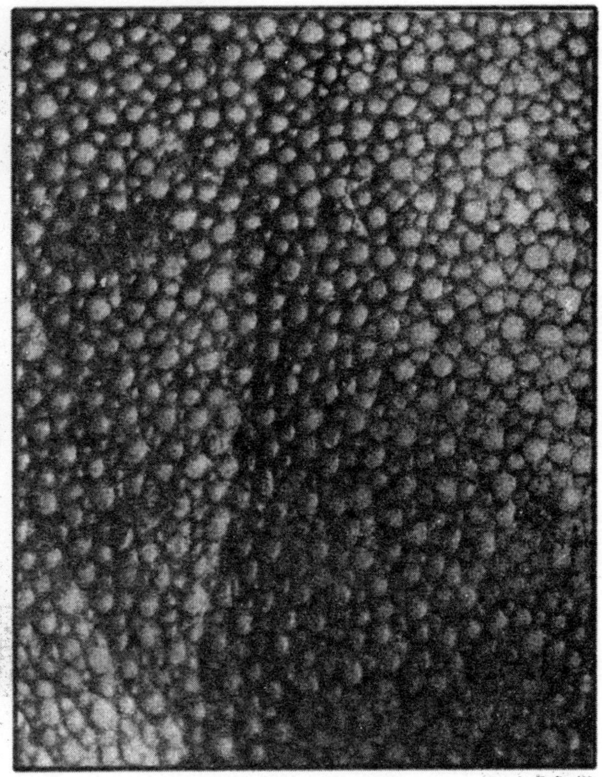

A. E. Smith

PARTS OF THE SKELETONS OF A LION AND A CRAB HIGHLY MAGNIFIED

The left-hand photograph in this page shows part of a lion's bone. Animal bones are made up of hard and soft layers which contain channels occupied by blood vessels. Bone contains over 60 per cent. of earthy matter such as calcium phosphate and calcium carbonate and rather more than 30 per cent of animal matter. This last consists mostly of a substance called collagen from which gelatine is obtained. The right-hand photograph shows a portion of the exterior skeleton of a crab—the shell, which is made of the substance called chitin.

number of hexagonal areas known as facets. When the cornea is removed and spread flat we see that each facet is a double convex compound lens, consisting of two plano convex lenses of different densities or refracting power when joined together.

The facets also vary in size, those at the periphery being larger than those at the centre. An example of this can be seen in the male glow-worm, whose facets are larger in the upper parts of the eye than those found in the lower parts. In the drone fly the facets are small and hexagonal in shape in the mid-region of the eye, whereas at the periphery the facets are large and square. Again, in the gad fly the facets in the mid-region of the eye are three times less than those found at the periphery.

The total number of facets present in various insects can be as low as 50, as in some ants. There are 4,000 in house flies, 12,000 in dragon flies, and 17,000 in butterflies; but they can also vary in the same species. One of the ants (*Formica pratensis*) has 1,000 facets in each compound eye.

The large compound eyes of insects are fixed and immovable, which explains why the eye is hemispherical in shape. All the facets have not the same length of axis, and so the image formed on the retina is blurred because it cannot be in sharp focus.

The blurred image formed at a distance of 2 inches from the object becomes more blurred at 12 inches; this distance in an eye composed of 72 facets is regarded as about the limit of recognition, and the degree of definition is reached at a distance of 3 feet in the tortoise-shell butterfly. On the other hand, at a distance of 20 feet from an object, the eyes of a dragon fly would see the same detail as is clear to the human eye at a distance of 160 feet. This power of vision in the dragon fly is necessary, because of the flight taken in long sweeps through the air, which increases the range of vision when in pursuit of prey. The wings are particularly adapted for these long sweeps. It must not be forgotten that vision and its limiting power are regulated to a certain extent by the flying powers of each insect, for larger insects naturally take longer sweeps in flight than do the smaller insects.

The compound eye is again modified in those insects which live most of their lives on the substances on which they feed. Here the eyes are found to be much smaller and flatter and possess a lesser number of facets in the cornea.

Such an eye is seen in the common greenfly, found in such great numbers on our rose trees; while another is found in the scarlet forest hopper. Here, however, a larger number of smaller facets

A. E. Smith

NEWT TADPOLE AND ITS TRANSITORY GILLS

For only about six months of its life, during the tadpole stage in fact, does the newt possess gills. These protrude through its neck, unlike the enclosed gills of fishes. The magnifying lens shows us the detail of these wonderful organs which separate the oxygen from the water and pass it to the blood.

is present, particularly suitable in an insect which spends most of its time on one plant, and at times wishes to change its position in search of food.

Those insects whose habitat is in water have compound eyes, with very heavy chitinous facets, which serve as a protection from the water: also the whole shape of each eye is circular, to enable the insect to see in every direction.

Eyes of this type are present in the water measurer, which spends its life skimming along the surface of the water. The water beetle also has a thick horny facet, for the same reason. The eyes are also larger in size, to give this insect greater power of vision when under water or flying at night in search of another pool as a change of habitat.

The compound eyes in the male species are found to be larger than those of the female. The greater amount of eye surface makes room for a greater number of facets and gives greater vision, enabling the male to find the female more easily. A peculiar adaptation of the eyes is found in the stalk-eyed fly of Natal known as diopsis. Here the eyes are carried on a lateral projection. In the female the length of this projection is less than that of the male, and in some species of diopsis the projections are not very long, which gives the insect a stereoscopic form of vision.

As if the compound eyes were not sufficient for vision, many insects have on the upper parts of the head two or three simple eyes arranged in the form of a triangle and known as ocelli.

This simple form of eye is a relic of the earlier form of vision in insects which preceded that of the compound eye, and consists of a bi-convex lens of simple form, surrounded by pigment cells resting on an aggregation of elongated rod-shaped nerve cells, separated by pigment and having a refractive cuticle.

Lubbock has stated that these ocelli see like the human eye. The lens throws an image on the back of the eye, and the image is seen reversed, which in the human eye has been reversed again in the right position. Whether the insect has the same faculty is unknown. The position of these ocelli on the back of the head of the insect suggests a protective purpose; it is thereby made aware of the approach of an object from above or behind. On the other hand, it has been stated that these ocelli are not used for real vision at all. As they are representative of the earlier form of vision, such a form of eyes is a degenerate type and can only be used, it is said, to distinguish between the effects of light and darkness.

The eyes of the ant lion show this ocellus structure distributed in groups on each side of the head as protuberances, each ocellus having a thick horny structure such as is necessary for an insect living among hard sand with sharp cutting edges.

Another striking wonder is to be found in the many types of legs and feet of insects which are adapted for the many functions such as walking, running, clasping, catching prey and digging through the soil or listening to insect music.

By far the greater number of insects use their forelegs and other legs for locomotive purposes. The normal leg consists of constant factors. These are, the coxa or haunch, a broad flat piece fused with the side or under surface of the body; the trochanter, a small triangular segment connecting the coxa with the femur or thigh, which forms the third elongated joint of the leg. Following the femur we have the tibia, or shin, which is the same length; then the tarsus, or foot, consisting of any number of segments up to five, terminated by two distinctive claws.

The tarsus is the only part of the leg which touches the ground, and its many joints give flexibility to the leg for securing a firm foothold when the insect is travelling on an uneven surface.

The legs of insects may undergo great modifications. They may be broad and thick for digging, have a comb for cleaning the antennae, be flat for swimming, or have hairy projections for collecting and holding pollen, and have a thin area which serves as an auditory organ.

By far the greater number of insects use their legs for locomotion, and the first or normal leg is of this type, the remaining two being modifications seen in an insect such as the earwig.

Chapter CXXI

Is Nature Really Cruel?

By H. Mortimer Batten

Author of "Nature from the Highways"

It is not to be wondered at that the early Victorian picture of Nature, "The dragon-fly torn by the swallow, the sparrow speared by the shrike," has proved so readily acceptable as "red of tooth and claw," for in our own lives we see, for the most part, the cruelty of Nature's world—the small bird in the talons of the hawk, the mouse displayed to the luxurious cruelty of our fireside pet, the fly in the spider's web, the half-devoured remains of bird or beast in every field and woodland corner.

We are familiar, too, with the rabbit's scream of terror and despair, with the cry of the small bird caught after dark in the talons of the owl, so that, over all and above all, the inexorable law of selection, the eternal weeding-out process, seems to occupy a foremost place in the activities of woodland life. Of the quiet backwaters of Nature, the field mouse weaving her nest, the fox cubs cuddled and caressed by their mother, we see little or nothing.

But *is* Nature cruel? I think not. Cruelty in its keenest forms is the invention of man, and we, for the most part, reap its royalty.

Let us try to sift out the facts. Not long ago I came across, in the aquatic world, a creature which I took to be about the most perfect instrument of torture I had ever seen. It consisted of a loathsome eight-legged beast, rather like a scorpion, and about two and a half inches in length. Protruding from its head were two powerful forceps, and its scheme of life was to lie at the bottom of some murky pool, pretending to be a waterlogged twig, its tail stuck upright. Little fish are wont to gather round any protrusion of this kind, and immediately a fish came within the insect's reach, down went its flapper tail, it projected itself through the water, and in an instant had the fish amidships in its powerful forceps. It would then proceed to suck the life juices from its unhappy victim, a process which occupied close upon an hour, while all the time the fish was alive and breathing.

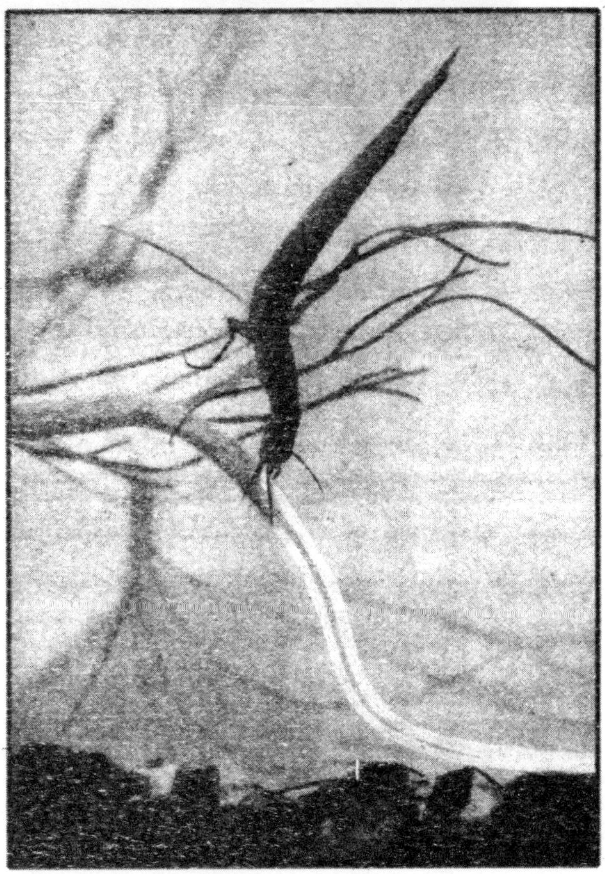

THE WATER-TIGER AND THE EEL

The larva of the water-tiger beetle lurks in pond and stream. We see one with its jaws fastened on an elver, or young eel, which it has sucked white. But an anaesthetic fluid is pumped into the victim as soon as it is seized.

Inquiry, however, revealed the facts of the case. The forceps of the attacking insect are hollow, and the instant they close, a fluid is ejected through them, on much the same lines as from the fangs of a snake. This fluid is nothing more or less than a powerful anaesthetic, which at once strikes to the spine and immediately paralyses the whole nervous system. The fish which has received its dose may live for a day or more, in fact till it dies of starvation, but so far as its feelings are concerned we are safe in concluding that it ceases to live immediately the anaesthetic is injected. As a matter of fact, the anaesthetic is pumped in and out in considerable quantities, and serves to dissolve the entire tissue of the captive, so that when it floats away it is no more than an empty skin. The facts of the case are not very pleasant reading, but they serve to illustrate that the most merciless and cruel methods of Nature may be rendered merciful by some special provision.

Spiders similarly dope their prey. In the case of these insects which absorb the juices of their victims, naturally a lengthy process, it would not meet the circumstances of the case if the victim were killed outright, for its "blood" would then congeal and dry in the atmosphere. They keep the patient alive, and anaesthetics are employed to make this necessary process as simple as possible.

Then let us take the cruelty of the cat with its mouse victim. It is part of Nature's scheme that cats and other creatures dependent on their quickness should take their prey home *alive* for the training of their young. Some years ago I knew a big game hunter who had

Neville Kingston

WHAT ARE THE FEELINGS OF THE RAT IN THE HORNBILL'S BEAK?

Human pity is aroused at once on behalf of the victim in this spectacle. It would seem, in terms of human feeling, that the rat's experience must be the most dreadful possible. But, from a careful study of the subject, it appears that once the animal has been seized a kind of paralysis sets in, as in the case of a mouse being played with by a cat, and that suffering exists more in the imagination of the spectator than in the consciousness of the animal. We must beware of judging the feelings of animals too closely by human standards.

been carried off by a tigress, which actually took him to her cubs, and played cat and mouse with him for an hour or more. Every time he tried to creep away the tigress dragged him back and this went on until an army of beaters arrived upon the scene. The tigress then carried him off but dropped him on finding herself in the centre of the din, and the hunter was rescued quite conscious and very little injured.

This man's story as concerned his mental condition during the unique experience was enlightening. He remembered every incident with perfect clearness; he remembered the terrific mental effort while in the tigress's clutches of trying to drag himself away. He had no fear, no dread. To all these sensations his mind was an entire blank. He was aware of the sunshine, aware that his position was a terrible one, but he suffered nothing mentally or physically. The nightmare experience through which he had lived was, in his own words, comparatively calm compared with half an hour in a dentist's chair!

So here we arrive at another kind of anaesthetic. People who have been as near to death as it is possible for a human being to approach have repeatedly stated that at a certain point their fears and their sense of pain ceased entirely, yet our minds are infinitely more sensitive and comprehending than the minds of any lower animal. The mind of a mouse, for example, is a very minute affair compared with

Neville Kingston

SOUTH AMERICAN TIGER BITTERN SWALLOWS A FISH

The South-American tiger bittern swallows a fish whole. Feeding is the most important thing in animal life, and we see this idea exemplified in the tense attitude and the outspread wings of the bird. We must not unduly excite our imagination about the horror that the fish must feel when in the act of being swallowed. Although in an element other than water, the fish still flaps and wriggles—movements which ordinarily take it away from danger. These movements are rather the outcome of blind instinct than terror.

the mind of a man, but if a man does not suffer in the clutches of a tiger, does a mouse suffer in the clutches of a cat?

Fainting is, in itself, an illustration of Nature's mercifulness. Why do we, or other creatures, faint under circumstances of extremity, be it mental strain, or nervous shock, or loss of blood? Is it Nature's merciful anaesthetic to close our minds to what might otherwise be a terrible conclusion?—inherited from the days when life was a struggle against animal foes, when we might be carried off and torn to pieces piecemeal by one or other of them.

Nature is not cruel—rather, for all her cruelties, she has a special provision, and it is possible for man (or any other creature) to faint, yet to retain full use of his faculties and his muscular powers. Thus an animal may struggle desperately against a foe, even though its mind is dead to fear and its body dead to suffering. There can be no doubt that the ability to suffer is in exact proportion to the brain, and thus we, with our super-sensitive and super-cultivated brains, can suffer infinitely more keenly than the highest of living things next to us. Man possesses an imagination, and by that power he stands not only superior, but far above the highest of the lower vertebrates.

IMAGINATION is the one power by which man possesses the earth. Eliminate it, and what do we eliminate with it? First and foremost the desire to improve, which is ambition. All possibility of a god,

Neville Kingston

THE END OF WILD LIFE IS TO BE EATEN BY SOMETHING ELSE SOONER OR LATER

Nature seems at first sight an extremely cruel force. To live long enough to reproduce their kind is lucky for many forms of animal life. On every side we see the scheme of wild life is one of hurried eating before the eater is himself devoured. Even when creatures like the herb eaters are not preying on each other they are consuming the supply of their neighbour. These roach, for instance, which we see being swallowed, the one on the left by a little bittern and the one on the right by a boatbill, are not themselves predatory, at least not on other fish. But they are as terrible enemies to aquatic larvae as the fishing birds are to them. Yet animals do not inflict, as a rule, half the pain on each other that human beings do.

SUDDEN DEATH ON THE VELDT: LIONESS LEAPS UPON THE BACK OF A FLEEING ZEBRA

It is common to speak of an animal's "last agony," and when this is referred to it is usually in connection with a bullet or other man-made wound. It is doubtful if there is much agony felt when an animal such as a zebra is killed by one of the big carnivores. This photograph, sent to us from Africa, is of a reconstruction showing how a lioness obtains a meal from a zebra in the veldt. The great cat has leaped on the zebra's back and has one forepaw on its quarry's forehead to wrench it back and the other forepaw is fastened in the chest. The powerful jaws are biting through the backbone and this will immediately paralyse the animal. The zebra's fate is infinitely preferable to that of, say, a donkey killed slowly by overwork in man's service.

Dorian Leigh

Shepstone

PYTHON FEEDING AND A MONGOOSE-COBRA DUEL

Animals kill each other more efficiently and less painfully than human hunters do. The python crushes the fowl in one constriction of its powerful muscles (bottom). The cobra, on the other hand, if it is worsted, as it usually is, in a duel with a mongoose, dies in the heat of battle. But in any case the end comes suddenly.

of worship, of admiration for higher things, goes. Such sense of worship as might remain would really be fear, as the young ape fears and dreads the old ape, though he may mimic him and watch his movements. Every thing which makes man what he is finds its root in imagination, and imagination is more than one half of suffering. It plays the leading part. First of all it makes possible the realization of death—the possibility of our own lives coming to a close, the vision of the body which has served us so well lying stark under the stars. No lower animal understands death as we understand it. Generally speaking, their fear of death begins and ends with the scent of blood, so half their sufferings are relieved at the outset; but there is a further understanding—pain. Animals do not understand pain any more than they understand death. What I mean by this is that their sufferings are limited to what they suffer physically—the actual sensation of pain. They do not wait for the next paroxysm, they do not realize how ill they are, they do not dread what to-morrow might hold. It is not a cheerful subject, but it helps us to understand a world which we, with our super-sensitive imaginations, are only too apt to paint in our own vivid colours.

If you or I lost a hand we would regard the dreadful mutilation with a sense of horror. Not so a creature of the lower world. It would suffer only the actual pain of the injury, which in the case of a severe injury is often very little, and not one-fifth of what man suffers. A winter or two ago a hedgehog came to my garden trailing a mutilated hind leg, but when a scrap of bacon was put under his nose, he ate it gaily enough and looked round for more. When fed he slept, and a few days later went his way quite happily, though maimed. A small bird which had newly lost one foot came as perkily as ever to the bird-table, and indulged in his usual quarrel with a hedge-sparrow, while an old spaniel I had, after breaking a hind leg in leaping through a deer fence one afternoon, escaped from his hospital in the evening and made his usual round of the village to see that canine affairs were progressing favourably.

A. H. Hall

BETTER TO DIE BY THE BEAK THAN IN A TRAP

It is surely less unpleasant for a rat to be seized and swallowed by a bird than to get caught in a trap. Indeed, to be trapped seems to excite more terror in an animal than anything else; whereas, when animals slay each other, the killing is either done quickly, or some deadening process comes into play so that suffering is automatically minimised.

Then let us take the squeal of a rabbit when a stoat or a weasel is on its trail. Once it has obtained a whiff of its deadly pursuer, the rabbit runs no farther, but simply lies down helplessly, uttering that plaintive cry. Here we have yet another anaesthetic, for the stoat and the weasel, like the insect with the forceps, take the blood of their victims. The paralysis of the rabbit is an affection of the brain, and to what extent does it suffer physically when its brain is so disordered that its muscles refuse to work?

We regard the stoat and the weasel and such-like killers as the most cruel and relentless of all wild creatures, yet they play a very merciful part in Nature's scheme of mercy. How long does a rabbit or a hare linger in a trap where it ranges for food? Not long. That first plaintive scream brings the hunter to the spot, and the creature which might have lingered for hours lingers no longer.

Throughout Nature we find a fixed and highly developed motive against lingering death and long suffering. Animals which dwell in herds, for example, do not allow one of their number to linger in an injured or mutilated state. If they did it would bring their foes about them, and the safety of the herd would be threatened. So by a merciful but inexorable ruling the fit set about to destroy the unfit.

I once saw this illustrated among half-wild prairie cattle. A man had left a scythe lying about, and, foolish as cattle are, one of the beasts had severely injured itself. The rest of the herd became wildly

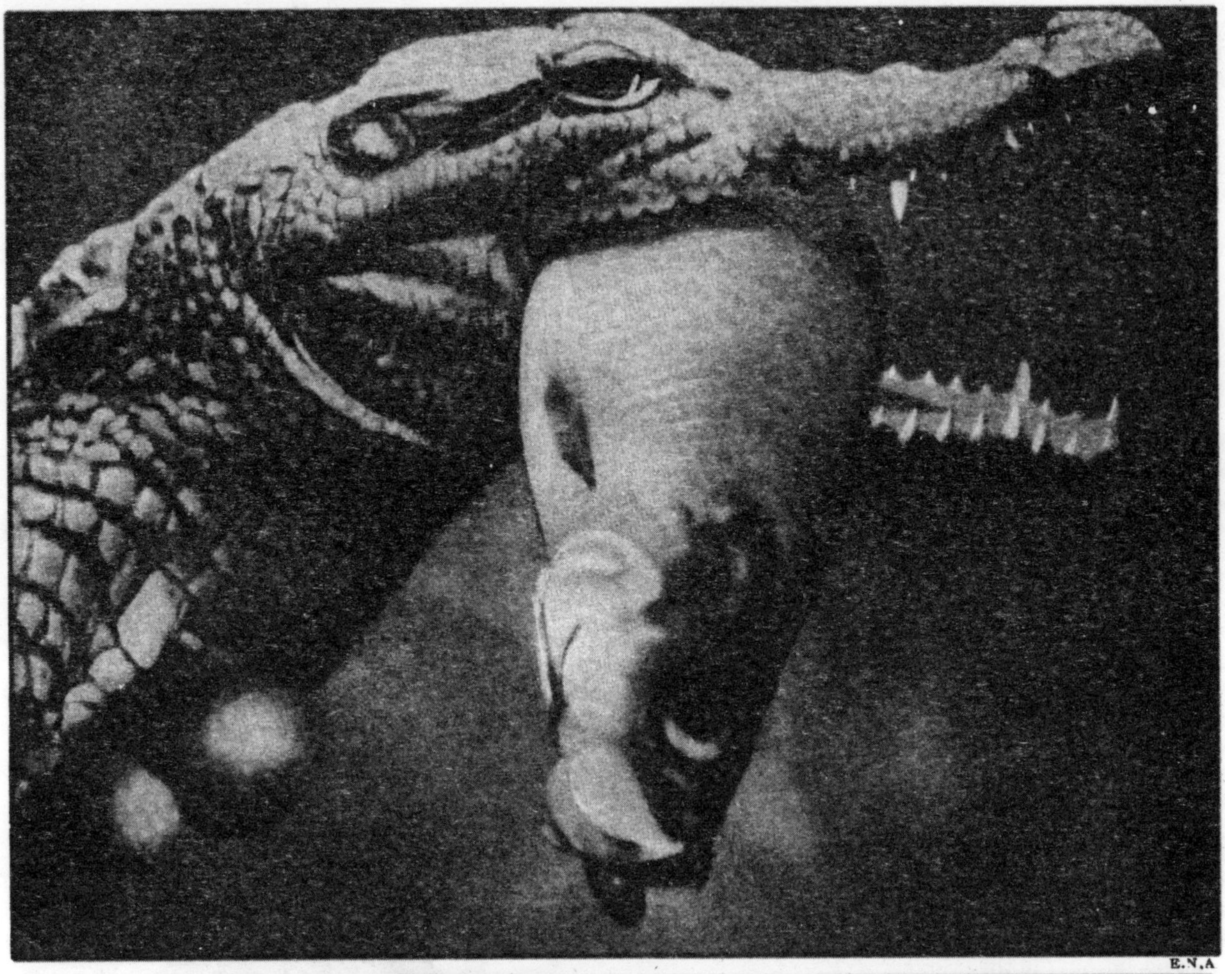

E.N.A

excited, and milling round the unfortunate beast, it was not long before they had it gored and trampled out of existence.

Another merciful provision of Nature is that when an animal falls ill, sleep comes to it. Either it sleeps till its strength is regained, or it does not waken. Of the tens of thousands of wild creatures that perish from injury, it may be taken that every one that can gain a place of shelter passes out of existence in the quietest and best way possible.

Nature may be inexorable, but Nature is not cruel. In all the wonderful and complex machinery of life, there is no cruelty compared with that of man's invention—as, for example, the keeping of wild creatures under unsuitable conditions. Better to adopt Nature's rule to kill, but not to keep alive in suffering

Neville Kingston

EGRET AND CROCODILE WITH THEIR PREY

Below is an egret with a rat which it has just captured, and above a crocodile with a large fish between its efficient teeth. The main diet of the great saurian is fish, and any caught are very quickly disposed of. But the crocodile is usually thought of with loathing as lying in wait for victims at drinking places and then dragging under any animal not too large.

Chapter CXXII

Living Representatives of Extinct Monsters

By Dr. W. T. Calman, F.R.S.

Keeper of Zoology, The British Museum

THERE is a widespread impression among those whose acquaintance with the subject has been gained from popular writings that in the ages vaguely referred to as "prehistoric" the earth was peopled by animals of gigantic size and terrific aspect, of which the animals now living are the puny and degenerate representatives.

While there is a certain basis of truth for this belief, it is far from being a correct picture of the history of the animal kingdom. It is true that at various periods in the long history of the earth, as revealed by geology, different groups of animals have attained to monstrous dimensions, far exceeding those of their nearest relatives in the living world to-day, so that in looking at their fossil remains in museums we naturally say, "There were giants in the earth in those days." But, on the other hand, there are other groups which seem to have reached their culmination in our own epoch, and it comes as a surprise to many people to learn that there are animals now living that are larger than any known to us as fossils.

It is curious that the mammoth, which has so impressed the popular imagination that its name is used as an adjective to indicate enormous size, hardly deserves its reputation, for it was not so big as some living elephants. During the Pleistocene period the mammoths ranged over a great part of the northern hemisphere, both in the Old World and in America. They even penetrated within the Arctic Circle in Siberia, and the islands to the north of it, where their remains are so abundant that their ivory has long been an important article of commerce. They seem to have survived in this region until a comparatively recent period, for their carcasses have been found preserved entire in the frozen soil, so fresh that dogs fed on the flesh. One such carcase was excavated on the banks of the Beresovka river in eastern Siberia by a Russian scientific expedition in 1902. Illustrations of it are given in pages 1337–1345.

In this instance it was even possible to discover the manner of the animal's death. It had fallen into a crevasse in the frozen earth, and in its struggles to get out it must have burst a large blood-vessel, for the cavity of the chest was full of blood. It had been browsing on grass, some of which remained between its teeth. The skin of this specimen was so complete that it could be stuffed and mounted in the attitude in which the animal died.

From this and similar discoveries we are able to form a fairly accurate picture of the mammoth as it appeared in life, and this is confirmed in a very interesting way by the rude sketches engraved on ivory and bone by Palaeolithic men. The body was clothed with a shaggy coat of long black hair with reddish under-wool. In other respects it closely resembled the living Indian elephant, but the tusks were much larger, sometimes more than twelve feet long, and strongly curved upwards and inwards. The back sloped down from the shoulders, whereas in the Indian elephant the highest point of the back is behind the shoulders.

Several different species or local varieties of mammoth have been described from different parts of its extensive range, and it is likely that in those from warmer climates the hairy covering was more scanty. It should be noted that some of the races of elephants found living to-day are quite conspicuously hairy, especially when they are young.

SOUTH AMERICAN ANT-EATER

Darwin remarked on the extraordinary continuity in the mammal fauna of South America. The long vanished ancestors of the ant-eater in the above photograph were often of vast size.

The various races or species of mammoth differed a good deal in size, but it does not appear that any of them were larger than the living Indian elephant. The "record" for the latter species is of a bull which stood ten feet six inches in height, measured to the highest point of the back. The average height for well-grown bulls is said to be nine feet. Both the mammoth and the Indian elephant are therefore smaller than the African species, which sometimes (though rarely) exceeds eleven feet in height, and of which the "record" specimen is said to have measured eleven feet eight and a half inches. In comparing these figures it must be remembered that it is no easy matter to estimate accurately the height of a wild elephant. Measurements taken from the dead animal lying on the ground

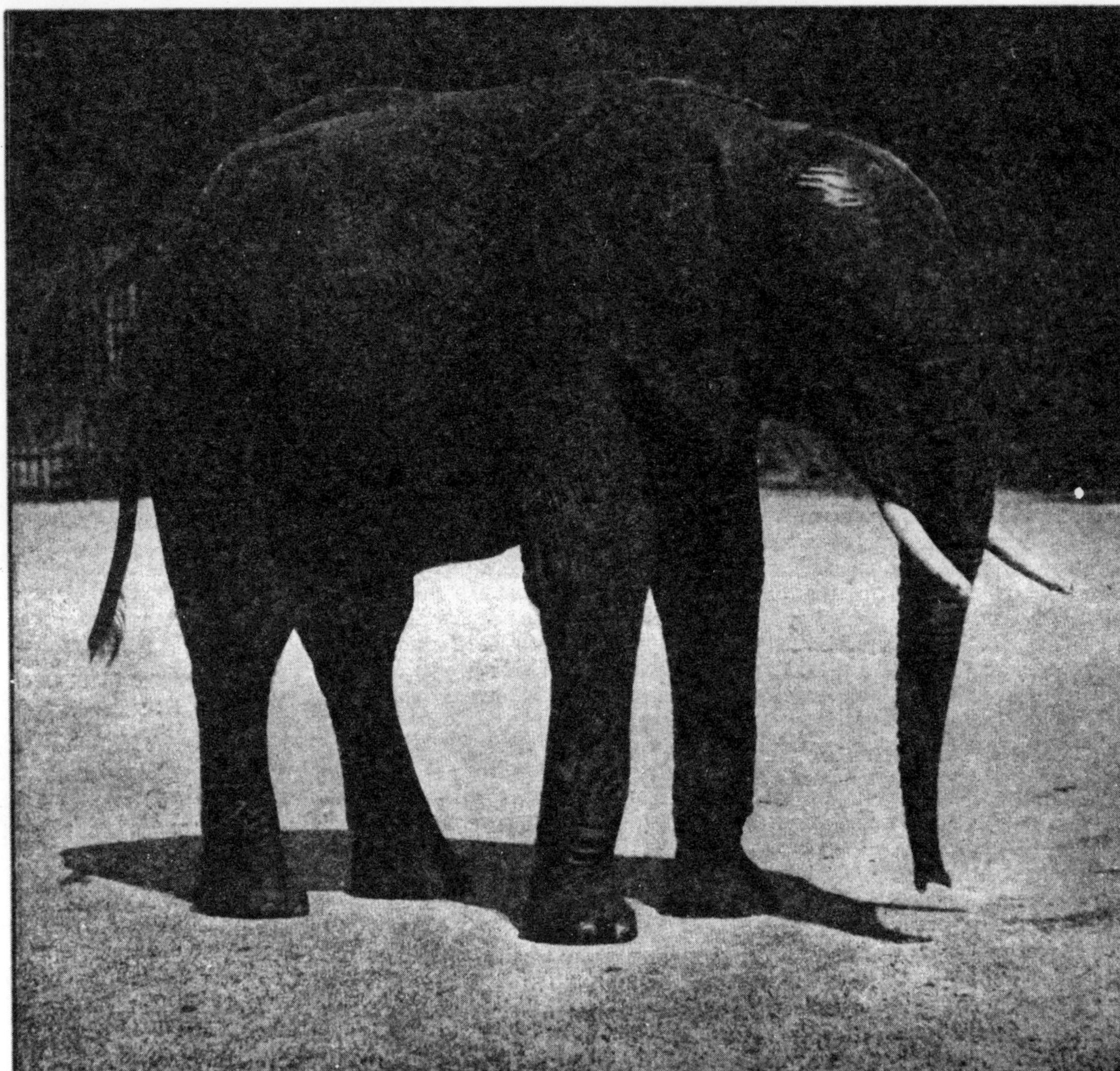

Autotype

HUGE AFRICAN ELEPHANT WHICH HAD EVEN LARGER ANCESTORS

Mammoths were ancestors of the elephants which exist on the earth to-day and " mammoth " has become a popular synonym for enormous size. Yet few if any of the mammoths were as large as the African elephant living in the forests of Africa in our time. Before the mammoths, however, there were two different species of elephant which exceeded any living specimen both in height and weight. One, whose remains were found in Kent near Chatham, must have been well over thirteen feet high. The record African elephant was only 11 ft. 3½ ins. high.

are obviously subject to error. It is clear, however, that the largest mammoth was inferior in size to the existing African elephant.

The mammoth, however, was not the largest among extinct elephants. Some years ago, the bones of a gigantic elephant were discovered near Chatham, and its incomplete skeleton is now mounted in the Geological Department of the Natural History Museum, South Kensington. It is an example of the species known as the straight-tusked elephant (*Elephas antiquus*), and the skeleton as mounted stands twelve feet seven inches high. Allowing for the soft parts, muscle, skin, and so on, the height of the living animal must have been well over thirteen feet, although an earlier estimate of " about fifteen feet " is probably too great. It is calculated that the animal must have weighed some ten or twelve tons. Another fossil elephant (*E. meridionalis*) which ranged from south Europe to England attained a similar or perhaps a somewhat greater size.

Fossil elephants, however, were by no means all of gigantic size. On various islands of the Mediterranean, Sicily, Malta, Crete, and Cyprus, fossils have been found which show that when these islands were first separated from the continents of Europe and Africa at the close of the period immediately before the Pleistocene, they were inhabited by elephants which speedily became dwarfed owing no doubt to their cramped quarters and unfavourable conditions. One of these dwarfs was only three feet high.

Mondiale

STATE INDIAN ELEPHANT FROM GWALIOR, SMALLER COUSIN OF THE AFRICAN ELEPHANT

Indian elephants form a race distinct from those of Africa and are smaller in size. This one was remarkable for the length of its tusks which grew so much that the ends had to be cut off because they almost touched the ground and prevented the animal from lying down. It was a beast used on state occasions and its trunk, forehead, ears and cheeks are brightly painted. The Indian elephant has been domesticated for centuries whereas, till comparatively recently, the larger African relative was thought too intractable to learn man's service.

The discoveries of palaeontologists within the past twenty years have enabled the evolutionary history of the elephants to be traced with considerable completeness. Without going into details it may be noticed that this evolution has been accompanied by a fairly regular increase in size. The earliest ancestor of the elephants yet known was a small tapir-like animal (*Moeritherium*), not more than three feet high, of which the remains have been discovered in deposits of the Eocene period in Egypt. In the successively later Oligocene, Miocene, and Pliocene periods, intermediate forms can be traced, becoming larger and larger, until we reach the true elephants which have existed from the Upper Pliocene, through the Pleistocene, to the present day. But while increase in size has gone on in the main line of descent it must not be supposed that it has always accompanied evolutionary progress even in this group of animals. The dwarf races of elephants mentioned above show that evolution may sometimes go from large to small.

While the existing elephants can thus challenge comparison with all but the very largest of their extinct relatives, there are several important groups of mammals of which the living members are but a feeble folk compared with their predecessors. This is notably the case with the South American animals belonging to the Order Edentata, the Sloths, Anteaters, and Armadilloes. These form a very remarkable and isolated group of mammals having no very near relatives among existing animals, although they

W. S. Berridge

F. W. Bond

ANIMALS OF DIFFERENT CONTINENTS ASSOCIATED IN ZOOLOGICAL CLASSIFICATION

Armadilloes and anteaters, animals peculiar to that continent of zoological surprises, South America, belong to the family named Edentata which signifies " toothless." Not all its members are entirely without teeth, but some are, while the rest have only imperfect dentition as compared with other mammalian families. The only race of animals coming anywhere near in relationship to this South American family is that of the pangolins and ant-bears. Here is a long-haired armadillo (bottom) and a white-bellied pangolin from W. Africa.

W. S. Berridge

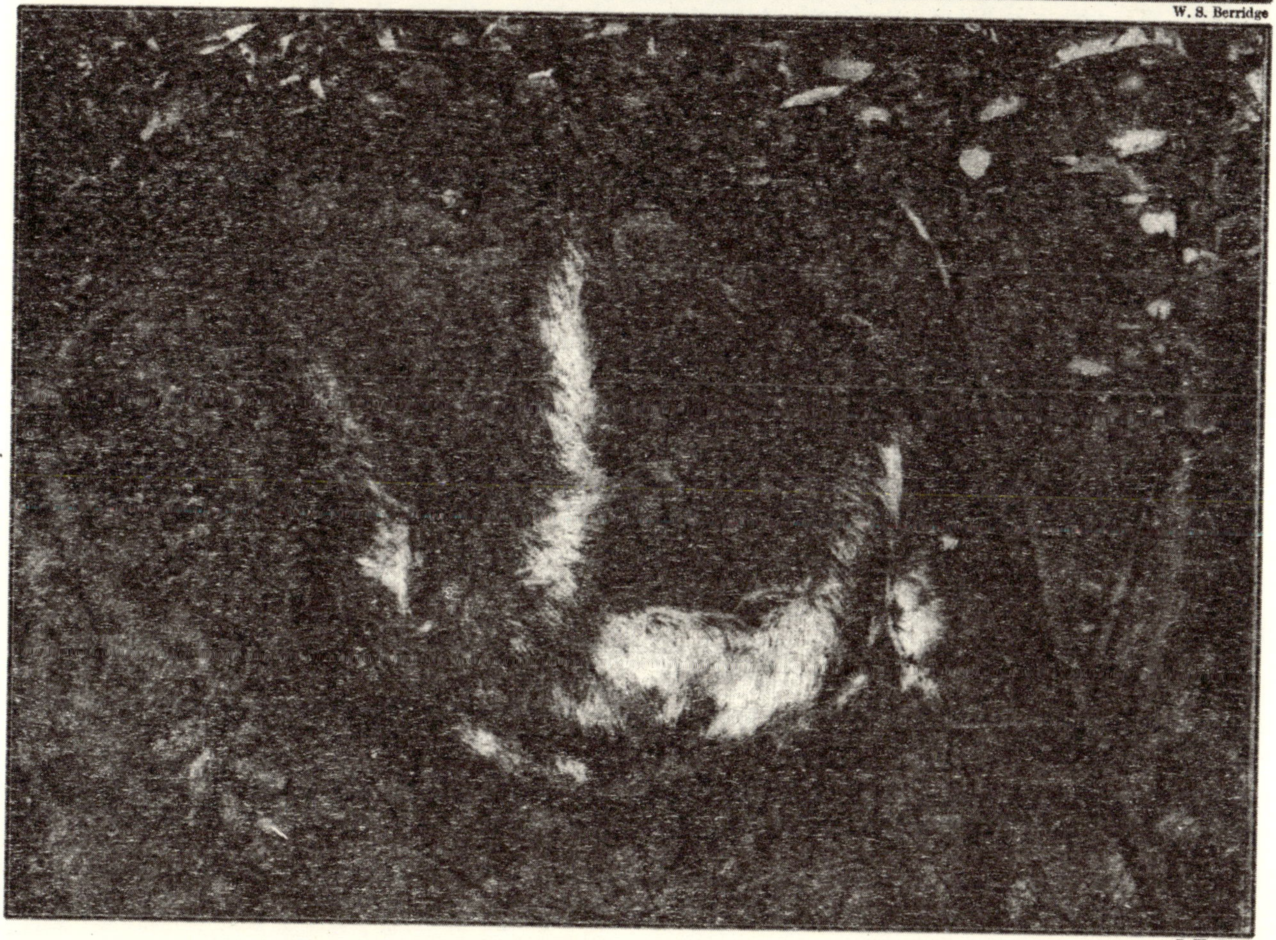

F. W. Bond

THREE-TOED SLOTH OF SOUTH AMERICA AND A PANGOLIN FROM CENTRAL AFRICA

A three-toed sloth up in the trees is an extraordinary sight as we may judge from a scrutiny of the lower photograph. It is difficult to tell which is the head and which the tail end. Above is a short-tailed pangolin, an African species. It has a more primitive-looking type of head than its cousin seen in the opposite page, and indeed it seems at first sight that the scaled body just comes to an end rather than that the animal has any separate head. These two animals are commonly associated together in zoological classifications.

are commonly associated in zoological classification with the pangolins and ant-bears of Africa and Asia. Animals related to them, however, have inhabited South America since the early part of the Tertiary epoch, which is a very long way back in the history of mammals. The remarkable continuity of the mammalian fauna of this region greatly impressed Darwin during the voyage of the "Beagle," and he has recorded in the opening words of the "Origin of Species" that it was this that first turned his thoughts in the direction of Evolution.

The existing sloths are small shaggy animals living in the dense forests, hanging back-downwards from the branches and clambering with great deliberation by the aid of their strong hooked claws. They rarely descend to the ground, on which they move awkwardly, walking on the outer edges of their inturned feet. Their long hair is of a greyish-green colour, owing to the growth on the hairs of microscopic green plants—algae—which flourish in the damp atmosphere and give the animals a close resemblance to the lichen-covered branches of the trees. They feed on leaves and have few and simple teeth. They have no tail and the length of the body is about two feet.

Some of the anteaters, like the sloths, live in trees, but the great anteater, which is surely the most grotesque in appearance of all living animals, lives on the ground. It may be more than six feet in length, half of which is taken up by the immense bushy tail. There is a tall mane of stiff black hair along the back and the long narrow head is drawn out into a beak-like muzzle ending in a tiny toothless mouth, from which a worm-like sticky tongue can be protruded to lick up the ants on which the animal feeds. The fore-legs are "club-footed," for the anteater walks on its knuckles with toes turned inwards.

The armadilloes are active, burrowing animals. They differ from all other existing mammals by having the body, head, tail, and legs protected by an armour of bony plates developed in the skin. Over the shoulders and hindquarters the plates are welded together to form solid shields, but in the middle of the back they are arranged in a number of transverse bands connected by flexible skin. The under side of the body is covered only with soft skin. In some species the animal, when attacked, can roll itself into a complete ball. The teeth are small and simple, and the food usually consists of insects, although some species feed on carrion. By far the largest of the living species is the giant armadillo, which measures about three feet to the tip of the tail.

It will thus be seen that the sloths, anteaters, and armadilloes differ widely from one another in general appearance, structure, and habits. In the Pleistocene period, however, South America was inhabited by edentate animals of gigantic size, which to some extent combined the characters of all three. These were the ground sloths, of which the best-known are megatherium and mylodon. These are described as combining "the head and teeth of a sloth with the backbone, limbs, and tail of an anteater." Megatherium was some 18 feet in length and mylodon not much less. They were heavily-built animals and must have weighed several tons, so that they cannot have lived in trees like the sloths of the present day. The strongly-built hindquarters show that the animals sat erect after the fashion of kangaroos on the tripod formed by the hind legs and the stout tail, grasping the branches with the forefeet and no doubt stripping off the leaves with a protrusible tongue like that of a giraffe.

The frequent occurrence of large numbers of little nodules of bone in association with the skeletons of mylodon had led to the conclusion that this animal was provided with a sort of skin armour like that of the armadilloes, and this was confirmed by a remarkable discovery made in 1897. In a cavern near Last Hope Inlet, in Patagonia, there were found numerous bones of a large ground sloth known as grypotherium which differs very little from mylodon.

With the bones were several pieces of thick hide which, like some of the bones, showed distinct marks of cutting tools. Such tools of stone were, in fact, found in the cavern, as well as some human bones. There were also masses of cut grass and other indications that the animals had been kept in a more or less domesticated state in the cavern and finally killed for food. Masses of excrement found with the bones showed that the animals had been feeding exclusively on grass. The hide was covered with thick coarse brown hair, and in the thickness of the skin were embedded close-set round nodules of bone which must have formed a very efficient armour. Among other remains found in the cave were the teeth and hoofs of an extinct kind of horse.

The fresh appearance of these bones, which, as may be seen in the Natural History Museum at South Kensington, still bear the dried remains of sinews and flesh adhering to them, led to the suggestion that ground sloths might still be surviving in remote and inaccessible parts of South America. This expectation, however, has not been realized, and there is no doubt that, in the dry air of the cavern, the remains had been preserved for at least many centuries. In "Mr. Blettsworthy on Rampole Island," Mr. H. G. Wells has drawn a vivid picture of what the ground sloths *may* have been like.

Living at the same time as the ground sloths were gigantic representatives of the armadilloes which differed from the living forms in having the body-armour welded together into a single rigid shield. The best-known of these is glyptodon, which grew to some eleven feet in total length, the body-shield alone being seven feet long by nine feet across, measured round the curve. The shield is made up of a mosaic of small plates of bone which must have been covered by skin. The top of the head was protected by a separate shield and the tail by jointed rings of armour. The animal, in fact, was a kind of mammalian tortoise.

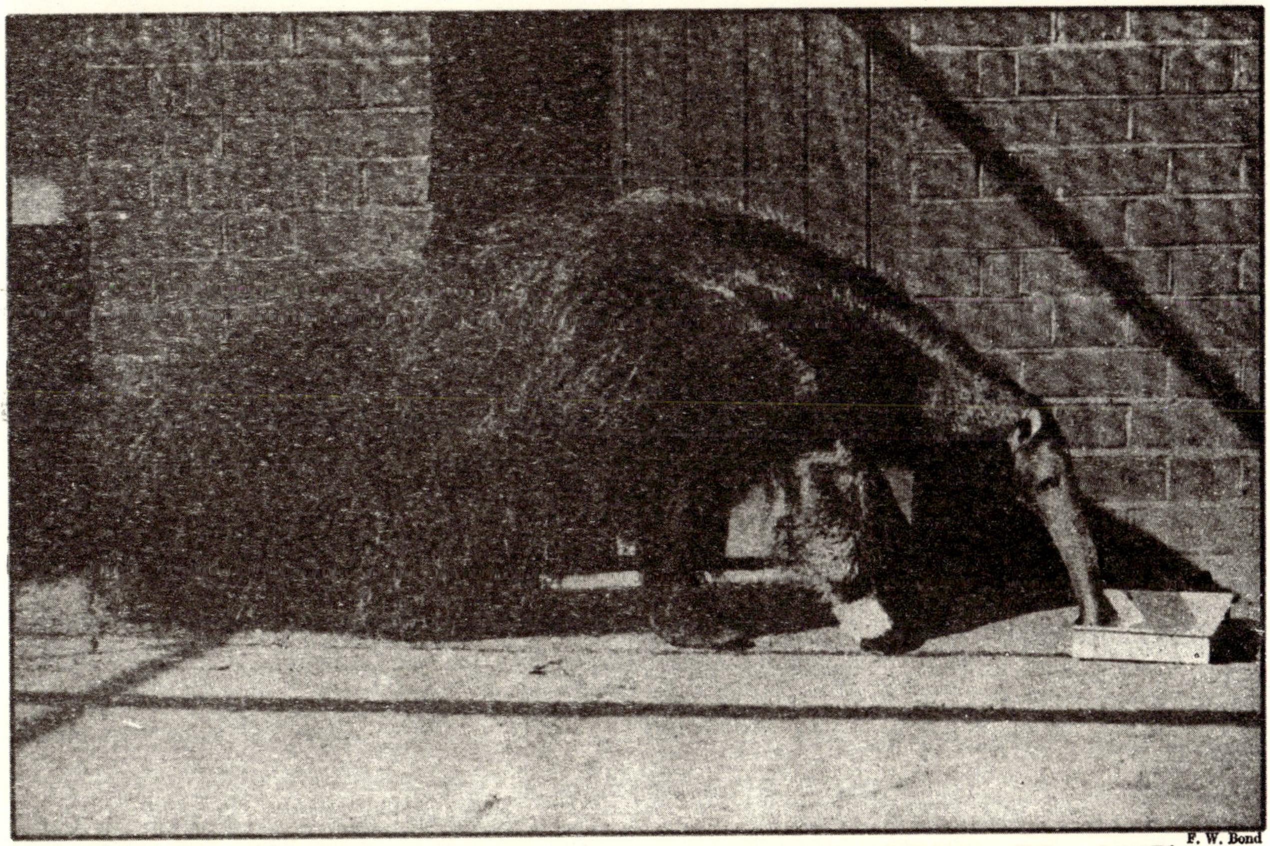

F. W. Bond

GREAT ANTEATER AND ITS SMALLER COUSIN THE TAMANDUA DESCENDED FROM GIANTS

The great anteater (bottom) like its forerunners in the South American continent, the ground sloths, mylódon and megatherium, is too heavy for a life in the trees such as is lived by the other sloths of to-day. But compared with the old ground-sloths, even these great anteaters are puny, for they measure only about six feet in length—quite half of the length is tail as we see—while megatherium was three times as long and probably weighed several tons. Above is a tamandua or lesser anteater, which lives in the tree tops and is only some 3 ft. 6 ins. long.

F. W. Bond

CHINESE PANGOLIN THAT HAUNTS CREVICES AMONG THE ROCKS

Asiatic pangolins are less addicted to tree climbing than their African brethren, but, like them, are nocturnal and live on termites. For eating these "white ants" they have specially modified tongues like the anteaters of South America, with whom they are often associated by zoologists for purposes of classification. Outwardly, the dissimilarity between these representatives of the Old World and the New—pangolins and anteaters—is very great, especially as concerns the scale armour of the former.

It must not be supposed that the existing sloths, anteaters, and armadilloes are the actual descendants of the giants that lived in the epoch immediately preceding ours. Their ancestors are imperfectly known, but there is every reason to believe that they have always been small and have survived while their overgrown relatives went under.

There are several other instances where a similar story has to be told, of small mammals inhabiting a country where their predecessors grew to much greater size. The marsupials of Australia, which to-day include no species larger than the great red kangaroo, standing as high as a man, were formerly represented by kangaroos of the size of a donkey and wombats as large as an ox, while the giant diprotodon had a skull three feet long, and was as bulky as a rhinoceros.

Although most of the Orders of mammals include extinct forms that exceeded in size any of their modern representatives, there are some that do not. No fossil ape is known that was nearly as big as the gorilla, although the imperfection of the geological history of the Primates forbids us to say that none ever existed. The record of the past history of the whales is also very incomplete, but it seems unlikely that they ever before reached a size so great as some of them do to-day. In particular, the great blue whale, or Sibbald's rorqual, which in Antarctic seas sometimes exceeds a hundred feet in length, is not only by far the largest of living animals but is, so far as we know, the largest animal that ever existed on the globe.

THE examples mentioned above have all been taken from the class Mammalia because it is chiefly in this class that we have living species so closely related to the extinct forms that we can fairly call them "representatives."

When we go further back in geological time, to the Secondary or Mesozoic era, the dominant class of the animal kingdom was that of the Reptiles. Many of these were of gigantic size, but nearly all of them belong to orders that have long been extinct and they cannot be closely compared with any existing reptiles. Among these we need only mention the dinosaurs, the varied forms of which include the largest land animals known. It should be remembered that the last of these "prehistoric monsters" died out ages before man appeared on the earth and the fanciful pictures which represent them in association with primitive man have no foundation other than in the artist's imagination.

Where the direct ancestors of living forms can be identified they are almost always found to be smaller, or at any rate no larger, than their descendants. Every now and then, however, collateral branches are given off from the main stem and in these the animals grow to a larger and larger size until finally they die out.

Chapter CXXIII

The Wonder of the Wing

By Dr. C. J. Patten

Professor of Anatomy, Sheffield University; Author of "The Story of the Birds," "Aquatic Birds," etc.

FLIGHT, the emblem of surpassing speed, of exquisite grace and beauty, surely is the poetry of motion. It has aroused admiration and wonder from ages immemorial.

Man, from time to time, has endeavoured actually to emulate the bird; but all in vain. The futility of launching himself into the air on artificial wings still looms large before him. The contour of his body, in contrast to that of the bird, presents a formidable barrier. None the less, he has led a triumphant march in aviation; he has at last conquered the air! He can travel, nay more, perform dexterous feats in this thin, invisible medium! Such a conquest has excited tremendous interest. Is it any wonder then that problems regarding the flight of birds are so exceedingly popular to-day?

The student of aeronautics has culled much information from observations on the bird. Indeed, the study of bird-flight has proved extremely important. Man has conquered the air, yes, but only in a sense; he cannot actually fly, but he can sit in a machine and fly it with speed and efficiency. Man's mode of aviation consequently depends upon two entities, and while he and machine may be co-ordinated in the closest possible way, yet the link which binds the two can become severed! However, aeronautics have made such wonderful advances that travellers are rapidly growing confident, and the time is nigh at hand when passengers will think no more of boarding an aeroplane or an airship than they would a steamship or a railway-train.

We ask, is it possible for a bird to "turn turtle"—in other words, to capsize? No; far from it. The raven, who of a sudden rolls upon his back in ecstasies of love before his mate, or of hate before the harassing falcon, is obliged to right himself instantly. The tumbler pigeon, which has acquired the art of performing a back somersault, must right himself "in the twinkling of an eye." If a bird endeavoured to float passively in the air, breast-uppermost, it would have to right itself speedily, as surely as a capsized lifeboat turns keel downwards. An aquatic bird seldom attempts to turn on its back in the water; it finds the manœuvre awkward. We find it easy and pleasurable. How then is the stability of the flying-bird so well maintained? By the perfect adaptation of its body. Structure and function are most exquisitely attuned.

In the first place, the remarkably deep keel of the immense breast-bone—to which the enormous breast-muscles are attached—imparts to the body its familiar boat-shaped contour. Unlike our breast-bone, which is small, flat, narrow, and confined to the region of the chest, that of the bird is very extensive in length and breadth, reaching almost to the root of the tail. Consequently a firm, bony, front-wall encompasses the greater part of the abdominal cavity, protecting the vital organs, and, in conjunction with the stout and rigid backbone, imparting additional strength and stability to the body during flight. The large breast-muscles are extremely powerful: in some species they weigh as much as all the other muscles in the aggregate. In man the ratio is only about one in a hundred. In the next place, the heavy internal organs impinge against the upper concave surface of the breast-bone.

We know that in order to safeguard a boat from being capsized, its keel must be sufficiently deep and adequately weighted. Furthermore, it is at times necessary to increase the ballast by filling the hold of the boat with heavy material. The boat-shaped body of the bird fulfils these conditions. In flight it may be compared to a boat moving through the water—a boat provided with a deep and weighted keel. The heavy organs are placed in the "hold" of the "boat"; that is to say, in relation to the deep surface of the breast-bone, and the "keel" is weighted by enormous breast-muscles. The ballast of the body is, therefore, very considerable. Organs, light in weight, especially the lungs and many of the air-sacs, occupy the dorsal region (in relation to the backbone), or, so to speak, the "deck" of the "boat."

From this level the wings arise, and can be spread on either side. It is quite evident that the centre of gravity is situated remote from the suspension of the wings; so remote that even when the bird cants to steer a new course, capsizing is out of the question. The body is so wonderfully adapted for flight that it may well be compared to a ship that is provided with a gyroscope.

LIKE the ship, the bird in many cases is provided with a rudder, to wit, the tail. When the feathers are of sufficient length the fine adjustments in steering are made possible. These are demonstrable in the superb wheeling and soaring movements in kites, rooks, pigeons, in the soaring skylark, and other species. The mechanism consists in partial or complete rotation of the fanned feathers. Here the action is that of a true aerial rudder. The fan can also be lowered and carried forward so that a column of air can be encompassed and the velocity of flight checked, as when a bird suddenly wishes to alight. In ordinary flapping-flight the rudder is often not called into use, and steering is brought about by canting. Heavy-bodied birds with small wings and short tails obviously must adopt this method.

Body-weight is quite necessary in the mechanism of flight. Otherwise momentum would not be acquired as the bird proceeded under way. A bird as light as air could not attain a speed faster than the current in which it was carried along; the wind would decide its course; it would drift aimlessly in space. A bird

The Wonder of the Wing

W. S. Berridge

EXTRAORDINARY WING STRETCH OF RUPPELL'S VULTURE

Stretching on its perch this bird shows the unexpected extent to which it is able to spread its wings. The flight feathers, that is, the feathers at the base of the wings, reach considerably beyond the end of the body and far below the perch. Being caged the vulture cannot exercise its wings much, and so goes through various contortions to keep the muscles from stiffening.

cannot rise passively (after the fashion of a balloon) by virtue of its extensive pneumaticity. Air-sacs are not direct essentials to flight. They are reservoirs, the contents of which can lend an aid in the outburst of song; in rapid respiration following violent exercise; and in regulating the body-temperature. Body-weight is no less in the air than on the ground. The initial movements of *rising* demand powerful muscular action. A falcon, if not adequately weighted, could not shoot down "like a bolt from the blue" upon its prey. A bird descending obliquely and gradually, as exemplified in gliding flight, gathers considerable momentum, and in closing its wings, comes to earth largely by its own weight. A bird, even a small one, having sustained a broken wing, drops with considerable speed, the cripple being much heavier than air.

Different birds, apparently similar in size when flying, may vary considerably in weight. A grouse is heavier than a lapwing; a partridge than a barn-owl; a goose than a heron. Birds with ample wings and small bodies are relatively light in weight. We are familiar with the extensive wing-surface displayed by the heron, lapwing and owl in flight. The wild swan is a ponderous bird, with none too ample wings. It appears to get under way slowly and laboriously, paddling on the surface of the water vigorously with its broad, webbed feet, while the powerful and measured strokes of its wings are at the same time lifting it into the air. Having made a fair start, however, its movements grow full of grace and beauty. Gaining the support of the air, it travels largely by the aid of its cumulative momentum, an economic factor in the expenditure of energy.

How is it that this hefty, short-winged bird, and others of like proportions, can succeed in gaining the support of the air? For a proper understanding we must now turn our attention to the mechanism of the wing-strokes, delivered, in ordinary flapping flight, at a moderate speed, by a bird, moderate in weight, and provided with wings, average in size and length. Our first mpression is that the wings move up and down in a vertical path, retaining at the same time a spread condition. Far from it: the strokes are not by any means so simple. Spreading (extension), folding (flexion), rotation, also backward and forward movements of a gliding character, follow in such rapid succession that in a large measure they escape detection. But the main object of the wing-strokes (commonly called the up-and-down-strokes), though constituting a flap-cycle of many phases, is but two-fold, namely: compressing and setting free a mass of air.

Let us analyse the down-stroke. As the wing descends, fully spread, its outer part, furnished with stiff unyielding feathers, encompasses a mass of air

FEATHERS INTRICATELY ARRANGED, SEEN WHEN THE PELICAN STRETCHES ITS WING

Power to separate or close the feathers, thus keeping in or letting out the air compressed in flight, is a very important virtue in a bird's wing. This pelican has every feather separated for the purposes of renovation, for no aircraft built by man is submitted to a more careful inspection than a bird gives to its own wings and feather-covering every day. In addition to inspection and readjustment and the removal of loose feathers, the pelican, being a water bird, has also to oil its plumage to keep the damp out.

and compresses it against the body, which becomes buoyed up sufficiently to derive a full measure of support. At the end of the down-stroke the rotatory phase comes into play. The under surface of the wing is swept forwards, forming a barrier which prevents the compressed air under the wing from making good its escape from behind. When the body proceeds forwards, the air which is held up offers considerable resistance. Consequently the bird becomes still more buoyant, and now mounts the crest of the compressed air column, like a boat riding over the billows. The main action of the down-stroke is to provide adequate support ; the rotatory action to aid in ascent.

APART, however, from the rotatory action, the body is elevated in another way—more important and fundamental—when the wing makes its descent. We have seen that the wing is fully spread during the down-stroke. Accordingly, as the stiff resisting quill-feathers of the tip and outer part press down upon the air, it in turn offers such firm support that it acts as a fulcrum, and can now elevate the weight at the other end of the lever. That weight is none other than the body of the bird ! Here we are presented with a lever system of the third order, in which the power (represented by the immense muscles attached to the wing) is situated between the fulcrum (the air) at one end and the weight to be raised (the body) at the other end. The down-stroke of the wing, therefore, acts with distinct mechanical advantage. It should be borne in mind that this stroke is accomplished by very powerful muscular action, the breast-muscles which are brought into play being relatively a hundred-fold more powerful than those in man !

During the up-stroke the wings are sharply folded. This movement is effected mainly by swift elastic recoil, so swift that it escapes observation unless the bird happens to be flying very leisurely. Even then it requires a well-trained and practised eye to discriminate the movement. The passive movement of the up-stroke is also largely aided by the active drop of the body. But the movement is not entirely passive in character, because smaller but definite muscles are present which contribute to the elevation of the wings, muscles which act at the termination of the down-stroke, that is to say when the great breast-muscles have ceased to act. These elevator muscles are also attached to the breast-bone, far below the suspension of the wings, but unlike their greater companions they do not pursue a straight course outwards to gain attachment to the wings. They pass upwards to the shoulder-joint, then through a ring and then downwards to reach their destination.

The direction of the pull of these muscles, therefore, permits them to act, pulley-like, as

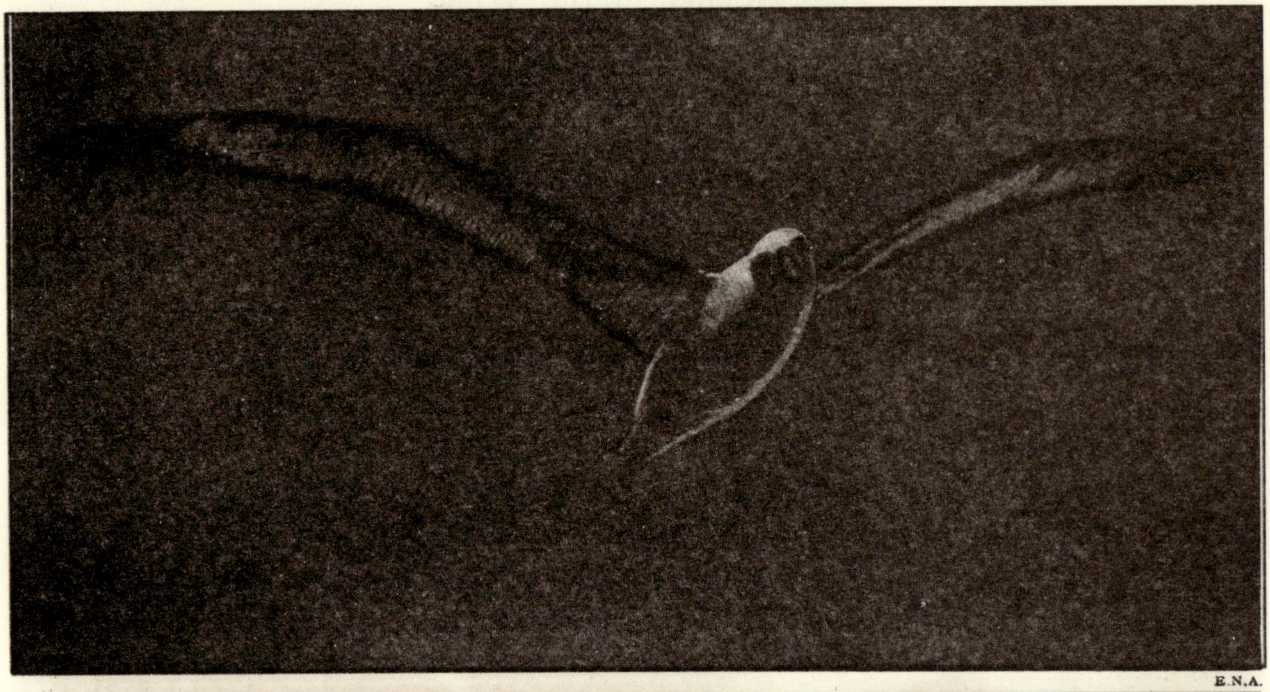

E.N.A.

Central Press

TWO TYPES OF WING THAT HAVE BEEN EVOLVED BY LIVING AIRCRAFT.

Pelicans have heavy bodies in relation to the extent of their wing-spread and do not take off quickly but have to flap heavily and hard to get off the ground. Notice the hook shape of the top of the wings. This hook is due to the formation of what is really the forelimb of the bird. Contrasted with the wings of this pelican we have those of an albatross (top). These are narrow and very long for the size of the body. Fourteen feet from tip to tip is the wing measurement of some of these birds.

Oliver G. Pike

Neville Kingston

PENGUINS' FLIGHTLESS WINGS AND A BANKING TURN MADE BY A FULMAR PETREL

When walking, especially upon slippery ice, the penguin uses its wings for balancing purposes. The lower photograph is of King penguins. On land, penguins will often lie on their stomachs, when, owing to the fact that their legs are set so far back, this position of their wings makes these limbs look rather like the flippers of a seal. The upper photograph shows a fulmar petrel going through the aeronautical evolution known as banking. This tilting half over on one side makes a very rapid turn possible.

elevators of the wings. These lesser breast-muscles are quite small, because they have light work to carry out, rendered very easy by an ingenious pulley system.

We have seen that during the down-stroke the stiff, resisting quill-feathers of the tip and outer part of the wide-spread wing gain such firm support that the air acts as a fulcrum, sufficiently strong to raise the body at the other end of the lever. But how has it come about that sufficiently great resistance is offered to the down-stroke to allow of the establishment of this strange, movable, highly-compressible fulcrum? To think of a featherless bird flying is certainly absurd. We might as well endeavour to fly by lifting and lowering our arms! Yet we must ask, why is the idea so absurd? Because the naked wing-surfaces are far too small and narrow to encompass and compress a sufficient mass of air underneath them during the down-stroke, which could give support to the flying body. Therefore, it has come about in the course of time that the bird of necessity has acquired a wonderful system of feathers which has enormously enhanced the comparatively meagre area of the naked wing.

KING PENGUIN AND THICK-BILLED PENGUIN OF THE ANTARCTIC

The penguin's wing has become reduced to a mere flipper. But this flipper is constructed internally, just like other birds' wings and, in fact, the penguin is as agile in the water as other birds are in the air. Its motion below the surface is much more like flying than swimming These photographs show (below) a king penguin and (above) a thick-billed penguin.

But since the ratio of the feathered wing-surface to that of the body of the bird has now become immensely greater, it follows that the down-stroke—in other words the work carried out by the great breast-muscles—must meet with considerable resistance from the air, collected beneath the enormously amplified wing-surfaces. The marvellous power and high-speed of the down-stroke hold up the air beneath the wings, so that it becomes more and more compressed, and the haulage

FLAMINGOES WITH WINGS OF ROSE PINK FOLDED TO FEED

Owing to the modification of their structure for wading flamingoes are only moderate fliers. Even for wading birds they have very long legs, much longer than the heron's, for instance, and, when adult, the birds stand six feet high or more. A flock in flight is a wonderful spectacle with the sunlight striking on the roseate wings. Folded, these wings make a coat of delicate pink for the bird's back.

E.N.A.

VOLUNTARY AND ENFORCED EXHIBITION OF WINGS BY MARABOU STORKS

The storks, as a family, take off fairly easily from the ground and this is because their wings have a very large spread. How large it is in the case of the marabou stork we can see from the illustrations in this page. Below the male bird's wings are being extended before its mate as though an impassioned harangue was being delivered—to which the female does not appear to pay the slightest attention. Above, some natives are extending the wings of their captive despite protests. Notice the draggled flight feathers.

Otho Webb

Arthur Brook

BLACK-HEADED GULLS RETURNING TO NESTS AND A GROUP OF CRESTED TERNS

In February or March the black-headed gulls are coming inland from the foreshore to their chosen nesting sites (bottom). The photograph shows the various wing positions of the flying gull excellently. Above is a photograph from an island in the Great Barrier Reef of Australia, and shows a squadron of crested terns, some flying and some resting on the ground. Gulls, which have to face the full force of ocean winds, are probably Nature's most efficient flying machines, and spend more time on the wing than land birds.

SEAGULL WINGS THICK AS SNOWFLAKES IN THE HARBOUR AT ST. IVES

Attracted by fish offal from a newly landed catch at St. Ives, Cornwall, the gulls arrive in almost a blizzard of wings and certainly scream as loud as any gale. Notice that the birds near the fishermen are in all sorts of wing positions but those higher up in the air are nearly all gliding with still wings just as a man-made aircraft does. Of all really wild birds gulls seem the most tame, perhaps because man has never persecuted them. Their flesh is coarse and fishy, according to those few people who have tried eating some.

Fox Photos

WINGS USED FOR INTIMIDATION, AND A STUDY OF THE FLIGHT OF A FISHING OWL

Wings are not always used for flight. The barn owl (bottom), for instance, makes very effective use of them to alarm an enemy. The bowed head and the down-flung wings make a very forbidding spectacle of this angry bird. Above we have a Malaya fishing owl with its long legs, and talons like clutching hands. The heavy wings, utterly different from the clear-cut pinions of the gulls, make movements not unlike the heavy flapping of a flag. The whole feather structure seems altogether more loosely knit than the seagull's or the hawk's.

E.N.A.

GRIFFON VULTURE AT REST AND A MEXICAN AURA IN FLIGHT

Vultures usually have a shabby, bedraggled look. Below we have a griffon vulture, stretching its wings on a tree stump and showing their span. Vultures commonly gorge themselves so full that, if disturbed at the end of their meal, they have to run quite a distance before getting enough speed to enable them to take off from the ground. The griffon vultures are native to the European borders of the Mediterranean, the open regions all over Africa and Persia, India and Siam. The upper photograph is of a Mexican aura.

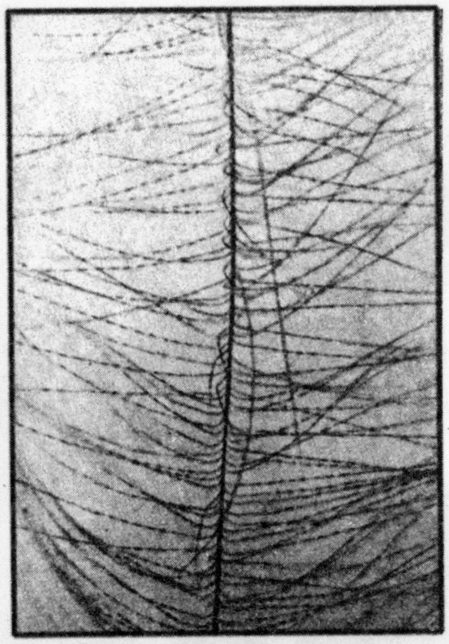

J. J. Ward

DETAILS OF DIFFERING FEATHER CONSTRUCTION

Only the microscope reveals the intricacy of a feather. Here are (bottom left) a humming bird's feather and (bottom right) a condor's feather and the interlacing of the barbs on which flying depends. Above are (top left) the loose filaments of the feather of the flightless emu and (top right) the soft filaments of an owl which give that bird its silent flight.

of the wings demands an increasing output of labour. Finally, the air offers such increasingly high resistance that it can act as a fulcrum or prop for the outer part of the wings

The great breast-muscles are an amazing pair of haulage machines, which, far from being assisted by gravity, pull down immense structures (the wings spread out like sails) by overcoming a high degree of resistance. Surely then it becomes hardly a matter of surprise to learn that these particular muscles in the bird are so enormous in size, so extensive in area, so powerful in action! We see then in the establishment of a fulcrum, subservient to the mechanism of flight, that the ratio of wing surface to size of body must be high, the haulage machinery must be powerful and swift, and the resistance offered by the compressed air must be sufficiently high to give support. We can now understand how it is that hefty birds, with relatively short and small wings, can gain the support of the air. Their wing-strokes obviously must be very powerful and rapid, in order that the resistance offered by the air may be raised to a high and almost continuous pitch.

MANY of us are familiar with the extremely vigorous manner in which the wing-strokes of ducks, grouse, partridges, coots, and other big-bodied birds are wielded. The slow, measured beat of the ample-winged small-bodied heron, offers a striking contrast. In the upstroke, the feathers also play an indispensable and at the same time a highly interesting part. It is necessary that the compressed air, at this phase of the flap-cycle, should make a rapid escape from under the wings. True, rapid folding and elevation largely aid; nevertheless, at the moment before flexion takes place, a draught of air is allowed to pass through a series of clefts between adjacent feathers, as beams of light stream through the separated laths of a Venetian blind!

The formation of the clefts depend upon the free manner in which the flight-feathers can be raised, separated, and rotated; consequently overlapping is prevented. It is obvious that elevated, folded wings beset with numerous gaps could not possibly lay hold of a column of air. Even when the wings begin to spread again at the end of the up-stroke, the air can pass through the gaps between the rotated flight-feathers. At the beginning of the down-stroke however, the feathers, one and all, are tightened, and all spaces obliterated. Compression of the air under the wings therefore again becomes possible.

So much for the flap-cycle, and the part played by the feathers. We can now put forward a definite, useful formula, namely, the down-stroke is actively performed by muscular energy, the body as a result

being passively raised: the up-stroke is for the most part passively performed, the body as a result actively falls. The greater the amplitude and length of the wing (provided that the down-stroke can be delivered with great strength and speed), the greater the height that the body will be elevated, and the greater the distance traversed passively when the wings are uplifted.

In flapping-flight, the body and wings make a series of reciprocal curves; here again it will be seen that body-weight is a great asset to progression. Additional buoyancy is granted to the body by induced currents. Indeed a bird, when once under way, travels, in a large measure, on a current of its own making.

HOW A BIRD MAKES A GOOD LANDING

When a bird is about to land it makes its downward glide and then suddenly puts its tail down so that, with its wings fully extended, it is offering the maximum resistance to the air in the direction in which it is travelling. It loses flying speed but rights itself with a flap of the wings. Below is a plover and above a seagull landing.

Birds can descend in a parachute fashion on partly spread, elevated, motionless wings. Pigeons often adopt this method. In flapping-flight, the wings strike downwards and backwards, allowing the compressed air to escape behind immediately. Planing downwards is effected on flexed and motionless wings, the path usually being steep. The swoop can be suddenly checked if the bird reverses its position so that its head and body are inclined upwards and forward, tail depressed and fanned, feet thrown forward, and toes spread widely apart. The wings all the while make short rapid strokes, mainly in a downward and forward direction. In other words the strokes are shallow and the wings are elevated only a short way above the level of the back!

In the mechanism of alighting, the maximum resistance offered by the air plays an all-important part. Hence, as large an area of the body and wing-spread as possible is presented. Gannets, about to alight on the face of a precipitous cliff, may be seen suddenly tilting their bodies to such an extent that their breast, abdomen, and under surface of their fully extended wings face the cliff, and the birds appear momentarily poised in the air, in a plane perpendicular to the horizon. When making a steep ascent, the body is erected in a plane at right angles to the ground, and the tail is carried forwards and fanned. Several very powerful and quick downstrokes are all the while being delivered, in order to raise the bird clear of the ground. During the down-strokes the wings are carried further forwards (toward the head) than in horizontal flight.

The joyous skylark, in making his steep, almost perpendicular ascent, either in long graceful spirals or head to wind, adopts this attitude and beat of

S. Arnold

E.N.A.

CONDOR OF THE HIGH ANDES THAT HAS A HEAVY BODY TO LIFT WITH ITS EIGHT-FOOT WING-SPAN

An eight-foot wing span supports the twenty or twenty-five pounds weight of a condor in the air. Exclusive of tail feathers, the bird is about three feet long. Thus, by comparison with, say, the albatross, which usually weighs less than twenty pounds for its twelve or fourteen-foot wing-span, we see that, as a flying machine, the condor must need enormous strength. Of course it does not spend such long periods in the air as the sea birds. Our left-hand photograph here shows a condor with its wings raised showing the structure of the feathers. The other illustration is of a condor making a difficult landing on a steep mountain side. Its wings are laid back to act as aerial brakes and its feet are outstretched stiffly against the impact of landing.

H. Wallace

Arthur Brook

BUZZARD AND SONG THRUSH AND THEIR WING POSITIONS WHEN THEY ALIGHT AT THEIR NESTS

On the left we see a buzzard with a shrew in its beak. It is returning with food from a hunting expedition to feed its young. The wings are spread so that if the bird's foot should slip from the edge of the nest, as in a high wind would be very likely, it can immediately recover itself. The right-hand photograph is a remarkable one. It was taken in summer, and the camera was hidden among plants growing near the nest of a song thrush. A foxglove with its cluster of bells is growing nearby. The bird, being much lighter than a buzzard, and building as a rule in much less exposed situations, lands on its nest much more quickly, but even so, usually indulges in a little preliminary fluttering before settling down.

Oliver G. Pike

E. N. A

Oliver G. Pike

H. H. Cleaves

THE WONDER OF THE BEATING WING: FULMAR PETREL, OSPREY, SANDWICH TERN AND GULL

Hovering in front of its sitting mate whose nest is on a little ledge in the cliff face this fulmar petrel (bottom left) is giving us a lesson in the very adaptive powers of flight. Quite a different aspect of that accomplishment is shown by the American osprey (bottom right) which has just swooped at a fish and is rising from the water. The splash of the bird's impact has not yet died down. This is the largest American hawk, and it lives exclusively on a fish diet. It sometimes goes right under the surface with the impetus of its dive after its prey just as the kingfisher of English streams does. Above are (top left) a Sandwich tern and (top right) a Californian gull.

wing. Here again the purpose is to increase the resistance offered by the air. Birds may be observed soaring in graceful circles on outstretched, motionless pinions, alongside a high precipitous cliff. Advantage is taken of the currents of air which, flowing in from the sea, are deflected upwards on striking the face of the cliff. Gulls, sailing on motionless pinions alongside the steamship, no doubt avail themselves of the support derived from the ascending currents deflected from the rolling billows below.

THE mechanism of fluttering flight—also known as hovering—is very different in character. The bird, supporting itself in the air over one spot, cannot travel on a breeze of its own making. It is only by the most vigorous and astonishingly rapid wing-beats that it can obtain sufficient resistance from the air to keep afloat. Who has not watched that charming little falcon—the kestrel—poised over the cornfield, as though suspended by an invisible thread; surely a motionless figure on outstretched wings! The wing-strokes of the humming-bird are wielded with immense power and velocity. The wings themselves, very long and narrow, appear misty or gauze-like. Their stupendously rapid vibrations raise the resisting-current of air sufficiently high to create a musically-toned humming or buzzing note.

The humming-bird can hover untiringly, as it sips the sweet nectar or snaps the juicy plant-lice from out the blossom. This fairy of the feathered world stands unique in this startling accomplishment. The albatross, by contrast the giant of the feathered world, also has long, narrow wings and they stream out like ribbons and yield a span, from tip to tip, of fourteen feet. This wandering ocean-bird uses its wings in a very different manner from those of its Lilliputian cousin. After making a few immensely powerful flaps, it can skim, sail, or glide on motionless pinions for a lengthened time, wheeling gracefully in different planes, so that its wings are set, now horizontal to the waves, now at forty-five degrees, now perpendicular as the mast of a ship. Such a master of the air, despite his ponderous body—weighing up to twenty pounds—when once fairly under way, can overcome gravity to an extent which renders him, in a large measure, continuously buoyant, indeed we might say quite self-supporting.

THERE are several species of albatross, all natives of the southern oceans, and, notwithstanding their wandering propensities, they seldom venture north of the Equator. Birds with ample wings and small bodies fly leisurely. They find no difficulty in rising off the ground immediately, and their buoyancy permits them to reach high altitudes in an amazingly short time. But they are not efficient at making a headlong plunge. A heron will float from the marsh into the air on a calm day without the slightest effort; up he goes like an open umbrella carried by the wind! A gull or an owl will rise softly and silently like a gentle puff of smoke. Birds with small wings and large bodies fly heavily, yet with great velocity. They are, however, not buoyant, and when rising must make a strong effort. We see this demonstrated in the rapid beats of the wings which, in many species, produce a whirring or swishing sound, so well-known to sportsmen. Grouse, partridge, woodcock, and pheasant are familiar examples.

Heavy-bodied birds, whether their wings be long or short, can descend with marked velocity. The long-winged peregrine falcon is considerably weighted by great development of breast-muscles and general massiveness of shoulders; yet he cannot on every occasion overtake the mallard in its descent to the water, its surest haven. The duck's wings are relatively short, but its heavy body often is the means of saving its life when tragedy threatens. Puffins, razorbills, and guillemots, are weighty birds with relatively small, short wings. At times they outrace the falcon in a dash from cliff to sea. Shore-birds, with moderate-sized wings and bodies, cleave the air with astonishing velocity. They can also twist and twirl in a most amazing manner. They are denizens of the open sand-flats and ooze-beds, and being unable to take cover readily, they rely upon their magnificent wing-manœuvres when harassed by the enemy.

BIRDS of a class, as a rule, fly alike. The raven, carrion-crow, hooded crow, rook, jackdaw, and chough exhibit much the same wing-beat, though the magpie offers an exception. The great black-backed gull, the lesser black-backed gull, herring gull, common gull, and several others of the family, fly remarkably alike. Many people fail to distinguish between the swallow, house-martin, and sand-martin, on the wing. Lastly, our familiar garden birds cut much the same figure. However, as they constitute a large group (some members of which are but distantly related), we must be prepared to find many variations in their flight.

The speed at which birds fly and the period for which they can sustain themselves in the air, vary enormously. The South American hoatzin is purely arboreal in its habits. Its short, degenerate wings, with relatively feeble muscle system only permit it to flit from branch to branch. In the nestling, the framework of the outer part of the wing (hand) is longer than in the adult, owing to the presence of prominent claws, used for climbing-purposes. These are lopped off when the quill-feathers have sprouted sufficiently to enable the bird to carry out its feeble flight through the trees.

The swift, by way of contrast, keeps on the wing, during the summer in Britain, from about 3 a.m. until 10 p.m. Nineteen hours out of the twenty-four, this bird is perpetually on the move, flapping, planing, gliding, and at times (especially towards nightfall, when one might expect it would be only too anxious to conserve its energy), dashing with terrific speed round the eaves of houses and other buildings!

The swift at its fastest can move at three miles a minute. On long flights, however, it probably travels

GANNET MAKING A SAFE LANDING BY ITS NEST ON A CLIFF

It is a delicate business alighting on a tiny ledge of a three-hundred-toot cliff, as we see this gannet doing. The upper illustration shows the bird, having swooped up to the right spot, spreading out its wings and also using its webbed feet to stop the impetus of its swoop. There are all sorts of air currents upon the face of such a cliff and it is a matter of nice adjustment of speed to land on the nest at the first attempt. Below we see that the landing has been safely made beside the sitting mate.

at the rate of half the distance in that time. It is hard to say how long a swift could keep in the air without a break. We fancy that were it granted favourable weather and eternal daylight it could encircle the Globe!

Many records have come to light to show that homing-pigeons can travel at a mile a minute. At that high speed they have endurance enough to keep on the wing until a journey of two hundred miles is accomplished. By dropping down their speed fifty per cent. they could remain on the wing all day. The swallow can travel at ninety miles an hour, and could complete a non-stop journey from Equatorial Africa to England without becoming fatigued! Our small garden birds travel, on an average, at the rate of about thirty-five miles an hour. Their endurance is remarkable. A goldcrest, smallest of European birds, and weighing but a dram, can make its way across the North Sea even on a dark November night!

A bird of prey can bear off in its talons a surprisingly heavy victim, provided it be killed outright. A female peregrine falcon (which is larger than her mate) finds no difficulty in ascending from the beach to a precipitous cliff, three hundred feet above the sea, with a dead curlew in her grasp, the quarry here being nearly as big as the captor. A golden eagle can rise a couple of hundred feet with the

Arthur Brook

H. H. Hall

EVOLUTIONS OF FEEDING SEAGULLS; A ROOK GLIDING TO ITS NEST

To study the wonder of the wing intensively the best way is to go where seagulls are used to being fed by human hands—such a place as the Thames Embankment in London. The birds wheel round the spot or the parapet where the food is being given, some of the bolder spirits alighting for a moment, while others prefer to snatch scraps thrown to them on the wing. These birds can in a moment alter the pace of their movement from a rapid swoop to a hovering. The upper photograph shows a rook gliding down to its nest.

lifeless body of a newly-born lamb, kid, or fawn. As a general rule it is a much more speedy business for the parent birds to feed their young upon smaller game. Hares, grouse, and rabbits form the eaglets' staple diet. Their bones and other indigestible parts are found for the most part in the eyrie. Likewise, the peregrine goes full speed ahead to the youngsters with a puffin, a rook, a plover, a jackdaw, or other abundant bird about that size. Large quarry, not killed outright, offers another and very different picture. A full-grown rabbit seized by the nape of the neck will kick and plunge so violently with its hind-limbs that the falcon may be obliged to come to earth before he reaches his accustomed and secluded ' dining-hall.' Here he falls into the ' hands ' of an angry mob, whose taunts and jeers urge him to relinquish his booty. He peers round suspiciously, then, under fierce protests, yields, lest the rioters should attract a dangerous enemy upon the scene. In an instant the bird of prey glides over the cliff-face, snatches up a puffin, kills it outright, reaches the eyrie post-haste, and in a twinkle his youngsters are enjoying their supper of puffin, whilst the querulous crows and yelping gulls hold a banquet below on the rabbit's carcase.

A GOLDEN EAGLE has been known to release a weighty, struggling victim, such as a lamb or a fawn, and then swoop down immediately some six hundred feet, there to devour the lifeless body on the jagged rocks. A full-grown fox was seized by an eagle, but not killed. Its struggles were so violent that it was dropped from a height of about sixty feet. It fell on rough, stony ground. A second eagle, perceiving its hopeless condition, pounced upon its flanks before the original captor could arrive. A moment afterwards, however, the body was being torn to pieces by both birds.

We may now briefly discuss a very interesting matter, namely, whether flightless birds, as we know them, were endowed with the power of flight in days gone by. It is difficult to imagine an ostrich—that huge familiar creature—capable of flight. The gigantic size and weight of its entire hind-quarters, including, of course, its gigantic hind-limbs, would necessitate tremendous compensatory development, not only of the wings, but of the whole framework of its fore-quarters (especially the breast-bone and muscles), with considerable enlargement of neck, head, and beak. Otherwise, the centre of gravity would fall so far behind the suspension of the wings, that it would be impossible for the bird when flying to prevent the front of its body from tilting upwards to an awkward extent. We are reminded of a little boat, in which all the occupants elect to sit astern, allowing the empty bow to rise clear of the water to an inconvenient height.

The same difficulty arises in regard to flight in the case of the emu, rhea, cassowary, and even the little kiwi. All have immensely-developed hind-quarters ; all would require immensely ample wings. If the forebears of ostriches ever flew, their bodily proportions must have been very different from those of their extant descendants. We think of smaller forebears with limbs built in proper proportions. *Eohippus*, ancestor of the proud winner of the Derby, was small ; so may have been the ostrich of bygone days. Indubitably, birds have sprung from nimble, swift, bipedal reptiles, long since extinct. The living bipedal iguanodon cannot be said to represent the direct line of departure along which the bird descended. Structurally, this reptile shows little affinities with the bird.

HOWEVER, some of the large bipedal reptiles, whose fossil remains have been submitted to the closest scrutiny, were astonishingly like ostriches in form and deportment ; in the proportions of front to hind limbs ; in the number of fingers ; in the relative size of head and neck to body ; and in other particulars. The tails of these reptiles were typically long ; the fingers and toes free and three in number. In the ostrich the tail has shortened and one toe is absent, though it is present in some of the other large flightless birds.

The wings of the rhea are better developed than those of the ostrich. On the other hand, we find degenerative gradations in the case of the emu, cassowary, and apteryx, and the tridactyl ancestral hand no longer maintains. It seems as though the queer ostrich-like reptiles had a forebear, arboreal in habits, whose leaping desires grew keener and keener, until at length the trees and their branches were relinquished and avian flight in the open became fully established. Millions of years ago the ostrich flew, but it should be remembered that flight had not far advanced ; in fact, among several species we may safely assume that it was little more than in its infancy. Millions of years have rolled on since the ostrich and its allies ceased to fly. In the vast vistas of time which have elapsed since that event, evolution has manifested herself in manifold activities. Flight—the wonder of the wing—among the many, has paid her a handsome tribute !

A WORD in conclusion, in regard to the penguin. Here a different historical picture presents itself. In a broad sense, it may be said that this bird never lost the power of flight. Once upon a time it flew in the air ; on that score we have no doubt ; the framework of its wings is large and strong ; the component parts complete, and designed in accordance with the aerial wing. At the present day, the penguin ' flies ' only in water. Its cousins of the Northern Hemisphere, the guillemot, razorbill and puffin, fly in both air and water. The penguin grew still more aquatic, until at length, Father Neptune claimed it almost entirely as his own. But its wings have never been denied a single day's work. There is something unusually attractive in the submarine ' flight ' of the penguin. Speed, grace, and adroitness in turning, have reached such a pitch of perfection, that we doubt if the fish in the water or the fowl in the air can emulate the penguin.

Chapter CXXIV

Animals in Human Warfare

By W. S. Berridge

Author of "Marvels of Natural History"

Few people realize what a large share animals take in human warfare, and although we can but deplore the fact that the lot of many is to suffer hardship, and even death, for a cause in which they have no interest, we can never forget the debt of gratitude we owe to them for the services rendered.

In the Great War, so fresh in the memory of most of us, horses, mules, oxen, camels, dogs, mice, pigeons, canaries, and even goldfish played a part; and although many of these were not in the front line, so to speak, they were all subjected to dangers of varying degree and the casualties were heavy.

At the outbreak of hostilities on August 4th, 1914, the British Army had some 25,000 horses, but this number was rapidly increased, and by the year 1918 the total was nearly 1,000,000, notwithstanding the heavy wastage that ensued in the meanwhile through disease and death. As many as 165,000 of these animals were obtained in the United Kingdom within less than a fortnight after the commencement of the War; but the bulk of them had to be procured from abroad and brought overseas to the various seats of action, vast quantities being purchased in North America, South America, Australia, New Zealand, India, South Africa, Spain and Portugal.

The first batch of Canadian horses arrived in England in the latter part of the year 1914. Needless to say, many of these animals were somewhat raw, and those destined to be used by the cavalry had much to learn before they could be regarded as efficient fighting units. They had to be accustomed to rifle fire, schooled in the art of jumping, and taught to disregard the rapid flashing above their heads of their riders' swords. But so little was heard about the cavalry during the eventful years of 1914 to 1918, that one was apt to think their activities were almost negligible. It is true that mounted troops could not be used in the deadlock of trench warfare, but they were ever ready to press forward when a break occurred in the barrier of earthworks. It has been stated on good authority that "Jerusalem would never have been entered but for General Allenby's cavalry," while "the crusade into the heart of Palestine was distinguished by the fine exploits of Yeomen of Warwickshire, Worcestershire, Buckinghamshire and Berkshire;" and had it not been for "Indian cavalry, Allenby's brilliant coup by which two Turkish armies were smashed would not have been possible." It will be seen therefore that cavalry did contribute very largely towards the winning of the War on the British fronts.

FOR TRAINING WAR DOGS

The German soldier in steel helmet and great coat is holding a canister of liquid. A hole in the bottom lets the contents trickle out leaving a trail. The canister is strapped to a man's back and the army dogs are trained to follow his "scent." This is a good example of German thoroughness.

Mules were employed solely as beasts of burden and for haulage purposes, and the assistance they rendered the Allies cannot be overestimated. About 250,000 of these animals were brought to Europe from North and South America during the period of hostilities. In spite of the fact that mules are somewhat difficult customers to deal with, their temperament being a mixture of stubbornness, cunning and willingness, they have the advantage of being far more

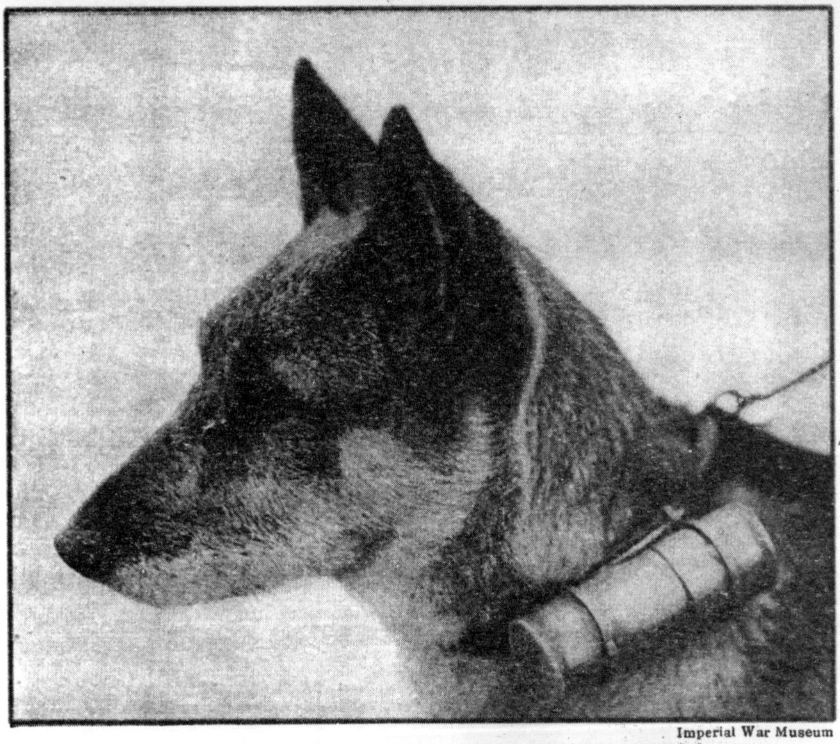

Imperial War Museum

MESSENGER DOGS AND THEIR BASE BEHIND THE LINES

During the Great War dogs were used by both sides in Flanders for carrying messages and other duties. The messages were carried, so far as the British were concerned, in a little metal cylinder strapped to the dog's collar (bottom). Behind the lines there was a special base (top) with kennels. The dogs were of varied breed, intelligence being of more importance than pedigree.

indifferent than horses to the din of battle, and far better able to withstand extremes of heat and cold.

The use of camels in warfare can be traced back to the time of David, and in more modern days they were employed by Napoleon, and later by Napier during the war in Scinde. In the Indian Mutiny the Gordon Highlanders rode on camels, each trooper being mounted with a native driver; while, moreover, the adaptability and speed of the creatures when travelling over sandy soil was recognized by the French during their punitive raids in Algeria, the troopers riding on horseback to within a comparatively short distance from the enemy, and, when making their final dash, mounting fast camels that had been held in reserve. British and Egyptian camel-corps played a prominent part in the Sudan campaigns, and in the Great War they were employed against the Turks. The Bikaner camel-corps, supported by the ruling princes of India, also took part in the campaign in Egypt, where it rendered conspicuous service.

When pressed, a camel can cover from seventy to eighty miles a day, supporting upon its back both its rider and enough food and water to last for a week. Unlike the horse, it is never controlled by a bit, but by a cord passed through a hole piercing the nostrils. The animal is by no means good-tempered, and no matter how well it may be treated it never appears to form any real attachment to its owner.

Although elephants are not utilised in modern warfare, they have been employed for that purpose in the past. The earliest reference to their use in battle is made by Ctesias, who mentions the ten thousand that were attached to the fighting line and transport columns of Cyrus. But a more detailed account is to be found in the First Book of

Imperial War Museum

SENDING A MESSAGE AND BRINGING DOGS UP TO THE FORWARD AREA

About to send the dog off with a message the soldier holds his four-legged messenger back for a moment for the photograph (bottom). In the next page the story of its adventures is continued. The upper photograph, taken towards the end of the Great War, shows four dogs being taken up from the base to the forward area. The party is skirting a small shell hole. The type of animal used for the work was usually bred from airedales or collies, though there were many dogs of somewhat mixed parentage.

Imperial War Museum

CROSSING A CANAL TO DELIVER A MESSAGE: A WAR-DOG AT WORK

These photographs were taken near Nieppe Wood in May, 1918. A messenger dog, sent down from the trenches, had to negotiate a canal before reaching its objective. We see the dog swimming (top) and the message being read (bottom). No human being could have run this obstacle race as quickly as the dog. But, of course, conditions as they existed in the Great War did not always permit of these animals being used. When given the chance, however, the dog proved himself as faithful, under new and more dreadful conditions, as ever before.

Imperial War Museum

MESSENGER DOG IN A GAS MASK AND TAKING A MESSAGE FROM THE TRENCHES

With characteristic thoroughness the German army put their dogs into specially constructed gas masks, as we see in the lower photograph. The dog looks the most grotesque sight possible. Notice the eye-pieces and the container for the chemical to neutralise the effects of the gas. This container is fastened to the side of the mask under the jaw, and does not hang from the point of the chin as the German soldiers' masks did. Above we see a British messenger dog jumping a shell hole in taking a message from the trenches to headquarters.

TEACHING DOGS TO FOLLOW A SCENT: GERMAN APPARATUS

This apparatus is suspended from a cable and consists of a wheel fitted with a number of clogs. When the wheel is pulled along the clogs engage the ground and, being correctly spaced, produce a number of footfalls approximating to human ones. Each of these clumsy pieces of imitation footwear is impregnated with scent and the dogs are trained to follow the trail.

Maccabees, in which is related the story of King Eleazar Savaran losing his life through being crushed by the falling of an elephant he had mortally wounded.

ANTIOCHUS EPIPHANES, King of Syria, employed elephants in warfare, and when he marched against Jerusalem his army consisted of "one hundred thousand footmen, and twenty thousand horsemen, and two-and-thirty elephants exercised in battle." It is further stated that "to the end that they might provoke the elephants to fight, they showed them the blood of grapes and mulberries," thereby, we presume, inducing them *to see red*. In the writings of Plutarch it is related how elephants trained to the work chased and knocked down the retreating enemy, impaling the men on their tusks, and then flinging them high in the air with their trunks. War-elephants were elaborately bedecked with armour that chiefly consisted of iron plates fastened together with rings and chains. Spiked and knobbed chains also hung from under the animals' throats and over their breasts, and others of a similar nature upon their trunks, but these, we are told, were "for ornament and to frighten horses." Although the Asiatic elephants are undoubtedly more tractable than the African, curiously enough, it appears that the latter kind were the ones employed in warfare. In the Punic Wars (264–241 B.C. and 218–201 B.C.), when Hannibal marched a herd of elephants over the Alps, it was the African and not the Asiatic species that successfully accomplished this surprising feat.

The last appearance of elephants in an engagement of any importance was during the Afghan War (1878–1879), in the battle of Peiwar Kotal, and although they still might be used with advantage for haulage purposes, they are liable to become restless and unmanageble when subjected to the noise of battle, and nowadays they have been superseded either by motor-power, horses, or teams of oxen.

The use of dogs in warfare is a very old institution. In the Middle Ages they actually went into battle clothed in armour, a suit of dog-armour preserved in the Tower of London testifying to this fact. Historical records show that King Henry the Eighth made use of a large breed of bloodhounds in the wars against France, and that in the days of Elizabeth the Earl of Essex had eight hundred of these canines in his army.

Christopher Columbus, moreover, employed twenty bloodhounds to assist his soldiers in his campaigns against the natives of Santo Domingo, and Mr. H. F. Suckling states that "there was a breed of large dogs in use in Northumberland, called slough-dogs, which were kept by the borderers for the purpose of pursuing offenders called Moss-troopers." War-dogs were also attached to the Greek army in the past, and we read that one individual so far distinguished itself by its bravery and fighting prowess that its owner had its effigy engraved upon his tablet.

We are all aware that dogs are utilised in Belgium for harnessing to small carts and barrows, but it is not

GERMAN ARMY DOGS LEARNING CONDITIONS OF MODERN WARFARE

This patrol of men and dogs (bottom) is equipped against the exigencies of poison gas. The difficulties of training men to breathe in gas masks were not a few. How hard, then, must it have been to get dogs to breathe in these unnatural conditions and with an encumbrance over their faces which all the animal in them must have hated. The upper photograph shows the outskirts of a pinewood where a patrol is training dogs to crawl and crouch on the ground as men have to do in modern warfare.

W. S. Berridge

Imperial War Museum

GOOSE, AN ARTILLERY MASCOT, AND A FIELD PIGEON LOFT

As mascots animals played a not inconsiderable part in the Great War. Below we see a goose belonging to the 52nd Brigade Artillery that was both gassed and wounded and finally, having survived many hazards, was taken to the Zoological Gardens in London to end its days in peace and quietness. Above is an old pre-war London omnibus turned into a pigeon loft for field service.

so generally known that during the Great War they were used for the transport of light guns. Their chief rôle in warfare, however, is for Red Cross work, although owing to their keenness of hearing they are also of great assistance in helping sentries in the execution of their duties.

Collies, Airedales and bloodhounds are the dogs most adapted for war work, but, needless to say, their training is both a long and arduous process, and they have much to learn before they become proficient in the performance of their humane duties. They are taught to search for wounded men on the battlefield, bringing succour in the form of water, bandages, and other first-aid necessaries,

Imperial War Museum

MESSAGE FASTENED TO A PIGEON, AND BIRDS IN THEIR MOTOR LOFT

Pigeons were used by the Saracens during the Crusades for carrying messages, the Crusaders' counter measure being the provision of falcons to fly after and kill them. Pigeons are invaluable to armies and during the Great War did fine service. Below is a bird and a message being put into the little container it carries, while above is a field pigeon loft at feeding time.

which they carry strapped upon their backs; while, even on the darkest night, by barking they are able to direct the stretcher-bearers to the fallen combatants.

The employment of pigeons in war-time may now be regarded as a necessity, for no modern army would be without its pigeon post. It appears that the Saracens were the first to utilise these birds for carrying messages, and as a counter-measure the Christian commanders then trained falcons to bear down upon and kill the avian postmen. During the Franco-Prussian war pigeons proved to be of inestimable value, and when Paris was besieged the birds are said to have carried therefrom 150,000 or more official despatches and 1,000,000 private messages.

Imperial War Museum

TAKING A BASKET OF PIGEONS ABOARD A SEAPLANE AND RELEASING A BIRD WITH A MESSAGE

Pigeons were employed by the thousand in the Great War, not only on land and sea but from aircraft, too. Our photographs show a basket of pigeons being put into a seaplane (left) and a bird being released with a message (right). The type of bird used is known as the homing pigeon, not to be confused with the carrier pigeon which is distinguished by the prominent wattles round the eyes and at the base of the beak. These homing pigeons can attain a speed of a mile a minute, though this is somewhat above the average speed for long distance flying. Before the War such a bird flew from Rome to its home in Durham, England, a distance of 1,093 miles, thus creating a record for long distance flying.

Imperial War Museum

SENDING OUT A MESSAGE BY HOMING PIGEON FROM A TANK IN FRANCE AND A SUBMARINE IN THE NORTH SEA

Many pigeons went into action with the artillery in France and some were even carried in tanks. Our left-hand photograph shows one being released from a revolver porthole under cover of a projecting machine-gun casemate. On the right another messenger bird is being sent off from a submarine and the vital piece of paper is being packed into the metal tube which is fastened to the bird's leg. During the War a pigeon was the means of bringing aid to a submarine after it had captured an enemy vessel, and other birds helped to save lives in the warfare on the sea when no other means of transmitting messages was possible. In fact it is scarcely an exaggeration to say that pigeons helped to win the war.

Imperial War Museum

CANARIES FOR TESTING THE AIR IN MINE TUNNEL AND UNITED STATES WAR PIGEONS

In compiling a list of animals used in warfare the canary would not probably occur to the average person. Nevertheless, these little birds were extremely useful in submarines and in underground mining such as was carried on under Hill 60, for instance, owing to their extreme sensitiveness to impure air. White mice were used for the same purpose. If the animals showed signs of being affected it was time for humans to go, even though the latter had not noticed any inconvenience. Above are some pigeons used for American naval air service

Imperial War Museum

HORSES TAKING THE GUNS THROUGH AWKWARD PLACES IN FRANCE

Below we see a team struggling out of the bed of the Canal du Nord at a point near Moeuvres in September, 1918. The smashed bridge is an eloquent answer to any question of why the team has to go to all this extra trouble. Above we see a gun team of a R.H.A. 13-pounder battery galloping through a ford. The horses make a brave show as they splash the water high above the drivers' heads. With the increase of mechanical transport such sights will be rarer in human warfare, though animal lovers will hardly regret it.

ARMY MULES IN TRAINING FOR THE SERIOUS BUSINESS OF THEIR LIFE

During the Great War about a quarter of a million mules from South America alone came to bear their part in the hostilities. And at one part of the Front, a road was said to have been built which had the bodies of dead mules for its foundations. These animals were used largely as beasts of burden and were found to be less worried by the din of battle than horses. Our photographs show (bottom) a mule being broken in and (top) a nursery for Army mules in Surrey. Here rest and quiet prepare a mulish physique for a strenuous life.

Imperial War Museum

MULES BEING TRANSPORTED ACROSS AN AFRICAN RIVER AND BEING CLIPPED

When a difference of opinion arises between mule and man the matter usually takes some time to settle. But, despite the traditional obstinacy of this animal, it was found that armies could not do without it. On all fronts of the war it was found a place. Our lower photograph shows one employed in the campaign in German East Africa. It is being carried across the Ruwu River by cable. Above is a mule in the stocks, where it cannot kick, for its first clipping. The mechanical clippers are being applied by the man in the centre.

ANIMALS IN TRAINING FOR WARFARE AT BRITISH ARMY MANOEUVRES

An incident in the British Army manoeuvres in the vicinity of Salisbury Plain is illustrated in the lower photograph. A mule-drawn timber has got into difficulties because the road is blocked by a heavy tank. In trying to turn in this narrow lane the limber has gone half through the hedge. It is in such circumstances that training in the management of animals for war tells, any embarrassment on the part of the drivers being soon communicated to the animals. Above is part of an artillery battery proceeding down a road.

Imperial War Museum

THE REAL THING AND PREPARATION FOR IT: HORSES AND MULES AT WAR WORK

Transport difficulties in war can never be imitated in peace. These two photographs show the horse and the mule as beasts of burden, the former in France and the latter near Tidworth in England. The horses (bottom) were photographed not far from Ypres in August, 1917. They are carrying shells for light artillery and are moving up to the battery positions. After crossing an area of liquid mud they are just gaining the road. Above is a mule on manoeuvres, serving a machine-gun battery.

HORSE AND DROMEDARY ON ACTIVE SERVICE ON FAR FRONTS: LANCERS AND CAMEL CORPS

On the left is a photograph taken in the famous Khyber Pass, which is really the bed of a stream cutting through the mountain mass separating India from Afghanistan. A patrol of Lancers is passing along this famous and much-fought-over route, which is thirty-five miles long. The horse has often served the Indian Army well on this ground, which has been a battlefield, at one time or another, from end to end. The right-hand illustration shows one of the magnificent riding camels, or dromedaries, used by the Sudanese troops in Egypt. Camels have been used in war since the time of David, and British and Egyptian and Indian camel corps fought against the Turks during the Great War.

Micro-photographs of documents relating to war matters and articles from the daily press were carried by this means, the records being enlarged when the birds reached their destination. Some idea of the remarkable homing instinct of these carrying pigeons can be judged by the story related of a bird sent out from the besieged city. It fell into the hands of the enemy, who kept it in confinement for ten years, but when it was ultimately given its freedom it immediately flew off and returned to its old home.

The type of birds used for message-carrying are known as homing pigeons, and these must not be confused with the so-called carrier pigeons, distinguished by the large, whitish wattles around their eyes and at the base of the beak, which are but indifferent flyers. A good homing pigeon can fly at the rate of sixty miles an hour, though such a speed is above the average and could not be sustained for any length of time.

W. S. Berridge

REMARKABLE HYBRID PRODUCED FOR HAULING GUNS

During the South African War an attempt was made by the Boers to evolve a new animal to supplement the supply available for transport work. A cross was obtained between a Chapman's zebra and a pony, and the above specimen was captured by the British and presented to King Edward VII by Lord Kitchener. The animal was produced chiefly for hauling guns.

In 1913 one of these birds, named "Prince of Rome," flew in a test match from the Italian capital to its loft in Spennymoor, county Durham, a distance of 1,093 miles. This feat then constituted a British record for long-distance flying, but whether it has since been beaten in these super-days we are unable to say. During the Great War homing pigeons were extensively used for flying over both land and sea. For the patrol boats and mine-sweepers they were often the only means which the occupants had of communicating with the shore. One bird, appropriately named the "Sweeper's Hope," flew 160 miles over the North Sea with the glad tidings that an attack made upon the mine-sweeping fleet had been frustrated by aeroplanes, and that the crews were safe; while on another occasion one of the birds was responsible for bringing aid to a submarine that required assistance after having captured a German trawler. A badly wounded pigeon also flew for a distance of ten miles from one trawler to another, and by its message saved the lives of many people.

Many pigeons accompanied the batteries at the Front, being sent off with their messages while the guns were in action, and even flying at night. At the Battle of the Marne a bird with a badly damaged foot through shell-fire was the bearer of news that enabled the French to frustrate the attacks of the enemy. The Germans had wheeled pigeon-lofts which they moved from place to place during the period of hostilities, and one of these that was captured during the War can now be seen in Regent's Park, London, at the northern end of the Broad Walk. Canaries were other birds that played a part during the War. They were carried in submarines and by sappers when mining underground, the birds by their sensitiveness to any impurities in the air giving a warning before conditions became dangerous. White mice were also used for a similar purpose.

One would hardly associate geese with warfare, but in olden days they were the means of saving the Roman Capitol. When the Gauls invaded Rome a file of men crept up the hill of the Capitol so stealthily that the leader succeeded in reaching the top without his presence being discovered. When he was clambering over the rampart, however, some sacred geese espied him and began to cackle, whereupon Marcus Manlius rushed to the wall, sent the man tumbling down the precipitous slope, and called out the garrison. Thus the Capitol was saved, for, to quote the words of Butler:

> Those consecrated geese in orders,
> That to the Capitol were warders,
> And being then upon patrol,
> With noise alone beat off the Gaul.

In the late War a pair of geese accompanied the 52nd Army Brigade, Royal Field Artillery, to the Front. These mascots went through the battles of Loos, Ypres (1915 and 1917), Ploegsteert, Somme (twice), Arras (1916, 1917, 1918), Vimy Wood, Cambrai and Mons. After the Armistice they were sent to the London Zoo, where they spent the rest of their days roaming about the spacious paddock.

In conclusion we must pay our tribute to those goldfish that suffered inconvenience, or even death, in the cause of humanity, for by placing them in water within which anti-gas masks had been soaked it was possible to a certain extent to determine the nature of the gas that had been employed in an attack.

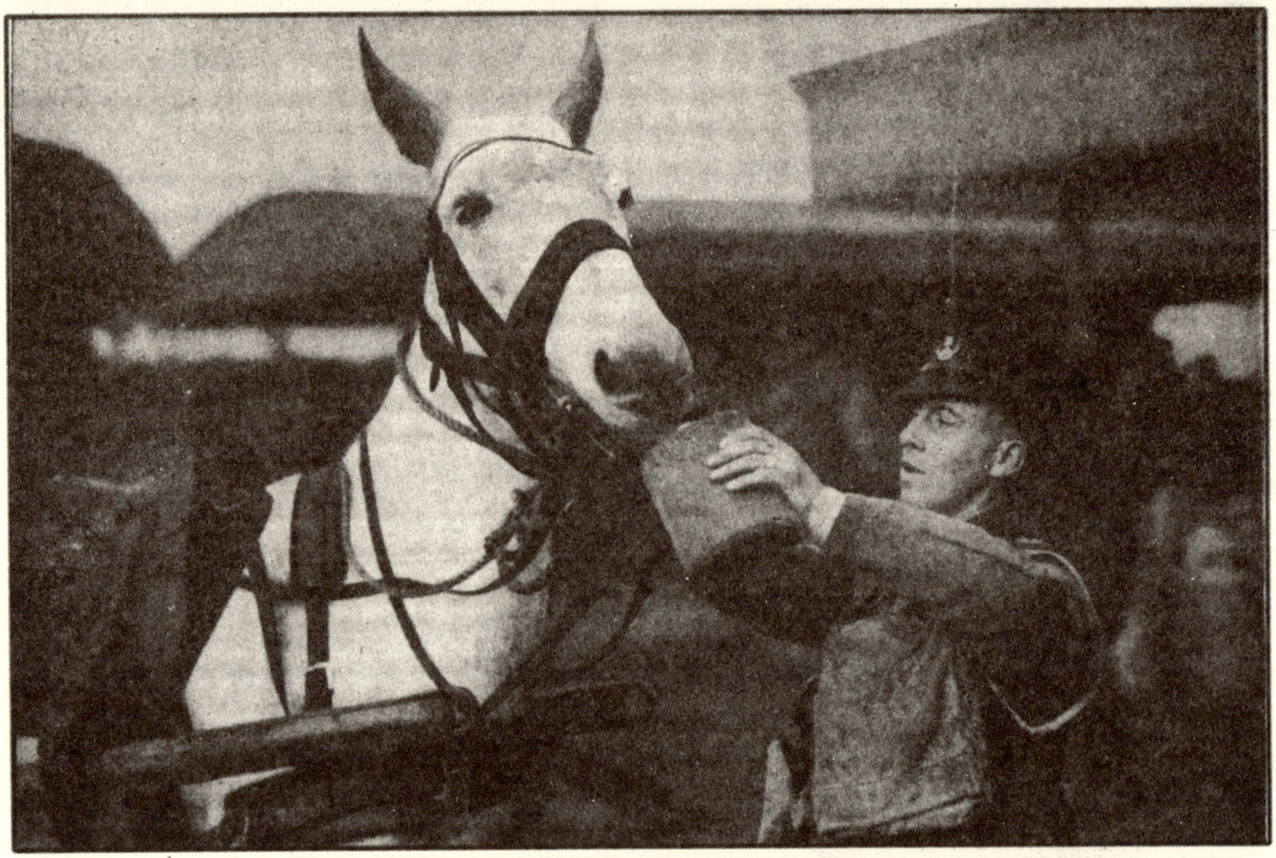

PREPARING FOR WAR IN TIME OF PEACE: INCIDENTS ON MANOEUVRES

Caught in the act of trying to make the best of a proffered drink from its driver's water-bottle we see in the lower photograph an army mule during a pause in the proceedings of the annual manoeuvres. Above we are in the horse lines with the animals resting from the day's work, and saddles and accoutrements piled in front. It is a rule in units using horses or mules that, when the time comes for rest, the animal is attended to before the man. In fact, few horses get so carefully looked after as army horses.

Imperial War Museum

CAMEL CORPS INSPECTION AND OX POWER ON A RAILWAY IN THE BALKANS

Napoleon employed camels in his Egyptian campaign, and so did Napier during the war in Sind which he undertook in 1841. In later years, too, the French have made extensive use of these animals in their dealings with the turbulent tribesmen of Algeria. The Bikaner Camel Corps, organized by the ruling princes of India, was one of the several camel corps which played a conspicuous part in the Great War. Below we see a camel corps paraded for inspection. Above we have an example of oxen used in warfare on the Balkan front.

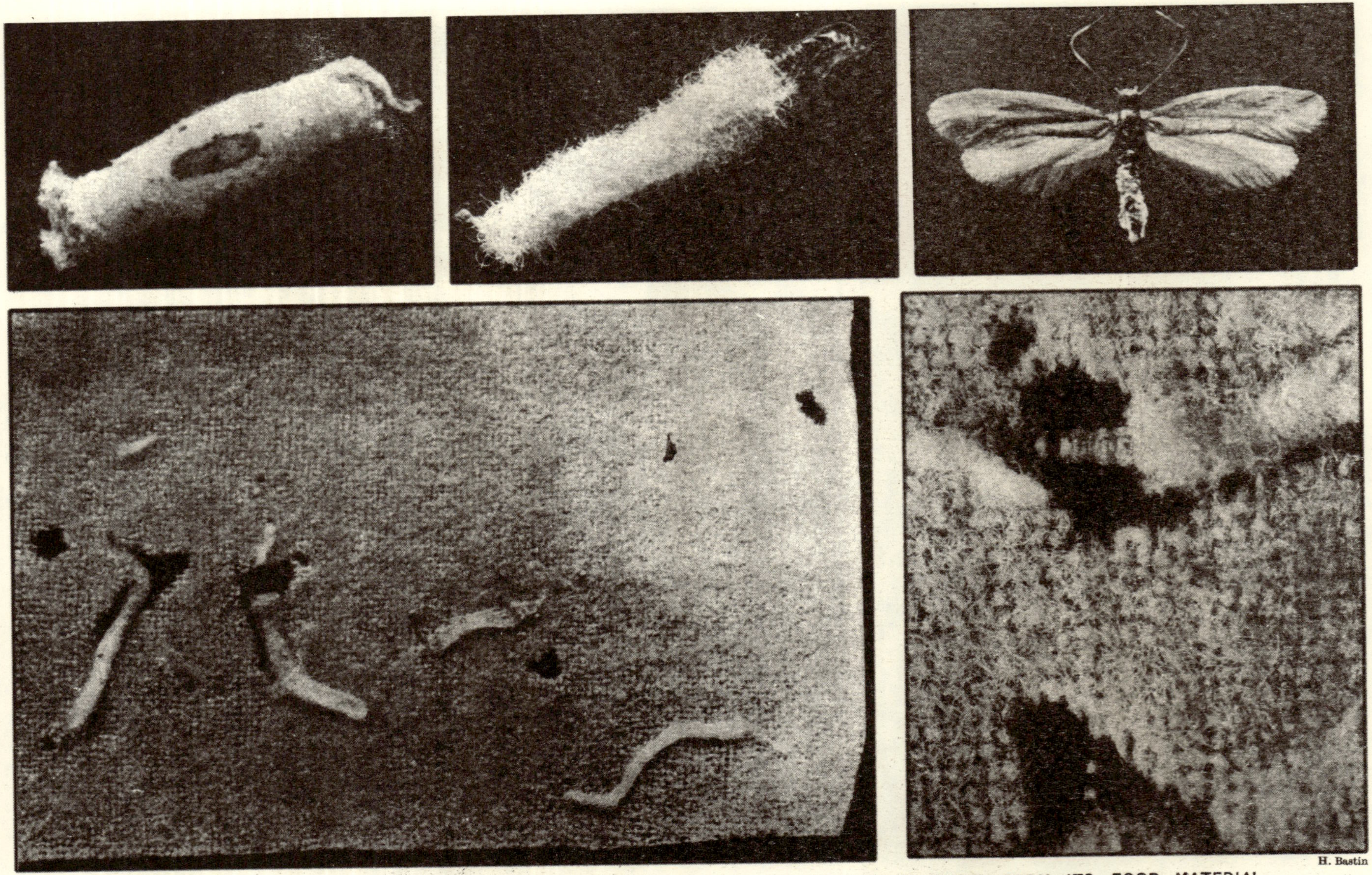

H. Bastin

CLOTHES MOTH, ITS DESTRUCTIVE CATERPILLAR AND THE CLEVER DWELLING IT MAKES FROM ITS FOOD MATERIAL

It is not the adult clothes moth which does the damage, but its caterpillar or larva. The adult flying moth lays her eggs on a dress, a coat or a fur, and as each egg hatches a small grub appears and begins to feed. From the material on which it has been placed the larva makes a little tube for itself (top left). In this it lurks, thrusting out its head to feed. As it grows it lets in a series of insertions of new material to enlarge its dwelling and also adds material at both ends. It never leaves its tube till it has made its pupa case (top centre), emerged from it and crawled out as a complete, winged moth (top right). The chrysalis has a number of small spines on its skin and by the aid of these it wriggles to the exit of its tube. Below are examples of its work.

Chapter CXXV

Twelve Insect Pests of the British Home

By W. Percival Westell

Author of "The Book of Nature"

FORTUNATELY the temperate climate of Britain is such that, except under very favourable conditions, insect pests are not nearly so formidable to human kind as in tropical countries. The Briton has not, as is the case with more unfortunate dwellers in foreign lands, to fight plagues of locusts which devour every green blade they come in contact with, or to do battle in mosquito swamps. Nevertheless, there are in Britain, even though the climate is not, except on rare occasions, of a tropical nature, quite enough insect pests to contend with both in and out of doors. The former are, of course, in the minority, the latter in abundance.

Advances made in the system of town planning, clearance of slum areas, healthier and better homes, cleanlier habits among the people, have all made their mark in lessening the numbers of insect pests of the British home. Even the most hygienic and careful housewife will, on occasion, find herself the unwilling harbourer in the home of some six-legged pest. Spiders, with their eight legs, not being insects, do not come within the survey of this chapter and, in any case, are allies, not pests.

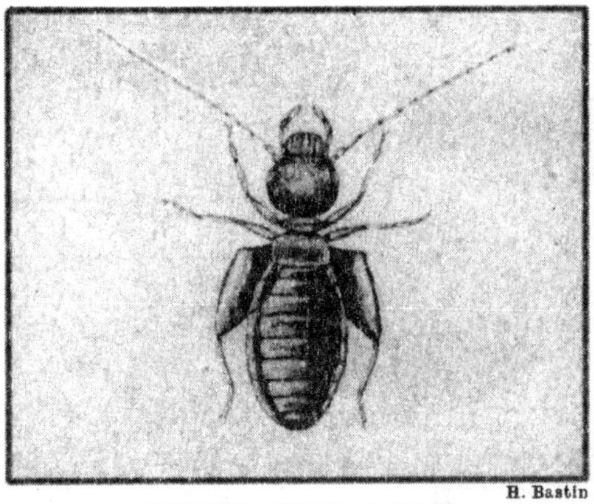

H. Bastin

MINUTE BOOK LOUSE

Book lice are very prevalent but are so minute that they escape attention. They are one-twentieth of an inch long and are seen as swiftly moving specks in books. This specimen is much magnified.

Old houses, bakehouses, shops, outbuildings, rubbish heaps near the homestead, offer invitations to certain kinds of insects to "walk into the parlour," and at times only ceaseless vigil and drastic measures are likely to stay the invading enemy. Sometimes tenants of the garden, such as the earwig and ground-dwelling beetles, will cross the threshold of one's dwelling, and the former seems especially partial to becoming a forbidden lodger in a new home.

It is, however, with a round dozen insect pests of the home that we are here concerned, and although detested by most people—and in most cases quite justifiably—these lowly forms of animal life present to the inquiring mind remarkable life histories worthy of consideration.

The flat, chocolate-coloured insect, often erroneously referred to as the black beetle—properly called the cockroach—is a lover of warm places indoors, and, like its cousin the house cricket next on our list, is very partial to bakehouses. The male cockroach has wings, and can leave its abode through the air if so disposed, but its wingless mate must, of necessity, stay at home. In some cases both sexes are wingless. The long antennae, or feelers, of the cockroach are features of interest, and, similar to others of its kind, this insect is a night roamer.

When I was a boy I lived in a large house that, in the days of Dick Turpin, was one of the old inns on the Great North Road at historic St. Albans, and in my school days I remember the bread cupboard was inundated with these distasteful household dwellers. Methods had to be adopted to keep down their numbers, and I call to mind how each morning I used to view with satisfaction the slain bodies of our unwelcome guests. Poison of some kind was laid down for them, but there are other remedies, such as sodium fluoride sprinkled on the floor, or in the places frequently occupied by the invaders. Poisoned baits can also be used.

At the end of the female's body there is a capsule, or purse, in which she carries her eggs. The eggs are splendidly arranged and admirably protected, but, contrary to the general rule in the insect world, in at least one foreign species the young are believed to be produced alive.

The cockroach was unintentionally introduced into Britain from Asia and the Levant. Its chief crime is that, when it comes into contact with food, it taints it with a distasteful odour, and as it can devour almost anything from a tender lettuce leaf to hard leather, the sooner it is given notice to quit one's premises the better. It is stated that if cockroaches find a house in which they have taken up their abode unsuitable, they will leave for another in a body, but of this fact it is difficult to get any conclusive proof, though such an exodus is quite possible.

CLOSELY related to the last-named insect, the house cricket will be known to many of our readers by the stridulating noise it emits. It is also a relative of that cheerful little acrobat of our grassy meadows, heaths, and waysides, the grasshopper. The male cricket is the "singer," but it is not a vocal effort, the curious noise being made by one wing being rubbed over, or drawn across, the other, and is thought by those who have made a study of this insect to serve as a signal to his mate.

To some listeners the note of the cricket on the hearth is irritating, to others it appeals. Leigh Hunt was evidently an admirer of the jumpy little

H. Bastin

EGG CAPSULES AND PARENTS OF THE COCKROACH

Cockroach eggs are laid in sets of sixteen packed neatly in a capsule (bottom, photo. magnified). The capsule is carried for some days and then dropped in a crevice. The larvae, on hatching, escape through the toothed edge of the capsule The upper photographs show (left) a male, and (right) a female adult cockroach

beast, for in his lines to "The Grasshopper and the Cricket" he writes:

> O sweet and tiny cousins that belong,
> One to the fields the other to the hearth,
> Both have your sunshine ; both though small are strong,
> To sing in thoughtful ears this natural song—
> Indoors and out, Summer and Winter, mirth.

The house cricket loves warmth, the hotter the better, and it has a habit of getting behind walls, skirtings, fireplaces, and other retreats where it may be heard every night, and yet never be seen.

The female has an ovipositor on the end of her body, and with this instrument she drills a hole and lays an egg. One female will deposit from two to three hundred eggs. Small wonder, perhaps, that, being such a lover of hot places, *Gryllus domesticus* should be a thirsty creature, and it is said that a damp wad of cotton-wool is a sure lure for this species.

Little, if any, damage is perpetrated by this fireside resident, although wet clothes are likely to be subject to its attention, as if the clothes-moth larva had been at work, but if it is desired to rid the house of these singers of the midnight watch, a mixture of equal parts of finely-powdered sodium fluoride, flour, and sugar should be spread about their haunts. Phosphorus paste might also be tried. There is, however, an old belief that it is lucky to have crickets in the home, so that the reader had perhaps better hesitate before he finally decides on a plan of campaign.

Hardly one lady among our readers will dispute the statement that in the wardrobe and drawer the clothes moth is the most undesirable tenant. The ravages of the larva of this moth—not the adult insect itself, as is so often supposed—among our clothes are only too well known, but moths, small and large, are frequently killed by the lady of the household under the belief that all and sundry are on evil intent. Most moths that are attracted to our homes in summer-time fly in at the open door, or window, because of the glare of gas or electric light, but the little brown-coloured clothes moth with very powdery wings has a set purpose in invading our homes and searching for the hiding-place of a nice woolly blanket, fur coat or dress.

The female clothes moth lays her eggs on, or in, the undisturbed garments, and when these eggs hatch out the larva actually commences to feed upon them. Having eaten sufficient, the time arrives for the destructive pest to change into a pupa, and it makes

a cocoon, or covering, of pieces of the garment it is attacking. The dead bodies of the perfect insects are often first indications of their presence, but the damage is soon afterwards discovered. Then, of course, it is too late.

A preventive is to place naphthalene or camphor balls in drawers, wardrobes, boxes and other receptacles containing clothes and other articles only used occasionally. It is a good plan, too, to dust articles before putting them away with flaked naphthalene. Clothes moths belong to a very large group of moths known as the Tineidae, and although tiny in name and stature, these are to be numbered among the most destructive insects of our homes, unless constant vigilance is exercised to combat them.

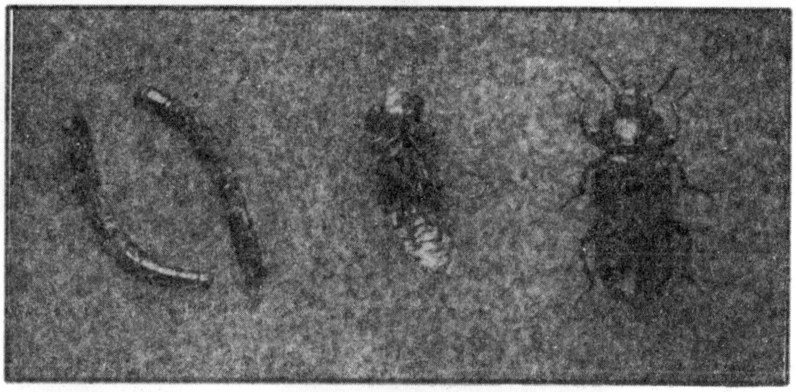

H. Bastin

MEALWORM AND COCKROACH, PESTS OF THE HOUSE

Where flour or meal is stored there will the mealworm beetle be found also. The lower illustration shows the larva, pupa and adult stages. Above is a cockroach group feeding on kitchen refuse. The insects are seen in various stages of growth. Cockroaches or "black beetles" were not known in England till the end of the sixteenth century.

NOT only are our clothes, household materials, and food attacked by unwelcome insect hosts, but our choicest articles of furniture—chair, table, piano, sideboard, mantelpiece, picture frame—are liable to serious attack by the furniture beetle. It is a small, brown-coloured beetle whose curious tapping noise may be heard in a room of an evening when the household is quiet. The belief is still prevalent in some districts that the so-called "ticking" is supposed to presage the death of a person—hence the name death watch beetle—but it is an unconscious act in this respect on the part of the industrious hidden worker, the noise being caused by the little carpenter knocking his head against the tunnel he is excavating. Some entomologists, however, are of opinion that it is a signal from one to another.

The prime object in life of this devastating pest is to pulverise wood, and in serious cases to reduce valuable articles of furniture to tinder. A large portion of a walnut bookcase in the possession of my family was riddled so completely by these furniture beetles that it collapsed, being reduced, all unsuspectingly, to matchwood. Immediately to burn the bookcase was the only thing to do. Watch should be kept for any dust thrown out of the round holes drilled in wooden articles, as this is a sure sign that the unseen worker is energetically engaged on its self-imposed task.

It is no use leaving the matter to chance, or to be attended to another day. Urgent measures are necessary. The eggs being laid in wood, and the

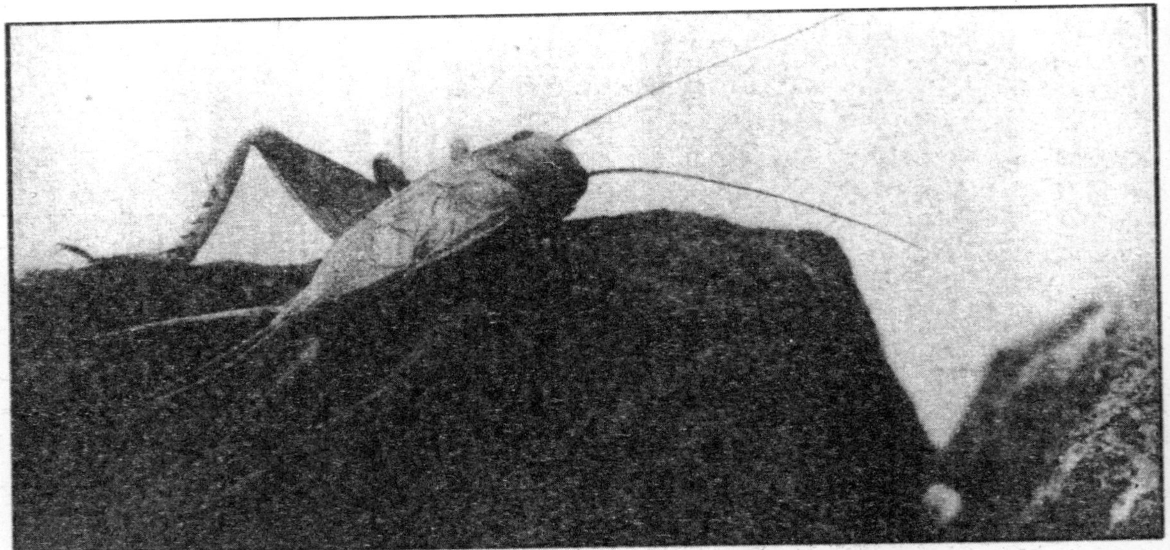

House cricket, considerably magnified

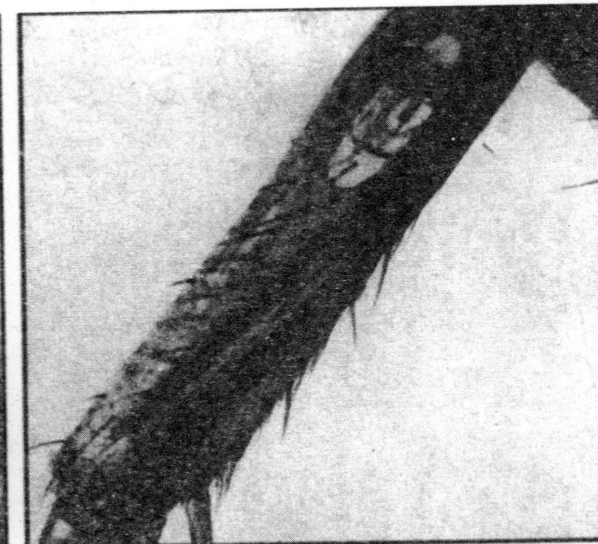

Part of cricket's foreleg, showing ear magnified

Wing cover of female cricket

Right and left wing covers of male cricket

Ovipositor of cricket

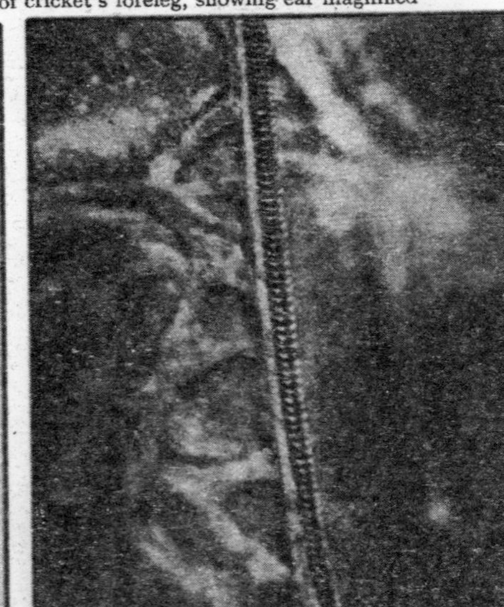

File-like vein on underside of male's wing

HOUSE CRICKETS AND THE ORGANS BY WHICH THEY "CHIRRUP," HEAR AND LAY THEIR EGGS

Lovers of warmth like cockroaches, crickets are very fond of getting in to chinks or cracks in floor or wall near a fireplace or kitchen range. The sound they make is produced by the male rubbing its wings together. There is a file on the underside of the wing cover and this, being rubbed against the other wing cover produces the familiar grating noise. The cricket also has an ear for hearing the noise and it is situated, not in the head, but in one of the forelegs, the aperture being covered by a membrane. The female has an ovipositor divided in two, and the eggs pass down between the two halves and into the hole drilled out by the points at the end of the organ. Photographs by J. J. Ward and H. Bastin.

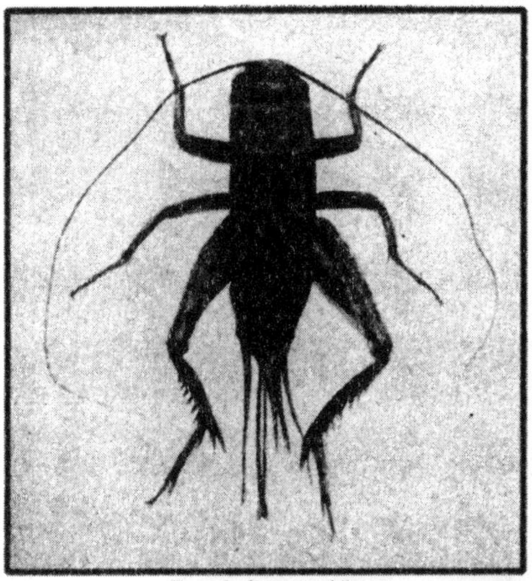

Female house cricket

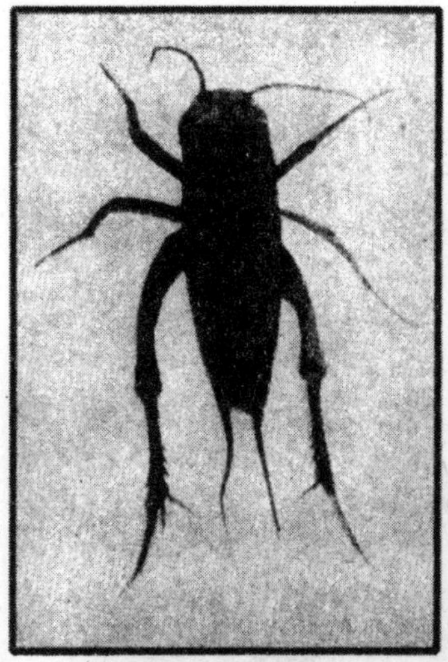

Adult male cricket

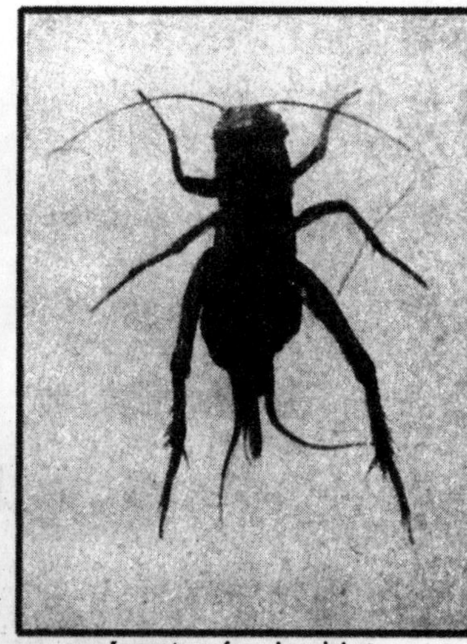

Immature female cricket

grubs, on hatching, tunnelling their way inwards, makes it essential to adopt drastic means to prevent further damage. Various remedies are at hand, such as paraffin, a mixture of oils, or boiling water to be run into the holes ; or the affected parts can be soaked in a weak solution of chloride of zinc, or sulphate of copper. These remedies should be applied in May, and again in July.

The silver-fish insect is a wingless creature found frequenting our larders. Unlike most other insects, it does not undergo any metamorphosis, just increasing in size from babyhood onwards. It is to be numbered among the most lowly of present-day insects, and it is considered that this species and its allies are not descended from winged ancestors, as is the case with the great majority of insect folk.

Silver fish insect, underside

Silver fish, top view

"SILVER FISH" THAT LIVES ON STARCH, AND SOME CRICKETS

Behind the wall-paper or in books is a favourite lurking place for the silver fish insect. It gets its name because some species are covered with scales. The body is tapered and has ten segments. Any substance containing starch such as paste on wall-paper, book bindings or lace curtains is food for the silver fish. Above are house crickets. **Photos, all magnified, H. Bastin**

THE name fish insect is given to this creature because some species are covered with bright scales like the finny inhabitants of our rivers and seas. Bristle tail is another popular name, and one of its cousins resorts to bakehouses and other places.

It has a tapered body, long antennae on the head, three pairs of legs, with three further pairs of hairy appendages towards the end of the body, and a straight, dagger-like one on the extremity. It has ten prominent segments on the abdomen. It feeds on flour and any appetising starchy fare in the larder, or will devour the paste of the binding in old books and the paste holding the paper to walls in houses.

Where a house has a damp cellar, as in the basement houses beloved by our grandparents, there, sure enough, the cellar beetle will be found. It is dull dead-black in colour, of inactive habits, and emits an unpleasant odour. It has undeveloped wings, and the elytra, or wing cases, are fastened together.

A number of insects belonging to the family Dermestidae perpetuate much havoc to food and other

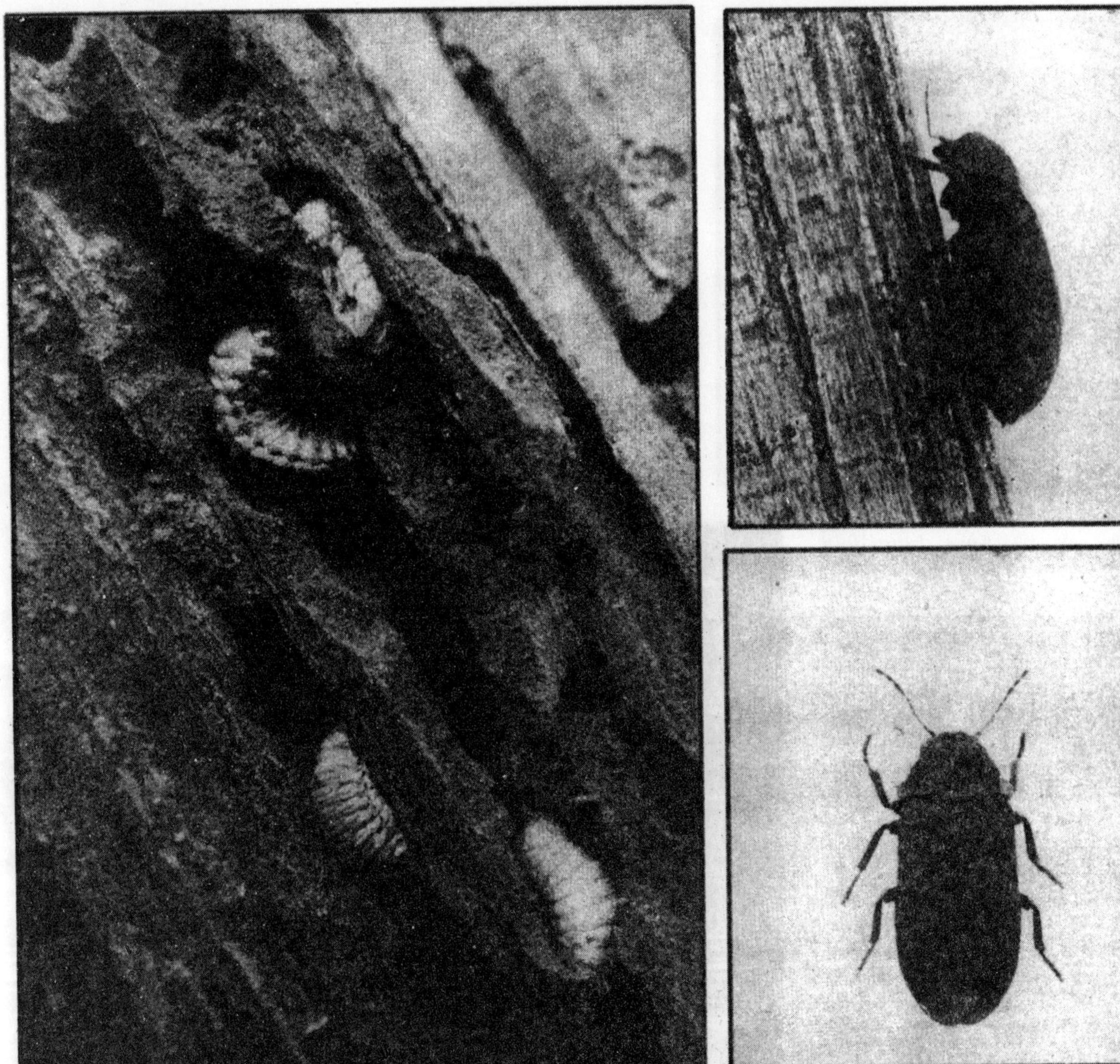

H. Bastin.

FURNITURE BEETLES, DEADLY FOES OF FURNITURE, AND THEIR WORK

Constant watch has to be kept against furniture beetles. Minute holes in the legs of tables and the backs of chairs and a little fine sawdust nearby are signs that the boring larvae of the furniture beetle or "death watch" have been at work. Valuable pianos and violins have been damaged seriously in this way. The holes should be treated with paraffin or a weak solution of copper sulphate, especially in the months of May and July. On the left are larvae burrowing and on the right enlarged views of a beetle from above (bottom) and from the side (top).

goods of a perishable nature, and among these the bacon beetle is one of the most notorious. The beetle has a club-shaped end to its antennae and short legs. The larva has a small rounded head, and its thin-skinned body is covered with a profusion of hairs. When the insect is alive and resting the head is generally bent beneath the thorax and the insect collector who wishes all his specimens to be well displayed finds it difficult to coax the head out of its curious position when he is mounting the bacon beetle for his collection.

Another pest to be included in our survey is the meal moth, or mealworm beetle, which resorts to mills and granaries, or farms and homesteads where meal is stored. The adult insect is a long, narrow, rust-coloured creature with a small head. There are three pairs of short legs on the thorax, and on the last segment of the body two further small appendages are present. The larva is the well-known mealworm, so readily devoured by our cage birds—an orphan nightingale rescued by a friend of mine greedily ate this, its favourite captive food—and is a long, hard-skinned cylindrical grub having short legs, and there are two prominences on the last segment which serve the purpose of extra feet. It does much damage to stored flour.

In the family Psocidae there are included certain kinds of insects in which the adults usually possess wings, the front pair being much larger than the hind ones. There are, however, other members of this

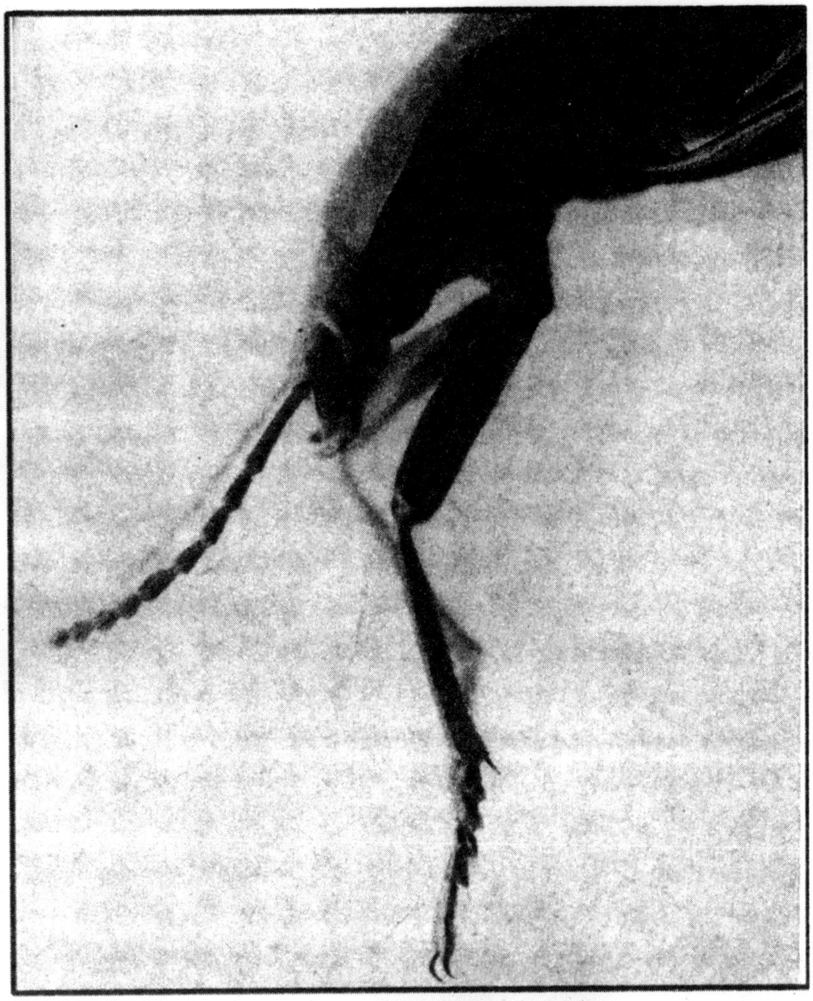

family in which wings are never developed, and to this latter section the book lice belong. They are small, soft-bodied insect pests, the bane of the book-lover and librarian, and in damp rooms one species, known as *Atropos divinnatoria*, is often found in some numbers. Hardly any substance of an edible nature comes amiss to it, but when it attacks books, papers, and preserved natural history specimens, means must be adopted for keeping it at bay. One often disturbs these small creatures when opening a book that has not been used for some time, and the best method of despatch is finger-and-thumb, a remedy I have found equally satisfactory when dealing with the countless hordes of green fly found on rose bushes and apple trees.

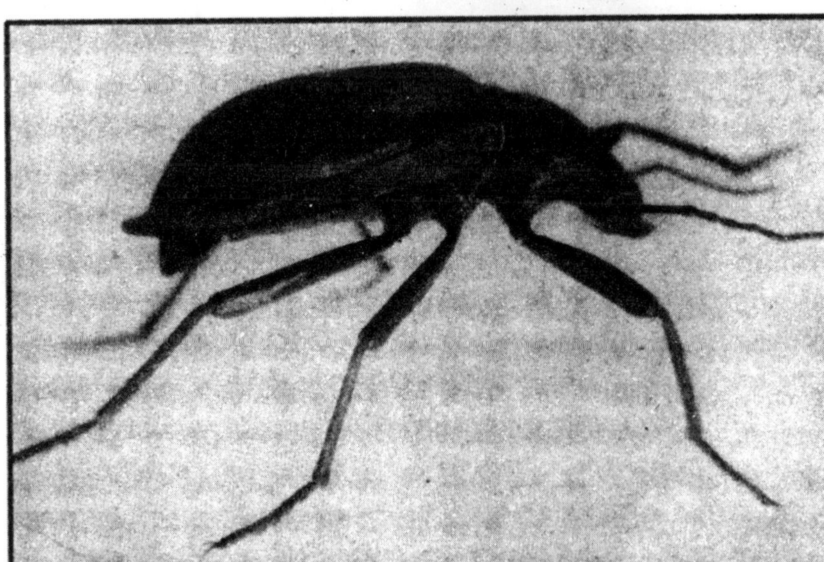

H. Bastin

CELLAR OR "CHURCHYARD" BEETLE, A NOISOME VISITANT

The chief objection to the cellar beetle is the smell associated with it, which is produced by the volatilisation of a liquid contained in two vessels near the hind end of the abdomen. The beetle is found always in dark places. It cannot fly, the wing cases being fused together (bottom) Above is the head greatly magnified and on the left a female (bottom) and a male (top)

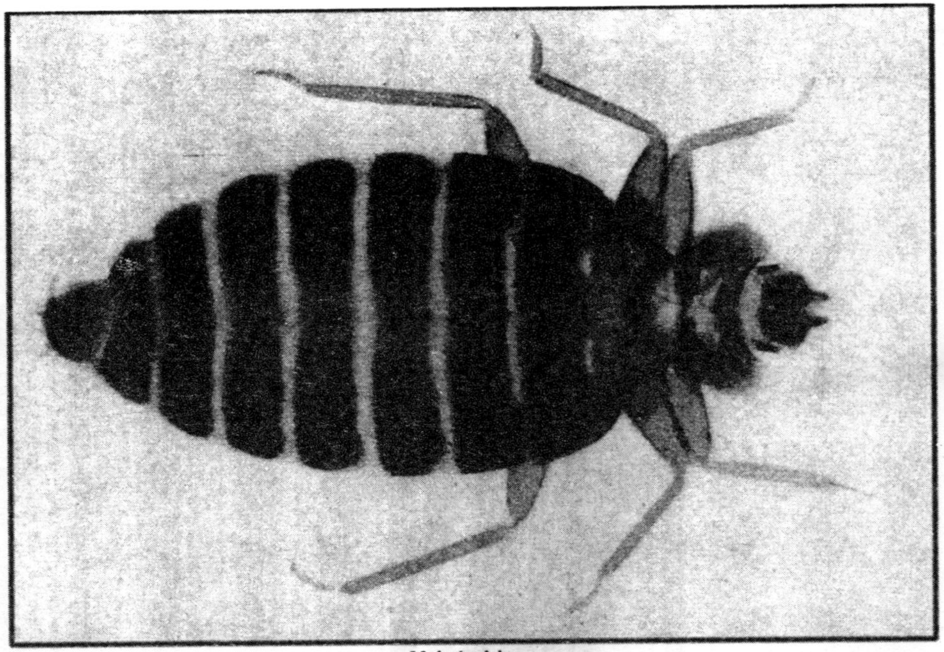

Male bed bug

Female bed bug

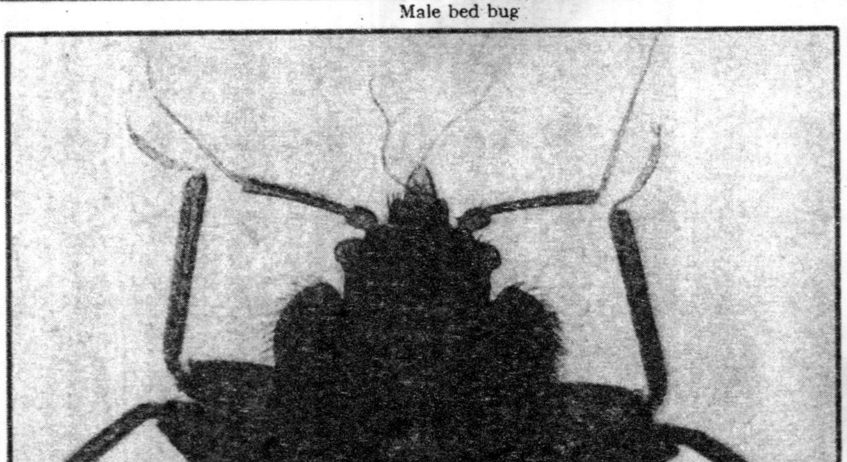

Head and foreparts of bed bug

Mouth palps and lancets of flea

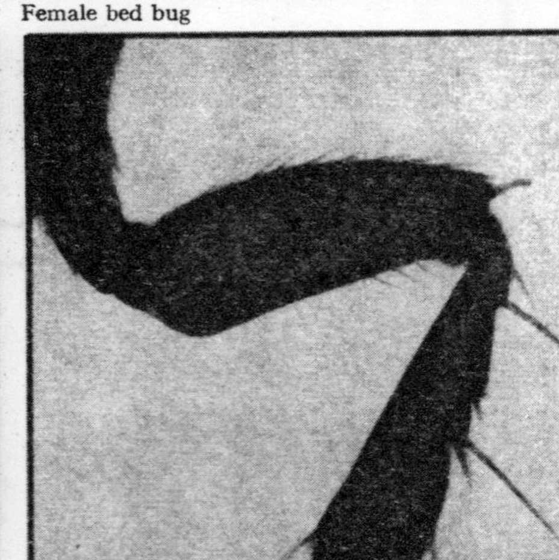

Part of jumping leg of the flea

DISGUSTING PARASITES ON HUMAN BEINGS THAT LURK BEHIND WAINSCOTING AND UNDER FLOORS

Bed bugs and fleas are not by any means always found on their hosts. They spend considerable periods away from human beings, living and breeding sometimes in empty houses. So soon as occupation begins these parasites are aware of it. Bed bugs show extraordinary cunning. If unable to get a person in bed they will crawl up the wall and along the ceiling until over the bed and then drop. These pests are flat-bodied and feed by thrusting the sharp proboscis through the skin and sucking blood. The common flea is also a blood-sucker. If a man could make a jump in proportion to that of a flea, size for size, he could clear the Nelson Monument in Trafalgar Square, London. These photographs are magnified. Photos by J. J. Ward and H. S. Cheavin.

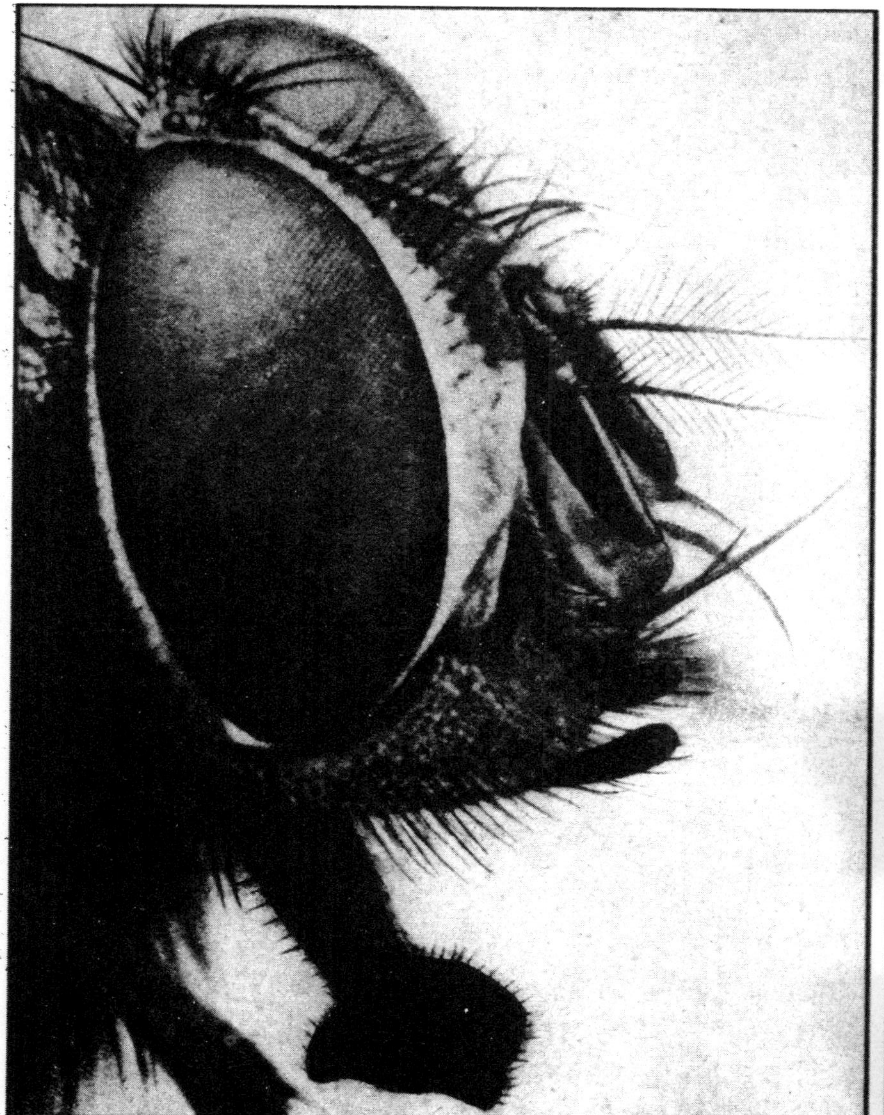

H Bastin

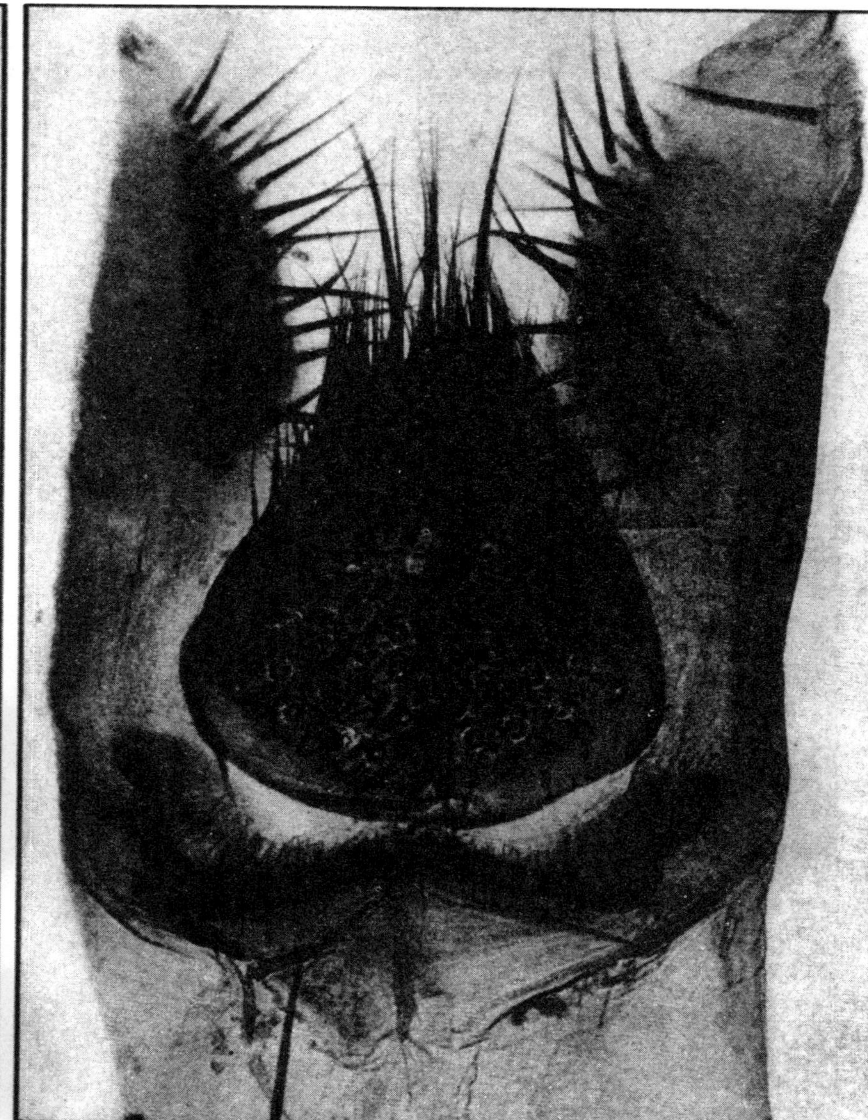

J. J. Ward

SIDE-FACE VIEW OF THAT HOUSEHOLD PEST THE BLOWFLY, AND CURIOUS ORGAN OF THE COMMON FLEA

The left-hand photograph shows a side-face view of a blowfly's head, and we can see the compound eyes of the insect quite plainly. On the right is a photograph of a curious organ possessed by the common flea, the use of which is not at present understood, though it is believed to be a kind of hearing apparatus. It consists of a number of disc-like orifices, carrying long bristles. The young flea has a rather short larval life, being full-grown in about twelve days, when it spins a little cocoon in which to become a pupa. This cocoon is made of tiny silken threads and particles of dust and cotton and woollen fibre are generally attached to conceal it from enemies. The flea remains in the pupal stage about a fortnight.

Insect Pests of the Home

There are various kinds of half-winged insects, as they are called, and among these are to be included the bugs, and the well-known frog-hopper whose amazing exploits, as it sets its mechanism to work and springs or hops from its resting-place, will be known to many of our readers. There are what may be called plant bugs and animal bugs, that is, insect parasites found on vegetables as well as animals. Many of our domestic pets, wild birds and other creatures are infested with some of these pests, and at least one species, known as the bed bug, is a terrible pest when it invades our homes. This it will do in spite of cleanliness and the fact that no previous tenant had left such unwelcome inhabitants behind.

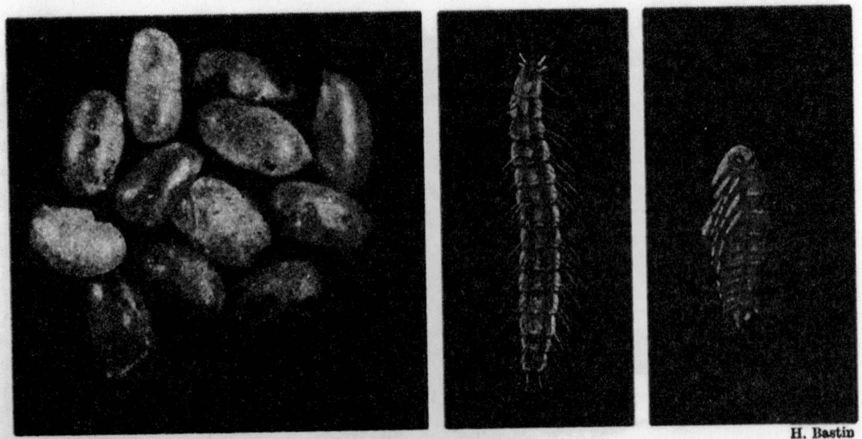

H. Bastin

J. J. Ward

BACON BEETLE OF CATHOLIC TASTES AND THE FLEA

So-called bacon beetles (bottom right) have earned the hatred of housewives for their fondness for pork. But their tastes are very wide and their larvae (bottom left) readily devour all skins as well as paper and cork. Some have even been found in a mummy in Egypt. Above we have the eggs, and a larva and pupa case of a flea. The photographs are magnified.

The bed bug is a flat-bodied, reddish-brown insect, and as it carries out its blood-sucking expeditions under cover of darkness, the result of its obnoxious presence on, or near, the human body may well be imagined. A solitary specimen is bad enough in all conscience, but when, as sometimes happens, a plague of these altogether distasteful household pests make their appearance, defensive war is inevitable and no peace pact can be considered. The proboscis of the creature is thrust into the body and blood sucked up.

It is supposed that this unwelcome visitor was unsuspectingly imported from Africa, and in addition to the irritation its presence causes to the body and the pain set up by its blood-sucking, the insect emits an offensive smell which makes it additionally discomforting. It is said that the cockroach, a pest already treated of in this article, is an enemy of the bed bug. Be this as it may, neither insect can be tolerated by humans, and constant warfare has to be waged against the bed bug and its numbers slain without fear or favour. This, in itself, is not a pleasant task, but it must be done at all costs if the home is to be rid of one of the worst insect pests it is ever likely to harbour.

The common flea (*Pulex irritans*), is another unwelcome tenant of our homes, and in spite of cleanly habits there are times when the most careful among our fellows manage to bring to the household one of these irritating little bloodsuckers, caught maybe from some person in train, bus or car. " First catch your flea and then kill it " is sound advice to offer, but this is easier said than done, for this active little creature is an adept at escape from human hands. It has eyes, and is a highly specialised member of its race. Its range is now cosmopolitan, brought about during the last fifty years or so by the facilities for travel vouchsafed to its hosts, yet we learn that among dirty races in certain regions of Africa the human flea does not occur. With cleanly Europeans it is present ; with unclean natives it is absent !

Refuse heaps are breeding-grounds for these parasites, and it appears that, without resorting to the sucking up of human blood, this insect can and does live and reproduce itself. It can even continue to live for some time without a meal of any kind. The piercing organs are strong and well developed, and it has been suggested that the serrated mandibles have been formed since the time when *Pulex irritans* found it so advantageous to prey upon the blood of human kind. From one to five eggs are laid at a time, and these hatch in a few days into small white wormlike creatures having many segments on the body. The mouth parts are adapted for biting, and on the front

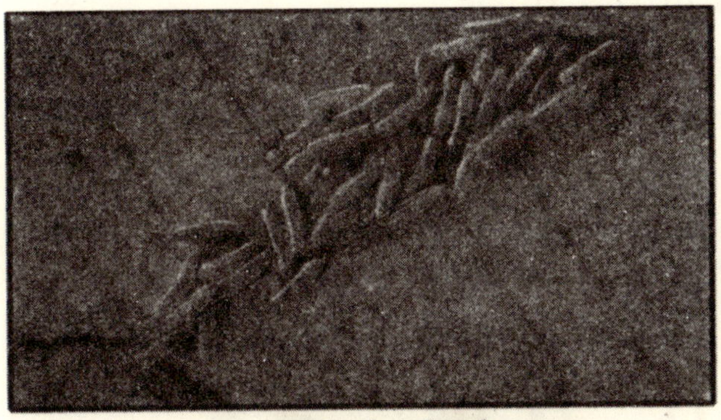

Eggs of blowfly, enlarged

Blowfly, enlarged

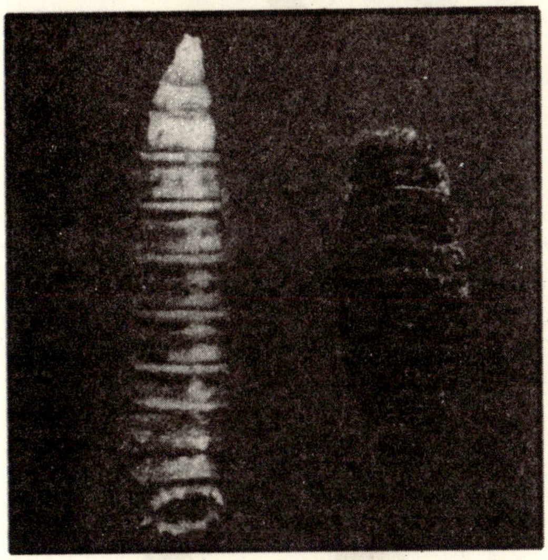

Blowfly's larva and puparium

Puparium with pupa projecting

Empty puparium

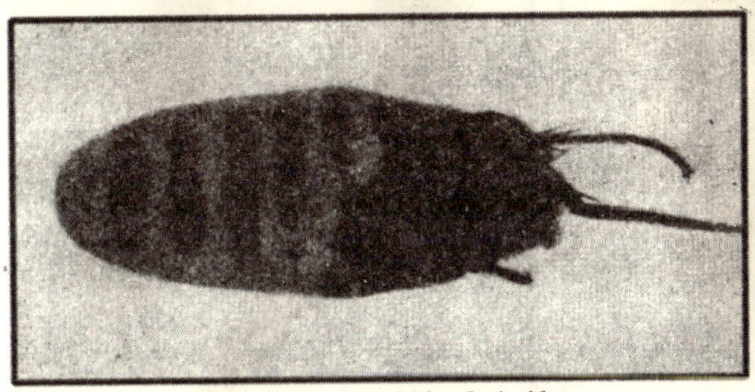

Puparium and dead blowfly inside

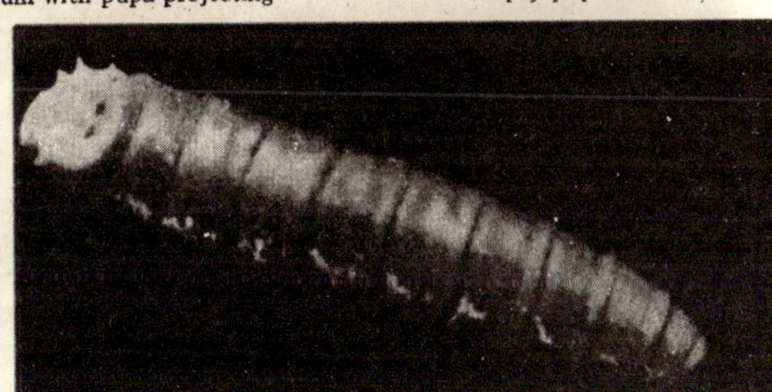

Larva with oval spiracles (top left)

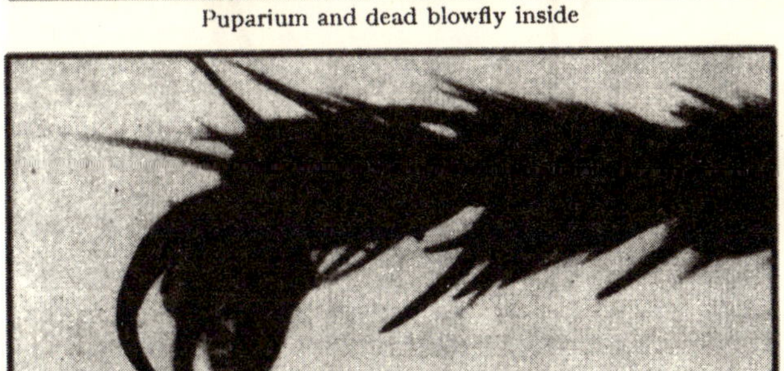

Side view of blowfly's foot

Front view of foot

BLOWFLY THAT FEEDS AND LAYS ITS EGGS ON THE FAMILY JOINT

Great precautions must be taken against the contaminating of our meat by the blowfly. If there is any hole in the meat safe the fly will find it and a gauze cover whose edge does not lie quite close against the shelf on which it rests will soon have its weak spot found. At times, blowflies will even drop their eggs through the wire mesh on to the meat below. The harm caused by this fly lies in the fact that it may have been feeding on some rotting meat—a dead animal or the contents of a dustbin, and so carry infection to sound meat. Photos by J. J. Ward

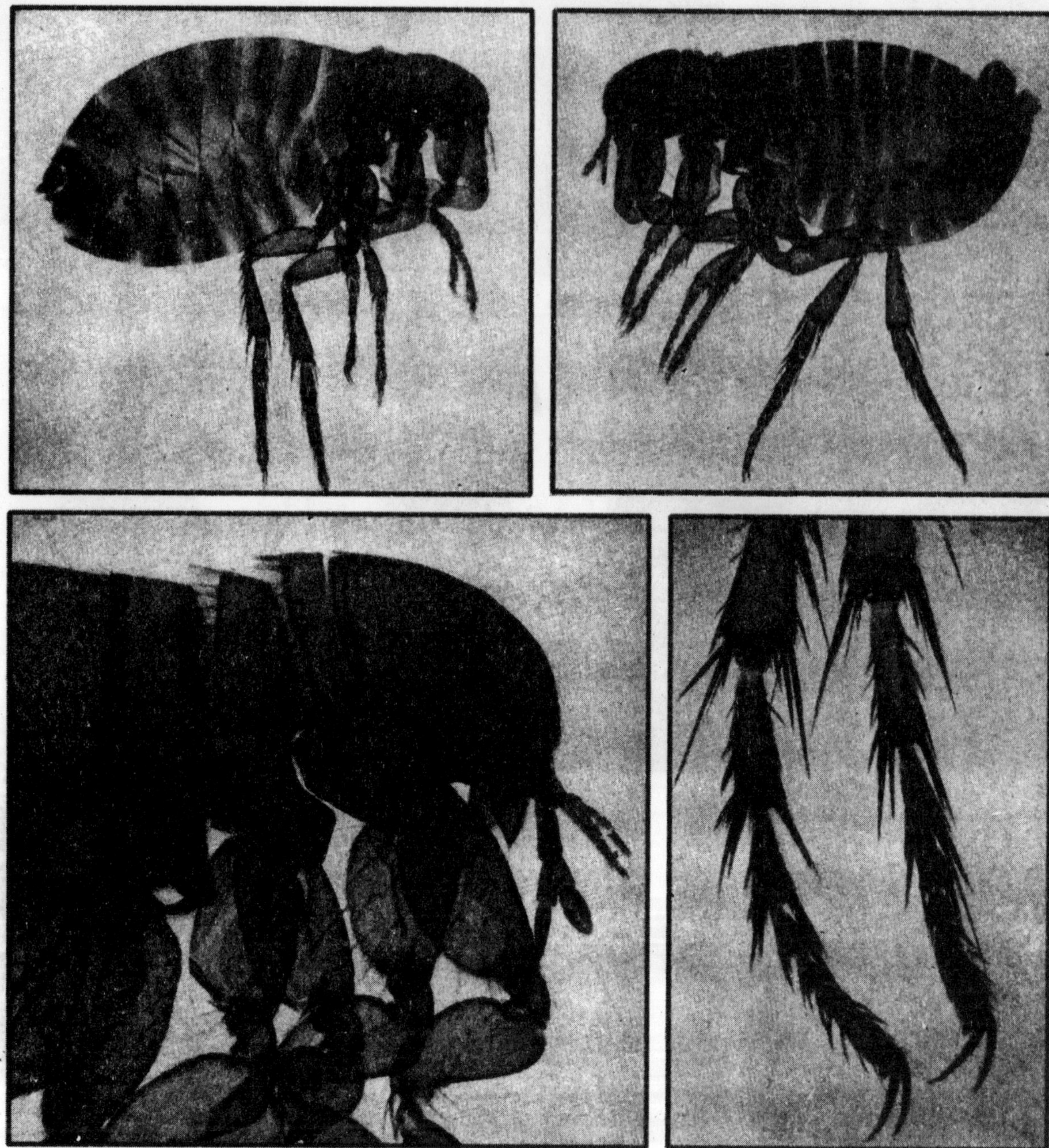

J. J. Ward

FLEAS AS THEY APPEAR UNDER A MAGNIFYING LENS

A flea can jump two hundred times its own length and thirty times its own height. Our photographs, all considerably magnified, show (bottom left) the head of a flea with the strong piercing lancets which cause the irritating "bite"—though "stab" would be a more correct term; (bottom right) the clawed feet; (top left) an adult female and (top right) an adult male. The flea starts life as a tiny maggot after emerging from its egg, and after twelve days or so, spins a cocoon. It remains in the pupa stage for about two weeks.

part of the head there is a knife-like apparatus with which the young larva is able to make an incision in the egg-shell and make good its escape. The larva eventually spins a small cocoon, and very soon after this the perfect insect comes forth. Fortunately the flea passes only part of its time on its host, but even temporary visits are very unwelcome and must be staved off if at all possible.

Last on our present list of insect pests of the British home is the blow-fly. The larva feeds on decaying animal matter, and its eggs are deposited there so that the hungry larvae may find an abundant food supply close at hand—but our own provender is also resorted to for the laying of eggs. The blow-fly enters our larder and will deposit its eggs on any unprotected meat that it may find, but even when there is a gauze cover over the joint the fly will drop its eggs through on to the meat. Outside the blow-fly may be regarded as one of Nature's scavengers, but in the house it is nothing but a pest.

Chapter CXXVI

The Music of an English Wood

By Sir William Beach Thomas

Author of "The English Year"

In countries where forests are thick and wild the darkness made by the boughs is strangely silent. No birds sing, and what animals live there are furtive and quiet. How very different are most English woods!

But even in England the smaller the wood the more musical. Happily most of the woods are small and open, and sunny enough to prove attractive to all sorts of animals, though even the smallest have a rival in the hedgerow, which is the most English thing in England and the most popular. It is often very much like a little bit of wood, as Mrs. Browning long ago pointed out, "run wild." In the open country the hour of the day most full of sound, especially of bird song, if the season is spring or summer, is the hour of dawn. In the wood most sounds are to be heard at sunset, all through the year.

A sort of queer hilarity possesses both the pheasant and the blackbird at this hour. The birds are not like one another in any other aspect, but they both crow and chatter with exceptional noisiness at the evening hour and give a sharp contrast to most notes.

You may hear in a wood every sort of sound: rustling, tapping, pattering, stamping, singing, scraping, barking, hooting, squealing, screeching, hissing, flapping; cries of hunter and hunted, cries of merriment and (very rarely) of pain; but most are rather subdued till their evening clatter begins. It is astonishing how noisily the birds go to roost. Though only the pheasant and blackbird crow and chatter at this moment, the wood pigeons, which are fonder of a wood than most other birds, make quite a fuss as they settle to roost in some tall pine or larch. The noise is as loud as the crack of the two wings against one another over the bird's back, which is a characteristic habit of the pigeon (and the pigeon only) in early spring. The sound is almost startling when flocks of pigeons, diving into the dark of the wood on a winter evening, suddenly clatter among the upper boughs.

But even in daytime the wood is seldom quite quiet. The mice rustle among the dead leaves, and the squirrels and many birds scratch and throw up the leaves behind them like a burrowing rabbit. Perhaps the most emphatic of all the sounds is the loud rap of the rabbit's hind foot when it is sounding the alarm. The magpies chatter, the jays, which are the noisiest inhabitants of the wood, continually scream. Now and again, though seldom in the daytime, you may hear the bark of a fox; and, especially if it is a moonlight night, three sorts of owl—the brown, the barn and the imported little owl will hoot, and cry and chatter. About sunset the little owl, which hunts while it is still light, is sometimes almost as noisy as the pheasant.

H. Bastin

ALIEN GREY SQUIRREL

A light scampering noise upon a tree trunk may betray the presence of a grey squirrel or we may hear it rustling in the grass. The grey squirrel though an imported species is now very common

Most of the sounds of the wood can suggest to us vaguely what is happening; and it is interesting to seek an interpretation for each and all. Most are interesting but few are musical. Music, as apart from noise, is confined to the song of birds and (perhaps) the whispering of the wind in the trees. It has happened to most haunters of the wood to be suddenly greeted by the thin soprano notes of the robin or the gushing energy of the wren; and so heard in such a place both are greeted as music indeed. Yet strictly speaking neither is music in our sense of the word. The intervals and scales are not our intervals and scales. They can be imitated by various devices, but not on a piano, which has definite and sharply separated intervals. Even good musicians with very sensitive ears find it very difficult to agree about the range of notes, and many very ingenious attempts to express the songs in musical notation have failed. The songs are delightful to our ear and seem to us to express joy and love and passion; but to analyse them is beyond us. We cannot even agree whether the song of the nightingale is sad or merry. However, there are just a few exceptions.

An expert musician, well known to the writer, declared that a blackbird on the elm trees outside his window used to sing accurately the first bar of "I have a song to sing, Oh," And always the blackbird goes nearer to human music than any others of our birds, except captives, such as bullfinch or starling, which can learn to whistle tunes under careful instruction. It is not, as is often supposed, only the parrot tribe and the Nepalese minah (the best of all mimics) which can learn to imitate definite human music

Arthur Brook

WOOD PIGEON "SNAPPED" WHILE FEEDING BESIDE A WHEAT-SHEAF

From some fastness in the wood the pigeon comes out to feed on the crops in the surrounding fields. The sudden, loud flapping of its quickly-beating wings is usually the first thing to bring the presence of this bird to our notice as we walk through the wood. But the cheerful and enquiring noise inadequately described by the sound "coo" is the more pleasant way the pigeon has of advertising its whereabouts. The one seen here is caught in the act of stealing grain.

That lovely bird the golden oriole, which now comes every year to the south of England, whistles very much like the blackbird. Its notes are pure, and can be reproduced very exactly by the human voice. We can more or less represent by our intervals the coo of the wood pigeon and the crow of the cock; but there is just one bird, and no more, that sings a perfectly true interval as we know it, the cuckoo. Generally speaking, its coo-coo is a major-third at the beginning of the season, though it changes and often becomes a minor third at the end. We call the bird and the sound cuckoo, but birds cannot strictly be said to pronounce any of our consonants.

It would be strange if birds and man had a similar form of music, for they possess very different instruments. Each has a "song box," but the human song box, which is called the larynx, is at the top of the windpipe; the bird's song box, which is called the syrinx, lies at the lower end of the windpipe. It is a complicated instrument; but the principle is simple enough The air, as it is breathed out sets certain membranes or cords vibrating, and these are loosened or tightened according to the bird's mood.

The song boxes differ in different birds a great deal. Some are much smaller and simpler than others; and you cannot be sure which has the more complicated instrument; but roughly and on the whole it may be said that the best singers or talkers have the most elaborate song boxes. For example, the nightingale and the rook possess complicated instruments; and the rook is perhaps the best of all the talkers as the nightingale is one of the best of the musicians.

But songs and notes differ so widely that comparison is scarcely possible. The "call" of the partridge, the "hoot" of the owls, the "boom" of the bittern, the song of the lark, the "coo" of the dove, the "quack" of a duck have little in common. Nor is there any likeness between the set song and the alarm note of a particular species. For example, the "pink, pink" of a chaffinch has little likeness to its lovely little song. Yet there is singularly little range of note in the song of any one species. The glorious bubbling succession of notes from a lark as he ascends is not the least monotonous, but most of the sounds are on one or two notes. Its delicious song has not anything approaching the range of the conversational tones of that wood-loving bird the rook, which does not sing at all.

Yet few if any songs are monotonous to our ear, though some calls are. The great-tit has a sharp double note that distresses some ears ; and when the summer is over the greenfinch, though he can sing pleasantly enough, wheezes out a single note that is one of the most monotonous sounds in nature. Everyone grants that the cuckoo can sing a true interval, but its double note affects us in different ways. The poet Wordsworth loved to listen to it—especially in a wood, because it could "beget the golden time again," could recall the pleasures of his boyhood. It is so insistent a sound that few country children can avoid imitating it, and the imitations are often very hard to distinguish from the original. Yet to some it is as irritating

Arthur Brook

A NEST OF WOODLARKS IN A WELSH WOOD

Photographed in a wood near Llandrindod Wells in Radnorshire, we see in the upper photograph a nest of woodlarks and their mother. Here we have the music of hunger, a loud and continuous squeaking from a group of gaping beaks. The eager heads are set in a mass of fuzzy down. The lower photograph shows the mother with something in her beak worth squeaking about.

as any other frequently repeated sound. A thing that breaks the monotony is the frequent change of place. The cuckoo, like the lark, the pipits, and sometimes the Jenny wren and the sedge warbler, sings as he flies, and is a very restless bird. If you listen, as Wordsworth often listened, within the enclosure of an English wood where the ground rises and falls as the bird moves and varying clumps of trees break the sound, it is too expressive of the charm of the place to be monotonous or anything but musical.

A good naturalist would often infer the time of year merely by listening. If he were stone blind he would tell, as he stood still in an English wood or spinney, whether it were day or night, spring or autumn or winter. There are some people with ears so acute that they can

Arthur Brook

GREAT SPOTTED WOODPECKER AND SOME JAYS

The great spotted woodpecker (bottom) hammers away at tree trunks and fills the wood with din. This it does not only to find insects but to call its mate. It also gives a short, sharp cry. The upper photograph shows a family of young jays—great screamers

guess the nature of the tree on which the wind is playing. The thin murmurs among the pine needles is a note totally different from the robust noises among the twisted twigs of the British oak. Certainly a wind in the chattering leaves of an aspen in summer foliage has little likeness to the wind scraping through the thin twigs of a larch in winter time.

One of the most distinct changes of the year comes in July, and is more noticeable in a wood than elsewhere. When the birds begin to fall into silence, as most of them do after the eggs are hatched, a host of insects begin to take up their part in the orchestra. The flies buzz and the gnats hum. The cockchafers go booming through the evening air, often blundering with a crash against this or that obstruction, and there is no sound that more definitely suggests a date and a time of day, though there are two species of cockchafer of which one comes out a month earlier than the other.

One standard difference exists between the way of a bird and the way of an insect in producing sounds. The birds breathe air out of their song box. The insects, with scarcely an exception, never make a note with the mouth. They scrape their leg against their wing, or they vibrate the wings so rapidly that they produce a murmur. One may compare their notes with the curious creaking of the wings of swans, geese and rooks, or the clamour of the wings of partridge or pheasant when they start their flight. These

may be called accidental notes, but just a few birds deliberately and of set purpose use mechanical methods of making informatory or musical sounds. The pigeon in spring strokes the wing over its back and seems to enjoy the queer sound, which is certainly very characteristic of spring.

The snipe has a method of producing song music that is quite his own, and it has a word to itself. The snipe alone "drums." It was for a long time disputed how the drumming noise was produced, and the dispute still arises locally; but the matter was finally settled by an ingenious naturalist who reproduced the sound exactly by fixing snipe's outside tail feathers to a cock and then revolving the toy rapidly. The

Arthur Brook

NUTHATCH AT HER NESTING HOLE AND A YOUNG FAMILY

Nuthatches make a strange noise which has been compared to the sound produced by a pebble bumping and bouncing across the ice of a frozen pond. It also has a short, high note sounding like "which." In the lower photograph we see one in characteristic pose at its nesting hole. Note the angle of this branch in which it has laid its eggs. Above are some young birds.

Oliver Pike

J. T. Roberts

TAWNY OWL WHOSE EERIE HOOTING IS HEARD IN THE WOODS AT DUSK AND IN THE NIGHT

By its alternative name of wood owl, we may guess that the tawny owl is to be heard among the orchestra of an English wood. The bird lives in the thickest part of the wood and its "music" consists of a performance of the familiar phrase popularly described as "toowit-toowoo," though in reality it seems to sing "who" simply with an occasional clicking sound thrown in at the end. On the left we see one of these birds on guard, just outside the entrance to its nest in a hollow tree. The daylight is causing it to close its eyes against the glare, for the owl is a night flyer. On the right we see the bird awakened by the noise of the shutter when the camera took the photograph.

Arthur Brook

GREEN WOODPECKERS THAT MAKE THE WOODLAND RING WITH THEIR NOISY CARPENTRY

Longer by several inches than the great spotted woodpecker, the green woodpecker, which measures over a foot from beak to tail, sometimes lets out a sudden sound like a loud laugh which is sufficiently startling to one who walks alone and unprepared among the thick trees. Of course, the more usual noise made by this bird is the tapping on the trees when it is looking for its prey which is hiding in the bark. Our left-hand illustration shows one of these birds thrusting an inquiring head from its nesting hole. This hole it will return to year after year if undisturbed. On the right is one of these birds climbing a tree, which it does in a series of jerky movements, aided by pressing the tail against the trunk.

S. Crook

E. A. Botting

TIGER BEETLE AND GRASS SNAKES, MAKERS OF THE SLIGHTER SOUNDS

Besides the birds there are many things which make up the symphony we can listen to in spinney and copse. The thud of a beetle clumsily butting against the bole of a tree as it flies on its heavy way, may come to our notice. Here is a Tiger beetle (bottom). Above we have a pair of grass snakes, harmless things and seldom heard unless a rustling of dead leaves betrays them.

wild snipe make the notes only when they are diving down rapidly, and it is made solely by the wind rustling through the stretched and slightly separated feathers on either side of the tail. The sound suggests to many people the low bleating of lambs. But there is no other sound in nature with which it may be compared, nor does any combined sight and sound stay more vividly on the memory than these falling streaks of life, sending their strange vibrations through the evening air. The particular feathers, when you study them closely, look as if they were especially designed for their musical purpose.

You will scarcely stay long in a wood, at any rate one where any old trees are allowed, without hearing a frequent tapping. The noise is mostly caused by birds hammering on the bark for food. It is surprising how far you may hear the nuthatch, and its hammer, hammer, hammer is often mistaken for the woodpecker's. The tit, especially the great-tit or oxeye, hammers too, and makes quite a loud noise when it is splitting the seeds of such trees as the hornbeam. But there is only one bird, in England at any rate, which treats the hammering as a part of its musical equipment and signals by means of it. This is the great spotted woodpecker, a fine black and white bird with a splash of red on the head. It is multiplying fast, but is still rare as compared with the green woodpecker, which is one of the commoner birds and in its way a most persistent tapper. It taps for food, and makes a real carpenter's noise when it is tunnelling into a trunk to make a hollow for the nest. But the green woodpecker hammers

Arthur Brook

POLECAT THAT KEEPS TO THE DENSER AND LARGER WOODLANDS OF BRITAIN

Although generally considered to be so rare the polecat is said to be on the increase in Wales and is not, otherwise, confined to the wilder parts of Scotland, as one might expect, but is also found in the larger woods and forests of the Midlands and on Dartmoor. It is about seventeen inches long, and lives usually in a rabbit burrow. As for noise, it is the noise it causes other animals to make which tells that a polecat is about. The lower photograph was obtained near Builth Wells in Breconshire.

W. S. Berridge & H: Willford

BIRDS RESPONSIBLE FOR QUEER NOISES HEARD IN THE WOOD

A sharp, quick series of rather shrill notes ending in a trill coming from hedge or wood will tell us that a wren is near (bottom left). The greenfinch (bottom right) is usually found on the edges of the wood where it will sit on a bough and call " did-it " for minutes together. The hawfinch (top left) is seldom heard unless it is frightened, when it will shriek " sit, sit " several times over. The golden crested wren (top right) seems capable only of a rather wretched squeak such as one might make when rubbing a window with a damp cloth.

solely for business. The great spotted, on the other hand, has developed its business notes into a love note, and intentionally hammers at a hollow trunk, as some savages drum on instruments of hollow wood. The fact has been recently denied. The device seemed so curious that a few naturalists could scarcely believe it and one of them stated the theory that the sound really came from the throat of the bird. But too many observers have watched the woodpecker at his hammering to leave any doubt at all that he hits the wood to make spring music, and for no other reason. It is just possible that some throaty gurgle may accompany the mechanical tap. After all, the bittern booms by uttering his note with the beak in the marshy water, just as Haydn in the Toy Symphony made the nightingale's gurgle; but only one sound can be detected when the woodpecker hammers, and that sound is the tap of the beak on the wood.

Almost all birds are more or less vocal, though some of the biggest rarely utter any note and in England have no song. The commonest of the swans is named "the mute swan" for this reason, and the old legend that swans sing only just before they die arose from their silence during life. In this respect birds differ greatly from mammals, most of which go about their common duties without making any conscious sound at all. Only exceptional events extract a note of any sort.

Death's head moth

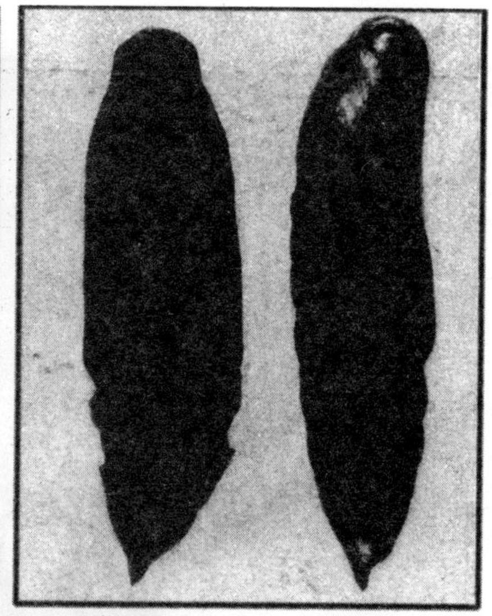

Pupae, front and side views

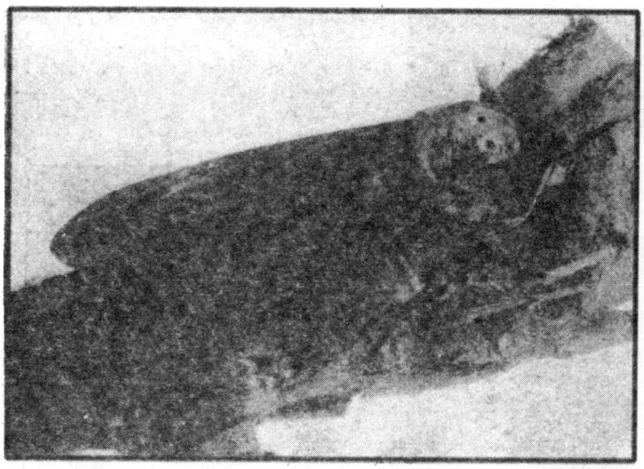

Living moth with wings closed

Magnified view of head

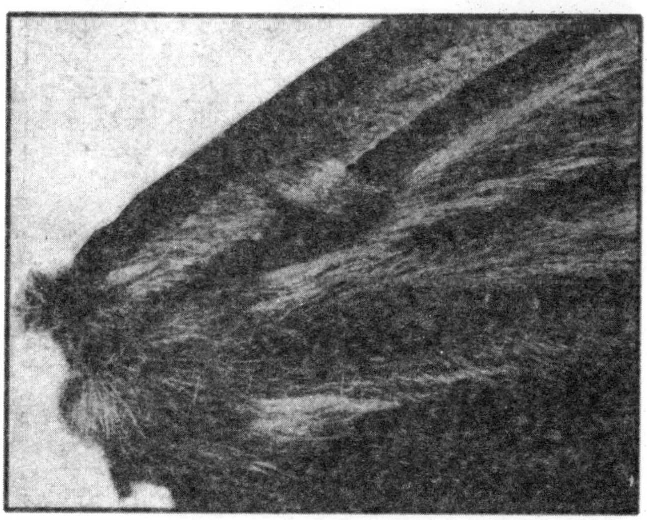

Enlarged view of retinaculum

Frenulum of moth, magnified

DEATH'S HEAD HAWK MOTH THAT SQUEAKS: AN INSECT PHENOMENON

Nothing would seem quieter than a moth, the most silent of flying things until it is confined in a room in a house and flaps against wall and ceiling. But there is a moth, the death's head hawk moth, that emits a squeak. Especially does it do this if handled, when most people leave go at once. The two bottom photographs here are of two tiny structures, (left) the retinaculum and (right) the frenulum. The former, on the forewing, connects with the latter in the secondary wing to lash the wings together when the moth is resting. Photos H. Bastin.

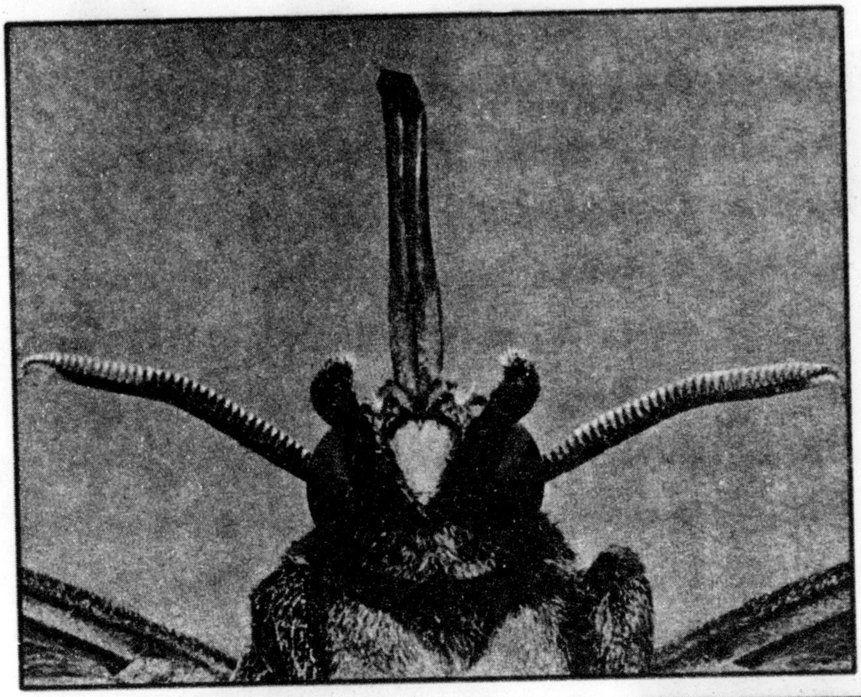

The weasel has a thin, strange, hunting cry, though it is so rare that some of the best observers have never heard it. The hare will squeal, almost like a child, when it is in pain and occasionally when it is frightened. So will a rabbit. Few sights or sounds are more pitiful in nature than when a stoat is hunting a rabbit and comes close to its victim. The hunted screams, and the stoat makes a queer whimpering noise almost like a dog's note of suppressed eagerness. A strange sort of paralysis often comes over the rabbit, and in spite of its superior speed it becomes an easy victim. When the end approaches both animals are usually silent. I have seen more than once a rabbit and a stoat fighting and wrestling without either hunter or hunted making the least sound. The badger and the otter are singularly silent, and the rats and mice and voles do little more than squeak. Foxes have a very dog-like bark, heard chiefly at night in the woods; but they, too, spend most of their day in utter silence. How different from birds, which even when their singing time is over have frequent and definite alarm notes and calls.

THE race of birds is supposed by the latest students of the subject to have arisen in the long course of evolution from creatures that belong half to the water and half to the land. They were once reptiles, and the reptiles may still be compared with birds in several respects. Most of the reptiles have the power to make some sort of sound. The chorus of frogs is a sound not to be missed in spring. It has interested people for thousands of years.

Two thousand and more years ago Aristophanes, the Greek comic dramatist, tried to describe the sound of the syllables " Brekke, ke, kex, koax, koax." It is a curiously ventriloquial note, extremely difficult to locate, and has often been mistaken for a distant engine. And it is produced by rather elaborate contrivances. Apart from the vocal cords, which are very resonant, it possesses two hollow internal sacs that make a sounding box, and in some sorts of frog swell out like two air-bubbles.

There is just one unmechanical sound made by insects which is almost frightening as well as surprising. What could be less audible than a moth, with its soft, furry body and delicate wings? What more silent than the corpse-like chrysalis? And almost all moths, caterpillars and chrysalises are wholly dumb. But there is one exception, the death's head moth, which is one of the rarest and biggest. The moth emits a fairly loud squeak, and sometimes the sound is heard even before it emerges from the chrysalis or pupa state.

It is produced, as is now proved, by the blowing of air through the proboscis, and we are not yet at the end of the vocal oddities of this queer insect. The caterpillar is also vocal, but the light crackling or tapping note is mechanical. It gnashes its teeth, in the strict and literal meaning of the term. The sound is made by the clapping of the jaws together.

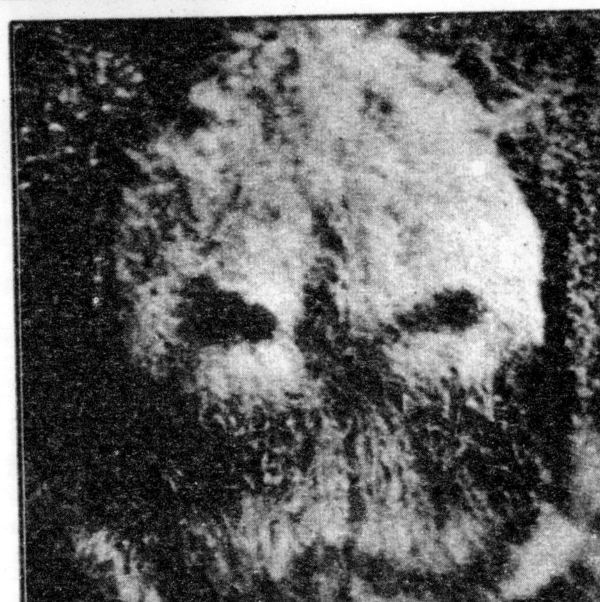

H. Bastin

HEAD OF THE "DEATH'S HEAD" MOTH

The distinguishing mark of the death's head moth is the skull-shaped patch on the thorax. This is seen highly magnified in the lower photograph. Above is the moth's head with proboscis extended. By forcing air through this the moth makes a squeaking sound

Chapter CXXVII

Life in the Tree-tops of a Tropical Forest

By Richard Palmer

of the Department of Zoology, University College, London

MAN is an earth-loving animal. Aeroplanes and skyscrapers have not yet converted him to a confident separation from the solid ground. In a thousand ways, in language and legend, Mother Earth has become the symbol of all that is firm and enduring, and fertile and life-giving. And so it is with most of our fellow-creatures that dwell in woods and plains. To them, as to us, she provides food and drink, and above all, shelter and security.

It is not, therefore, easy for us to imagine a situation in which to live on the ground is anything but safe and easy, and in which the choice lies between Mother Earth and light, food and air. Yet such, in fact, is the dilemma that the animals of the rain-forests of the Amazon have had to face. Let us see how it is that this choice has been placed before them, and by what means they have overcome their difficulties.

Two things are essential to the existence of a true tropical forest—great heat and abundant moisture. Combined they make possible the amazing luxuriance of plant-life that gives the rain-forest its unique character. But the moisture is not confined to the heavy rains that fall for a few hours almost every day. The low-lying forests of the Amazon basin are intersected by the countless streams that join to make the great river. In times of flood the water-level may rise as much as forty feet, and forest dells are converted for the time being into muddy swamps. At such a time Mother Earth is no safe hiding-place for any but water-loving beasts. The rest, if they are not already tree-livers, must take temporarily to an arboreal life. But floods are not the only objection to life on the ground in the Amazon basin. The main problem is not to avoid drowning, but to get about at all. We in Europe are accustomed to woods each consisting mainly of the same kind of tree, reaching to approximately the same height, and among which we can walk about at will. In the Amazons, on the other hand, you have not one forest, but many, one within another, giving in all an impenetrable tangle, in which only an arboreal animal can hope to make any headway at all.

Firstly we have the great forest trees, towering upwards like the pillars of a cathedral to a height of 150 feet or more. They possess no branches except at the top, where an almost continuous canopy of foliage is spread out to the sun, plunging all beneath it into semi-darkness. The size of the leaves that form this canopy is amazing. Some of them have a continuous expanse of nine feet in length by four or five feet wide. Those which are broken up into leaflets are even larger, sometimes reaching fifty feet in length. It is obvious how effectively such foliage can shut out the sun.

Within this greater forest we have a smaller one of medium trees, forty to fifty feet in height. These are more comparable with our own in magnitude, and give us something by which we can measure the immensity of the major forest. Then there is the thick undergrowth of small trees, dwarf palms and tree ferns, reaching perhaps six to ten feet. But that is not all. Twisting round the bigger stems, hanging in festoons from tree to tree, and lying in tangles on the ground are all manner of climbing plants. In length many of these vastly exceed even the greatest trees of the forest. For instance, the rattans, which climb by means of prickly leaves, may reach six hundred or a thousand feet in length, although their thickness rarely exceeds three inches.

It is easy to see how such immense lengths can be attained. A climber will grow to the top of one of the great trees and flourish for a time in the light and air. Then, perhaps, a branch of its giant support will come crashing to the ground, bringing with it much of the climber, part of which, however, will remain caught among the tree tops. Once again it will start on its upward struggle towards the light, and in this way a climbing plant may zig-zag up and down through the forest like the shrouds of a ship. Clearly in the course of time this endless growth makes the forest almost impassable.

We may well ask, " Why this mania for tallness ? " The answer lies in two things. Firstly, there is the immense fertility of the humid soil, which makes possible a vast luxuriance of vegetable growth. Secondly we have the fact that sunlight and plenty of it is essential to the life of plants. One without the other could not produce this tremendous struggle upwards. In English woods the soil is not sufficiently fertile to bear great trees set very close together. Consequently there is always enough light even for a comparatively short plant, and height does not become such an important factor. In the Amazon valley, on the other hand, the trees grow so thickly that any that cannot reach to the top of the forest must die out altogether unless they can produce some mechanism for making use of a scanty illumination. And finally there are the climbers, that have not the strength to grow tall by themselves, but climb on their neighbours' shoulders.

SUCH is the forest from below. It is a picture of great luxuriance of vegetation combined with an eerie gloominess that is difficult to describe. During the heat of the day the forest is silent except perhaps for the distant crash of some great bough hurtling to the ground, or the cry of some animal seized by an enemy. And then there is silence again, until at evening the howling monkeys fill the air with their din. Some of the sounds are difficult to account for,

on the roof of the forest. They need not grow tall in order to reach it. They have only to develop organs fit for life in a tangle of leaves and boughs. And this they have done, in a vast variety of ways.

Most monkeys are well adapted for living in trees, but nowhere is this better illustrated than in those of the Amazon forests. Nearly all possess long tails which can act as a fifth hand. Just under the tip there is usually a bare palm very sensitive to touch, which at once coils itself round any branch with which it comes into contact. The agile spider monkey can easily support its weight by the tail alone. Bates tells us how he shot at a spider monkey but only succeeded in wounding his victim. " It fell with a crash headlong about twenty or thirty feet, and then caught a bough

and these the natives say are made by the Curapira, the spirit of the forest. Their unknown origin adds to their eeriness.

So much for the terrors of the basement. What of the roof? The forest from above presents a very different picture. Imagine an immense green carpet overstrewn at all seasons with flowers of every colour, with gorgeous butterflies the size of sparrows flapping lazily from bloom to bloom under the burning sun. Imagine the flowers in their turn followed by luscious fruits of every description. Is it then a matter for wonder that nearly all the larger animals have forsaken the gloom and danger of Mother Earth for the light and food and freedom of the tree-tops? They, like the plants, have come up for light and air, but even more, for food. Unlike the plants they cannot obtain their nourishment from the rich soil, but this disadvantage that sends them to the tree-tops in search of fruits and insects, is at the same time a boon in that it leaves them free to wander

F. W. Bond

CAPUCHIN AND DOUROUCOULI MONKEYS OF BRAZIL

The resemblance, at a distance, of the head of the capuchin monkey (bottom) to a tonsured head has led to the animal being named after the Capuchin order of friars. The monkeys belonging to the capuchin group go about in the trees in gangs with a leader. Another habitant of the tree-tops is the douroucouli (top) whose face has a certain resemblance to a human one

Dr. Francis de Loys

WONDERFUL DISCOVERY OF A NEW ANTHROPOID APE IN THE SOUTH AMERICAN FORESTS

While an expedition to the great forests of South America was exploring the country in the neighbourhood of the Tarra River, two apes broke cover and threatened to attack the party. One was shot dead and proved to be a specimen of unprecedented kind. The corpse was propped in a sitting posture on a packing case and photographed as we see here. The ape was a female, a little over five feet in height and had no tail. This animal partly bridges the hitherto complete gap in evolutionary process in the New World between Man and Simians.

F. W. Bond

ARBOREAL ACROBATS OF THE TROPICAL FORESTS: HUMBOLDT'S WOOLLY MONKEY AND A SPIDER MONKEY

Besides the tree sloths (illustrations of these animals will be found in pages 923 and 924) and various birds, the chief inhabitants of the tree tops of a tropical forest are the monkeys. These live together in colonies, and all of them have long prehensile tails. Upon their tails the lives of these monkeys depend very frequently, for they make considerable leaps through the air, catching at branches as they fly through the foliage with their tail as often as with their hands. Our left-hand photograph shows a captive specimen of Humboldt's woolly monkey demonstrating the practical use of the tail, which is here pushed through the wire roofing of its cage. On the right is a black-faced spider monkey, another arboreal acrobat.

with its tail, which grasped it instantaneously, and then the animal remained suspended in mid-air. Before I could re-load it recovered itself, and mounted nimbly to the topmost branches."

The spider monkeys can travel with great rapidity through the tree-tops, swinging from branch to branch and from tree to tree, and using all their five limbs in the process. . The Indians are very fond of them as pets, and obtain them alive in a rather curious way. They shoot them with poison darts from a blow-pipe, catch them as they fall, and counteract the poison by putting a little salt in the mouth.

The capuchin monkeys are almost as much at home in the tree-tops. They travel in single file in groups of twenty or thirty. When they reach the outermost branches of a particularly tall tree, they jump fearlessly down into the foliage, perhaps fifty feet beneath. Rapidly righting themselves, they proceed on their journey. The howling monkeys are more often heard than seen. They possess a special apparatus in the throat for increasing the volume of sound, and can be heard for a great distance. In the drier forests curious little monkeys known as night apes are sometimes found. These are hardly tree-top animals, as they live during the day in hollow trees, usually fairly near to the ground. Although they sleep in the day-time they are easily aroused, and in passing by a tree in which they happen to be concealed, one may be startled by the sudden appearance of a number of little striped faces at a hole in the trunk. They have the large, staring eyes of many nocturnal animals, and live on both insects and fruits.

The tree-sloth is another well-known inhabitant of the Amazon forests. Its strong claws serve as hooks by which it can hang on to branches upside down, moving slowly and cautiously about in search of food. The long shaggy hair is frequently covered with microscopic plants, which give it a greenish colour blending perfectly with

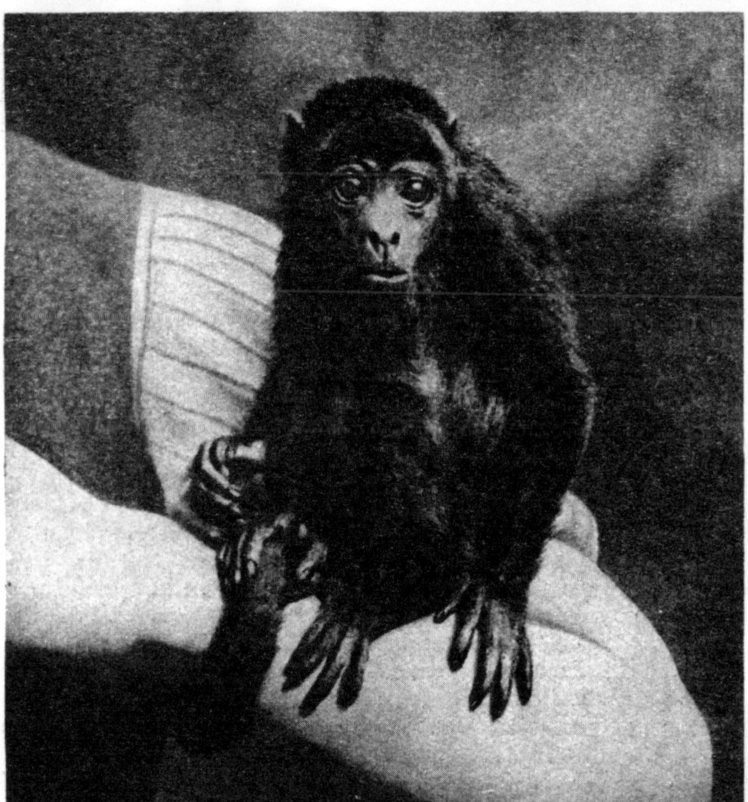

F. W. Bond

HOWLING MONKEYS THAT MAKE EVENING HIDEOUS

During the great heat of the middle day the green dimness of the Amazon forest is silent save, perhaps, for the occasional cry from some captured animal. But when the evening comes certain monkeys, called howling monkeys, fill the forest with their noise. Here we have a black howler (bottom) and a red howler (top).

Ray Jones

TREE-TOP NEST BUILDING

Taken in the vast Amazon valley the lower photograph shows an almost bare tree selected as a residence by an egret colony. The nests look like some strange sort of fruit. Above is the tiny nest of a humming bird in a fork of a branch from the top of a tree

the moss-covered branches. One species possesses an oval mark on the back resembling the broken end of such a branch. A good example of an animal whose relatives elsewhere generally live on the ground, is seen in the tree-porcupine. The tail is very long and prehensile like a monkey's, while the spines are slender and flexible. Even some of the ant-eaters have acquired prehensile tails and become arboreal, though the great ant-eater still remains on the ground at the edge of the forest, and shows no arboreal modifications.

It is interesting to note the divergent lines of adaptation that have been followed by the great group of pouched animals. In Australia these have become the kangaroos with long legs for running rapidly over the broad plains, and a stout tail for balancing purposes. In America, on the other hand, they have taken to the trees and become the opossums with short legs and a slim prehensile tail. In certain of these, the young, when able to leave the mother's pouch, are carried on her back, with all their tails gloriously intertwined with hers!

Flying animals like bats and birds are already fitted for a life in the tree-tops, and little need be said about them. Among the bats, however, the vampire is worthy of mention. These bats descend upon cattle and even on human beings at night, and, making a small hole with their needle-like teeth, proceed to suck the blood of their victim. It is a curious fact that the gullet of these bats is so small that only liquid food can pass down it. The birds include parrots and toucans in great variety, all of them adapted for perching on branches. There are, however, a few that live on the ground and prey on the teeming insect life. Among them the ant-thrush sometimes serves as a friendly warning to the traveller, of the advent of a horde of the biting ants on which it lives.

Reptiles have followed the example of the rest and taken for the most part to the tree-tops. Lizards are quite at home on the broad leaves, where they live chiefly on butterflies. On the trunks of trees are found the grotesque geckos, nimbly running up and down with the help of the sucker-like discs at the ends of their fingers. The lizards are in their turn preyed upon by tree-snakes, whose colours blend marvellously with the foliage, and whose long, whip-like bodies enable them to slither safely from branch to branch. If they should happen to fall they coil body and tail like a watch spring and land safely on the spiral, which breaks the fall. It is noteworthy that the only large reptiles have taken to the water and so escaped the danger that the periodic floods present to large terrestrial beasts. They include the alligator and the largest of the snakes, the anaconda. The latter may sometimes reach twenty-five to thirty feet in length.

One would imagine that frogs would take quite happily to the swampy rain-forest. And yet, in the Amazons, we

F. W. Bond

BIRDS THAT FLY OVER THE ROOF OF THE FOREST

While, owing to the two thicknesses of leaves, those of the tall trees and those of the short ones in the Amazon district, colours are dimmed, yet out in the sunlight there is a riot of tints. Seen from an aeroplane the forest presents a wonderful sight with many beautiful birds among the blooms and fruits. Here are (bottom) a black-capped lory and (top) a great-billed parrot.

F. W. Bond

TRIO OF CAPUCHIN MONKEYS FROM AMAZON FORESTS

Also known as the sapajous, the capuchin monkeys that live up in the trees of the hot, damp Amazon forests have golden fur deepening to brown on the back and paling to yellow on the cheeks and chest. These monkeys never leave their high retreats except to drink, for they have a great dread of coming to the ground.

find that even they live in the trees. Like the geckos they have developed adhesive finger-discs by which they can sit quite tight on the leaves on the look-out for insect food. Their brilliant greens match those of the leaves to a nicety, though some have "flash colours" on parts concealed when the animal is still. These possibly serve to dazzle their pursuers, when they suddenly flash out as the frog leaps away. Many of these frogs lay their eggs in pools of water trapped in leaves or holes, while others possess a kind of pouch on the back in which the eggs are carried until they hatch.

The protective coloration shown by the tree-frogs is quite a common feature among these forest animals. The best examples, of course, are the leaf-insects and stick-insects. These so closely resemble leaves and sticks that foraging ants may run right over them without suspecting the presence of their succulent prey. Some of them that resemble dead leaves have even a transparent patch on the wing which gives the impression of a hole in the leaf!

It will be noticed that so far nearly all the animals mentioned have been small. In point of fact, large animals are very few and far between in the Amazon valley. The forest is too dense for them, and life in the tree-tops is not suited to heavy animals. The only really large cats are the jaguar and the puma, and neither of these is often seen by the traveller. The puma never attacks man unprovoked, but the jaguar may sometimes be dangerous, and in some districts is reputed to have become a man-eater. The tapir is the only South American representative of the group to which the horse and rhinoceros belong, and is chiefly confined to the edge of the forest. The lack of large animals brings the South American forests into sharp contrast with those of Africa. In this continent the rain-forests are less damp, there is more continuous sunshine and the struggle for light is therefore less intense. Climbers are not so numerous and the jungle is therefore more easy for a large animal to penetrate. Consequently we find in Africa such forms as the elephant, the lion and the great anthropoid apes that have never found a foot-hold in the American forests. And since the need for tree-top existence is less urgent in Africa, we find there very few adaptations for that purpose. Prehensile tails, for instance, are confined to certain scaly ant-eaters which in point of fact are really immigrants from Asia.

It is interesting to turn from the rain-forests of America to the rather similar conditions that exist on the other side of the earth. In the low-lying parts of Borneo and the Malay Archipelago are forests almost as impenetrable as those of the Amazon. Here the animals have had the same kind of problem to face as in the West, and it is interesting to see whether, working independently, they have solved it in the same way. It turns out that they have not. In America they took to prehensile tails. In the East they have gone in for parachuting. Here, for instance, we find "flying frogs" which have extended their natural leaping powers by a great expansion of their webbed feet. Here also are "flying dragons," lizards with wide flaps on each side of their bodies, supported by ribs, and by which they can volplane for considerable distances. Flying squirrels are also found, possessing membranes uniting the front and hind legs. They are said to be able to parachute for seventy to eighty yards, and to guide themselves to some extent while in the air. We have here, then, the same kind of problem solved in a totally different way. But perhaps that is only an indication of the fact that the forests of Borneo are never quite so impenetrable as those of the Amazon. The presence of one of the great apes, the orang utan, is further confirmation of that fact.

The main point that emerges from any study of tropical nature is the immense adaptability of animal life to the most unpromising of habitats.

Chapter CXXVIII

Short Lives and Long in the Animal Kingdom

By Dr. A. D. Peacock

Professor of Natural History, University College, Dundee

WHO would not add to his length of days? Every living thing disputes with death, for to live seems instinctive. Tradition is richly storied of man's quest for longer life; a crude science once sought an elixir in witches' brews of animal parts; to-day we ask the living things themselves. To the simple question: What is length of life? there are two answers, namely, the span which an organism lives, the "normal life period," and the possible age attainable, the "potential life period." The former takes account of the hazards of existence and the latter is realized only by a few Methuselahs of their kind.

Direct observations on animal age are meagre and many ingenious methods of estimating it exist. Certain structures are used as indicators, for example the "ear stones" and scales of fishes, the shell of mussels, the shield of the tortoise and the "whalebone" of whales, the material being deposited by the living stuff in certain fashion and at a certain rate. The age of horses is gauged from the wear of teeth. Evidence concerning whales has been gathered in one specially curious way, by the harpoons found sticking in them. One such weapon was dated forty years previous to the time of recovery. Then there is the quaint story of the South American parrot, certainly of venerable age, for its speech was unintelligible to the Indians with which it lived because it spoke the language of a bygone tribe.

Beliefs in the longevity of certain animals must have been born of primitive credulity, a native instinct to exaggerate and a desire for a miracle. Unthinking tradition has handed them on and they have lost nothing in the telling. The list of long-lived animals is really very short. The figures given here represent years:

Giant Tortoise	200	Crow	100
Carp	150	Parrot	100
Vulture	118	Raven	100
Eagle	104	Man	100
Whale	100	Shark	100
Salmon	100	Eider Duck	100

Under ordinary circumstances of life these figures are much too high.

Authorities agree that the giant tortoises of the Southern Hemisphere certainly live 150 years and probably over two centuries. There still lives in St. Helena the Aldabran exile that knew Napoleon in the days of his eclipse. But the Galapagos Islands giants that must have seen a greater man, Charles Darwin, in the hey-day of youth, have fallen to the hunter. Certain sacred crocodiles of India go over the century; tradition credits them with two.

The proverbial example of brief existence is the may-fly insect with its "life of a day." Actually there are shorter lives. It is difficult however to state what animal is really the shortest-lived, though most probably it is one of the pigmies in size, the green-fly insects, for their total span narrows to a month or less. The may-fly's day is its wedding day and to say its life is one of a few brief hours is to speak in parable; for the age of a typical insect includes the feeding period of the larva—the caterpillar, maggot or grub—the transformation period of the pupa and the adult period. In this light wherein lies the wonder of the may-fly's little life? The common *Ephemera vulgata* emerge from the water in thousands for a wedding dance of an afternoon, lay their eggs, and die. But these performances occur only in the final act of a long life-history. This same ephemera, hatching as a small wingless larva with six legs and three tails, dwelt in the stream for anything from one to three years, almost a veteran among insects really.

EVEN respecting brevity of adult life the may-fly is probably outrivalled by strange insects called Stylops whose larvae are parasites within the grubs of "solitary bees." The winged and flying male lives but two or three hours; the egg-laying female however lives some days.

Other midget lives are those of Daphnia water-fleas, a month maybe, for many generations arise during the spring and summer. Under certain conditions the gnat and house-fly behave similarly.

The simplest animals, Protozoa, are single minute cells of living matter, "protoplasm," and they may divide into two organisms in a few hours and carry on so indefinitely. It is impossible to state the longevity of such animals for, except by mischance, each never dies. Yet any given one does not endure as a solitary being. When such ceases to become one, and becomes two, we may not say that its day is done for there is no corpse. The protozoan type of protoplasm is immortal.

The fresh-water sponge of our streams is an annual, but the sea forms, such as the bath sponge, live under stable conditions and probably support sedentary lives for many years.

The zoophytes and swimming bells seem annual, but our common little red anemone, *Actinia mesembryanthemum*, can live 66 years. In 1828, Sir John Dalyell of Edinburgh put one in a small glass of sea water where it remained until its natural death.

Some land snails are annuals, some biennial; the familiar Helix species, including the Roman edible

YOUNG ELEPHANT AT THE START OF ITS CAREER THAT MAY LAST A CENTURY

The problem of the elephant's age is not an easy one to solve because African elephants have been domesticated regularly only within recent years, and there was little means of finding out the extent of their longevity in the wild state. The Indian elephant has been known to live in captivity for more than a hundred years. Remains of wild elephants' carcases are, strange to say, very seldom found in India. How these huge bodies vanish so completely is a mystery In a wild state the elephant will probably live longer than in captivity, accidents excepted.

pomatia, lives from two to five years; common Limnaea water snails attain two to four, and Paludina species eight to nine; a giant sea snail, *Natica heros*, thirty. The fresh-water mussel *Anodonta* probably lives ten to fourteen years, but one giant, *Tridacna gigas*, supposedly lives sixteen to a hundred. The smaller species of octopuses and cuttlefishes live a year, some ten and more, while the monsters probably require many decades.

Of the earthworms, marine worms and the Echinoderms—starfishes, sea-urchins and so on, the smaller kinds die in less than a year, but slow growers, whose mature individuals show great disparity in size, are inferred to exist some years.

Very small crustaceans, for example, water-fleas, have pigmy lives of two to three months, but the edible crab, and probably the lobster, can attain nine years and the crayfish twenty—a very "respectable" age.

Small millipedes and centipedes presumably are annual but those measuring a foot and more are assumed to live a few years.

E.N.A.

POLAR AND BROWN BEARS WHICH LIVE FROM TWENTY-FIVE TO FORTY YEARS

As a general rule it is found that animals that live in the Temperate Zones live longer than those of the Torrid or the Frigid Zones. Of these two bears then, the polar or white bear which we see (bottom) so busily engaged in scratching its chin, would live a shorter time than this brown bear (top) which comes from the mountains of British Columbia. The average age for a bear is from twenty-five to forty years. While captivity affords safety from accident, yet a bear, if uninjured, would have more vigorous health in a wild state.

Short and Long Lives

Insects generally are short-lived. The range is wide, however; compare the green-fly's four weeks with the 37 years of the "fire beetle," *Buprestes splendens*. This age was known because the specimen was taken from a desk that had served for that period in a London counting house. An American bug, *Cicada septemdecim*, also has long life, seventeen years, the stages being curiously disproportionate, the winged adult having four short weeks while the long juvenile years are spent underground as a wingless larva.

Among social insects two queens of the slave ant (*Formica fusca*) lived at least 13 years and a queen of the brown garden ant (*Lasius niger*) at least nine. In the termites, or "white ants," the queens attain four to five years, while in the honey-bees the queens live from two to three, though exceptional cases of five years may occur, such being possible by reason of their sheltered and pampered lives. Worker and male ants live dangerously and die sooner, the latter in a few weeks, though the former could possibly live as long as the queen but for their occupational risks. The worker bee may survive a year, but the drone succumbs after four months. Less socially specialised, the fertilised female wasp lives only a year, including the winter sleep, and the males three summer months.

Insects whose larvae feed on poorly nutritive material, such as wood, have their years extended; for example, the larvae of the giant Sirex sawflies bore two to three years in timber before the few free summer weeks of maturity.

Most water types, caddis-, alder-, stone- and dragon-flies follow the may-fly plan of several months' larval life, but with a short adult period attaining at most a few weeks. Certain large dragon-fly larvae, however, supposedly live over two years.

A considerable proportion of insects, however, live under a year. The maximum ages of crickets and grasshoppers vary round six months, but cockroaches may overstep the year. The beetles appear in similar case, but the grub of the large cockchafer, *Melolontha vulgaris*, builds up a great body during a subterranean existence of four years, after which the adult flies a brief month. In the giant water-beetle, *Dytiscus marginalis*, the larval span is four to five weeks, and that of the adult several years.

Butterflies and moths are in a lower longevity category though, where the caterpillars are long feeders and winter sleepers, the species may attain a year or so. The wood-eating goat moth caterpillar, *Cossus ligniperda*, lives two to three years. Adult life in butterflies and moths is usually a few days, though worn and weary veterans, six weeks old, of "tortoise-shells" are known. A "painted lady," *Pyrameis cardui*, has actually been kept for three years.

Plant-bugs live a few months, the flea, if fed, 18 months, and that abomination the louse a too long life of seven weeks. In the two-winged flies of lower longevity grades life is measured in days; under very favourable conditions the minimum for the house-fly may be about 34 days, and for the gnat 30.

Spiders usually perish during the first winter, but can be kept for two or three years. Ticks also survive two years.

Vertebrates generally are long-living forms, especially the carp, vouched by Buffon as being a century and a half, and even, possibly, 200 years. The account of a German pike, 19 feet long, weighing 350 pounds, and presumably 267 years old—for it was found to carry a ring inscribed, "I am the fish which was first of all put into the lake by the hands of the Governor of the Universe, Frederick the Second, the 5th of October, 1230"—must go the way of many fish stories, for a critical zoologist—a doubting Thomas—proved that the giant was built from smaller ones! Trout and large fresh-water fish live several years; sticklebacks, minnows, and so on, probably only a few. Other notes are: shark and salmon, 100 years; Arctic plaice, 60 probably; eel, 60 (in Roman aquaria); Danube giant catfish, 50; fresh-water sturgeon, 40; North Sea plaice and herring, 20; Aphya goby, one year.

The potential longevity of the toad and frog may reach 36 and 12 to 16 years respectively. A Japanese salamander has lived 40 years in the Zoo. Exact European records show 40 years for captive alligators. Experienced students believe that no great ages are attained in lizards and snakes.

For birds the figures tabulated below are not exact in all cases, nor average, but as they relate to actual observations a certain value attaches to them. The figures represent years.

White-headed Vulture	118 (in captivity)	Cuckoo	32
Parrakeet	120 probably (in captivity)	Oyster-catcher	30
Parrot	120 probably (in captivity)	Rhea	30
Golden Eagle	104 to 150	Cassowary	26
Falcon	100 to 162	Skylark	18 to 30
Eider Duck	100	Canary, Peacock	24
Crow	100	Crane, Goldfinch	23 (in confinement)
Swan	70 to 100	Linnet	23
Raven	69 to 100	Magpie	20
Eagle Owl	68	Kiwi	20
Heron	60	Nightingale	12 to 25
Goose, Duck	50 to 80; 57 certainly for the goose	Turkey	16
Ostrich	50	Pheasant, Partridge	15
Crane	43	Pigeon	10 to 20
Pelican	41	Hen	10 to 30
Gulls, Dove, Sparrow	40	Robin	12
Hawks	30 to 40	Thrush	10
		Goatsucker, Swift	8 to 9
		Starling	8
		Wren	2 to 3

Nothing is known of the longevity of the most primitive mammals, the Australasian duckbills and spiny anteaters. A phalanger marsupial lived in the London Zoo for over ten years, but that is little guide to the longevity of kangaroos, opossums, and so on. The smallest mammals generally have the briefest lives. Thus, in the rodents, the porcupine lives up to 20 years; the hare, 10; the rabbit, 5 to 10; the guinea pig, 6 to 7; the squirrel, 6 to 15; the rat and mouse, 6. In the strong active carnivores 25 years is not often exceeded, representative lives being:

Facing page 1512 (Vol. VII)

ELAND: A BIG, LONG-LIVED ANTELOPE OF EAST AFRICA'S WOODLANDS

Because elands—largest of the antelopes—are far less nervous and truculent than most others of the family, are of big size and provide quite good meat, attempts have been made to domesticate them. They did quite well in private parks in England, but the animals took so long to mature that the experiment was found uneconomic. A bull eland stands nearly six feet high at the withers. The average antelope age limit is 15 years.

tiger, up to 25 and even 35 ; bear up to 25 and 40 ; sea-lion, 17 ; cat, 9 to 10 and occasionally 40 ; dog, 10 to 15 and, rarely, 35 ; hyaena, jackal and fox, 14 ; badger 12. The longevity of ungulates is similar. The elephant may hold the record with over 100 years, but the oldest case authenticated gives 70. The camel is credited with 100, but 40 is more probable. Hippopotamuses and rhinoceroses possibly reach 70 to 80, though London Zoo observations show 39 and 40 respectively. The horse spans 25 to 40 years, the donkey and zebra 25 to 30, the cow 25, the pig and wild boar 20 to 25, deer about 20, the giraffe 19 (London Zoo), llama 17, antelope, goat and sheep about 15. Of more highly evolved forms, the tropical fruit bat records 17 years, while for the primates the following figures exist : grey lemur 11 and chimpanzee 31. Thirty years is regarded as possible for monkeys. In civilized man the average life is about 50, but the Psalmist's span is often exceeded and centenarianism is well-known.

TIGER AND LION THAT SELDOM OUTLIVE THE QUARTER CENTURY

Active carnivores of large size are far outstripped in longevity by many of the ungulates. The tiger does not usually exceed a span of twenty-five years, though some specimens are believed to have survived for perhaps ten years more. The lion (top) also, does not often live longer than the quarter-century.

Longevity can sometimes be prolonged to an astonishing degree in certain insects by special habit adaptations, such as " hunger sleep," " winter sleep," and " pupal oversleep." In hunger sleep the vital processes are reduced to the veriest ebb ; the bed bug can live so for six years, likewise certain Blap beetles. In winter sleep (hibernation) similar body conditions result, only they are attributable to cold and not starvation. Female wasps hibernate and the tortoiseshell and related butterflies ; so do the dipterous cluster-flies and the malaria-carrying mosquito. Pupal oversleep, a curious phenomenon little known and studied, is an adaptation of great value to the species. By it the time of adult emergence is postponed. Thus the flea may lie " doggo " for an indefinite period in its cocoon, instinctively awaiting a suitable host. A certain fern saw-fly pupates in soft wood, but

Autotype Co.

BACTRIAN CAMEL, A HARDY DWELLER AMID THE EXTREMES OF THE SALT-LADEN SIBERIAN DESERTS

Credited with the power of attaining a century of years, it is probable that the average life of a camel is about forty. Longevity is a distinct advantage in the fight for survival which every family of animals must sustain if it is to survive. The longer the life the more chance of producing offspring, and since the long-lived animals usually take a long time to wean it follows that they will have the maximum of care and attention during their early years when the foundations of sound physical development are laid. The bactrian camel is a very hardy beast for it has to survive both great heat and great cold in its native Siberian deserts and live on vegetation and water which is often impregnated with salt to such an extent that few other animals would tolerate.

W. S. Berridge

instead of emerging ten months afterwards, it may defer its debut for one or two years. The rhythmic cycle is altered, a tricky insurance scheme whereby life expectation is increased.

In the tsetse fly, however, the larvae are nourished in the mother's body, so that independent existence, a few weeks, is thereby shortened to the pupal and adult periods.

We must really abandon most of the travellers' tales of prodigious old age in animals. For recent research of the "Discovery" Antarctic Expedition shows that the largest whales are only eleven months in the womb, are full-grown at two years, are mature at three, and probably live only about 40 years. Great growth, then, need not necessarily require great time. And surely this is just as marvellous a thing as the old yarns of five century longevity. A great many cases of great age correlated with great size certainly exist, but there are too many inconsistencies for the framing of a general law.

Lazy habits and long life are linked, witness the tortoises and crocodiles, but this is not of general truth, for the birds, which live the most excited lives, show notable long-livers, while their general longevity is probably greater than that of reptiles.

E.N.A.

CANADIAN PORCUPINE AND A BRAZILIAN TREE PORCUPINE

Generally speaking, the smaller mammals have the shorter lives, but usually they make up for a briefer span of existence by having more offspring than the larger animals. The young of the Canadian porcupine (bottom) are born with their eyes open and with well developed quills. Above is a Brazilian tree porcupine.

Gambier Bolton

FOX AND CAT WITH LIVES OF MODERATE LENGTH

As we go higher in the development of animal life we find that the regenerative power of the physical system becomes less. A one-celled animal is virtually immortal under favourable conditions. In the higher animals the units of the body carry on for just so long and no more. The fox (bottom) lives for about 14 years and the cat ten, though sometimes it grows older.

Concerning climate and longevity, and arguing from the case of man, who affords the best, and best investigated example, normal and potential duration of life is greater in temperate zones than in the Tropical or Polar.

Let us now bring our subject into relationship with fundamental principles. In biological language longevity is a " character," an attribute or quality of the living thing just as is red-headedness or blue-eyedness. A character cannot live to itself; it is correlated, it may be, in a very subtle fashion with all other characters. What affects it affects the society of which it is a member; the reverse holds good likewise.

Species preservation is a first law of nature—only the race counts—so the question arises, of what use is the character longevity? It certainly is of great survival value to the species, for the greater the time the greater the chance of rearing young to repair species wastage due to death by many causes. This seemed so important to the great Weismann that he believed that reproductive capacity had determined longevity. Others, however, consider the reverse might be the case. But animals survive by such a diversity of expedients, and characters are so intimately linked that we cannot be dogmatic. No one denies the especial importance of reproductive capacity and of

Autotype

DOGS THAT OFTEN HAVE TO LEAD STRENUOUS LIVES: ESKIMO DOG AND COLLIE

There are records of dogs which lived over thirty years, but such an age would be rare of attainment by so active and hard worked an animal as the Eskimo dog (bottom). It has constantly to expend an amount of concentrated energy that no other dog is called upon for. Dragging sledges across snow in the biting cold climate of North America does not make for longevity. On the other hand, life is lived to the utmost of vigour and healthiness. The collie (top) is a favourite breed for sheep dogs and these, too, have often to work under arduous conditions.

AFRICAN AND HAIRY RHINOCEROS, VETERANS AMONG UNGULATES

In the case of a rhinoceros it is probably its comparatively staid life that makes it enjoy longevity beyond the majority of ungulates. The rhinoceros is credited by some scientists and explorers with seventy or even eighty years of life in the wild state, though the records of the London Zoological Society show only thirty-nine years for a captive animal. These photographs show (bottom) the African rhinoceros and (top) a hairy-eared rhinoceros enjoying the effects of a mud bath in its pen.

W. S Berridge

PELICANS AND AN OSTRICH THAT ARE AMONG THE PATRIARCHS OF THE BIRD WORLD

Actual observation has revealed that a pelican can live for forty-one years, but the average life of wild pelicans is probably considerably less. Under ideal conditions such as obtain where they are kept in places like St. James's Park, London, with plenty of space, a private island where they are unmolested, and plenty of food, these birds must thrive even better than in their natural state, where the keener struggle for food would outweigh the advantages of climate. Above is an ostrich. One such bird is known to have survived for half a century.

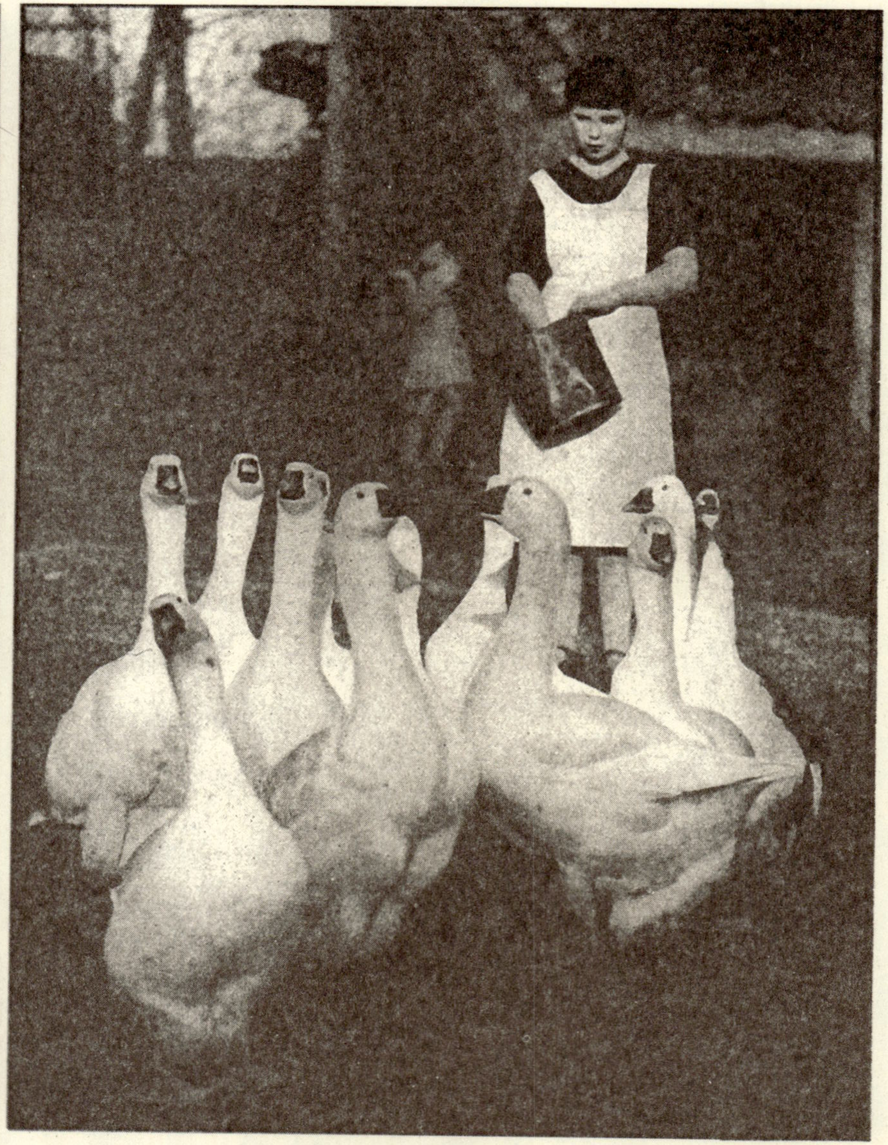

Fox Photos

SWANS CREDITED WITH OCCASIONALLY BECOMING CENTENARIAN AND THE GOOSE THAT MAY SURVIVE FIFTY YEARS

From seventy to one hundred years has been credited to a swan for its life span, and certainly, in England, where the birds are almost entirely without enemies, such a length of life seems not improbable. The swans seen above (left) are displaying a peculiarity of their species. Each bird has its own stretch of water and if another should trespass, it immediately retires before the wrathful approach of the accredited owner. The attacking swan in this photograph seems the incarnation of rage and rapid motion. On the right we have some fat geese. These are destined for an untimely end for the benefit of the poultry market, but, otherwise, fifty years is quite a possible life for a goose.

PINK AND SLENDER BILLED COCKATOOS WHICH CAN ATTAIN CENTENARIAN DISTINCTION IN A CAGE

Naturally the length of time lived by a captive cockatoo depends almost entirely on the treatment it receives. Once acclimatised, cockatoos are extremely hardy and can survive English winters without artificial warmth other than that of the interior of a house. They can live in a room without a fire. A century is recorded as being attainable by these birds, though they often harm themselves by escaping, their abilities as prison-breakers being prodigious. With their very formidable beaks they can saw and hammer and unfasten screws, and even metal chains have failed before their onslaughts. On the left is a pink cockatoo, and on the right a corella or slender-billed cockatoo. Notice their beaks.

Autotype Co.

MARTIAL HAWK-EAGLE AND KOREAN SEA-EAGLE BELONGING TO A FAMILY THAT IS LONG LIVED

An eagle is a singularly impregnable creature when adult and, as it can vary its prey, is not likely to suffer from a food shortage. Under these circumstances it is to be expected that individuals may reach a great age. For the eagle a total of 194 years has been recorded though such a figure would, of course, be very exceptional. Our photographs here show a martial hawk-eagle (left) and a huge Korean sea-eagle (right). Hawk-eagles are found in Africa, India and Australia. The Korean sea-eagle is a very large bird preying principally on fish and water-fowl and haunting coast-lines and the banks of rivers or the shores of lagoons and lakes. It has a particularly loud and penetrating scream.

longevity, nor their close linkage, but it is impossible to measure how much each has influenced the other.

Some clues to understanding the life span may be obtained by studying what ends it. Death gains access to the body mainly through attack on the food canal, the breathing organs and the blood system, the two former regions being the most mortal. Food canal fatality is greatest in reptiles, less in birds, and least in mammals; this means that this system has increased its powers of survival. Yet the reverse is the case in the respiratory organs. Metchnikoff believed that the main cause of death was poisoning by food canal bacteria, and though all his views are unacceptable today there can be no question that disease of one region causes functional disturbances elsewhere. The animal's hold

Neville Kingston

SHORT OF, AND JUST OVER, THE HALF CENTURY: CRANE AND HERON

Crowned cranes are natives of Africa and get their appellation from the ornamental head-dress they wear as we can see in the lower photograph. A crane has been known to live for forty-three years but the heron (top) seems to have a greater expectation of life, for sixty years is the number accorded to it. The specimen in the top photograph is a giant heron.

W S. Berridge

M. Duncan

CARP THAT IS OFTEN A VETERAN AMONG FISH, AND THE SHORT-LIVED SNAKE

Carp, those staid and ponderous fish, are notoriously long-lived. A century and a half in one case is vouched for, and a hundred years seems not uncommon, especially in such places as castle moats and ornamental water. The carp (bottom) seems to be content with a little stagnant water and a good deal of mud, and with such simple needs thrives where other fish would languish. Compared with the carp the snake (top) has but a short span, and naturalists believe that neither snakes nor lizards attain great ages.

Jacques Boyer

FRESH-WATER CRUSTACEAN THAT BEATS THE LOBSTER FOR LONGEVITY

This photograph, taken from a remarkable point of view, shows a crayfish which seems to be a great cluster of pointed legs. The camera has been placed just over the ends of the feelers. The crayfish appears to exceed both the edible crab and the lobster so far as long life is concerned and is known to reach its twentieth year. Found in many British rivers the crayfish is a fresh-water crustacean and feeds, at night, upon plants and insects. It is a slow-growing creature and takes about five years, or a quarter of its whole life, to mature.

E.N.A.

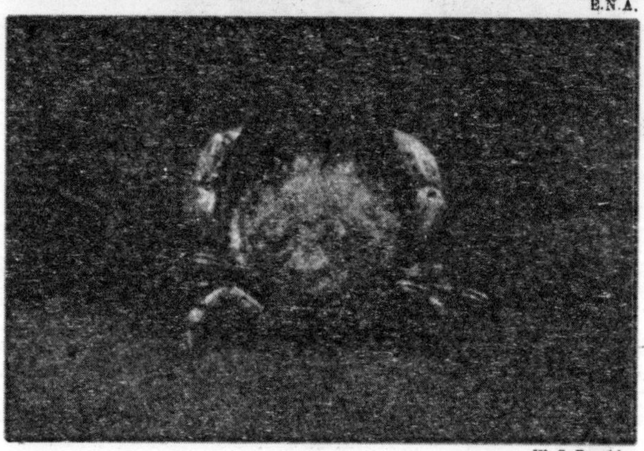

W. S. Berridge

CRAB AND CRAWFISH

Crabs and lobsters usually live about nine years unless accident overtakes them. Below we have a crab and above a crawfish or spiny lobster weighing seven and a half pounds and caught off the American coast at thirty-seven fathoms.

on life is as the strength of its weakest part. Moreover, the resistant powers of the various regions have not evolved in step so that there is actually a mal-adjustment of the system. True this imperfect body can, and does work with surprising harmony, especially if it be nicely adapted to its mode of life, and life may not be such a bad thing, after all. But despite all this there is rarely a passing like that of the "one hoss shay," where

> It went to pieces all at once—
> All at once and nothing first
> Just as bubbles do when they burst.

A finer analysis shows that what really counts is the viability of the cells which compose the tissues. In the system we call the body these units can carry on their work for just so long. They are mortal by the very fact of their having to accommodate themselves to other cells differently specialised. Given suitable conditions the one-celled animals are immortal, as also tissue cells appear to be if grown experimentally, but the higher the organism the less becomes the regenerative powers of the parts composing the system.

The stuff of life is immortal, but in the achievement of complex organizations of tissues an ancient virtue has become frustrated. If higher types were physically immortal or possessed of the greater gift of

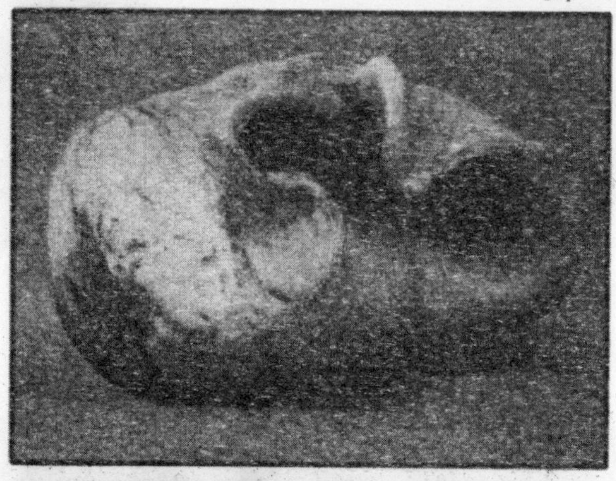

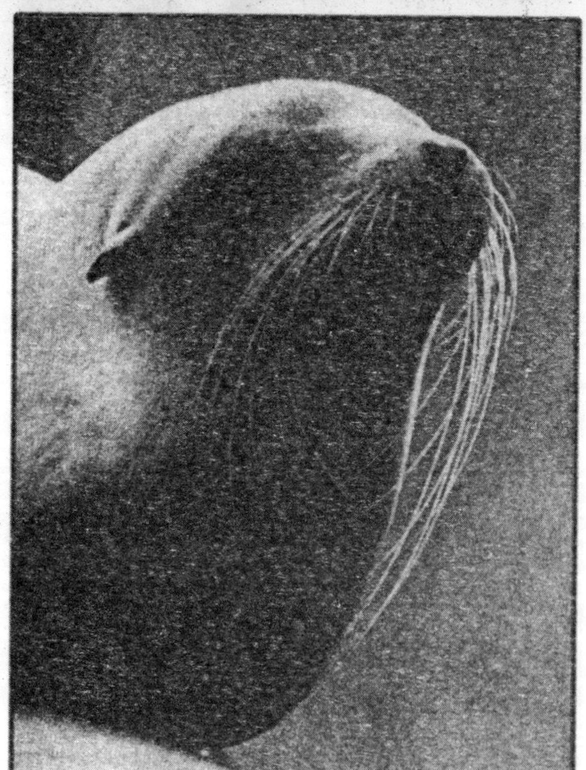

H. Bastin

SEA LION AND A GAUGE FOR AGE

The sea lion (bottom) lives for about sixteen or seventeen years Our upper photograph is of an otolith, the ear stone or small vibrating calcareous body found in the ears of fishes, by study of which their age can be determined

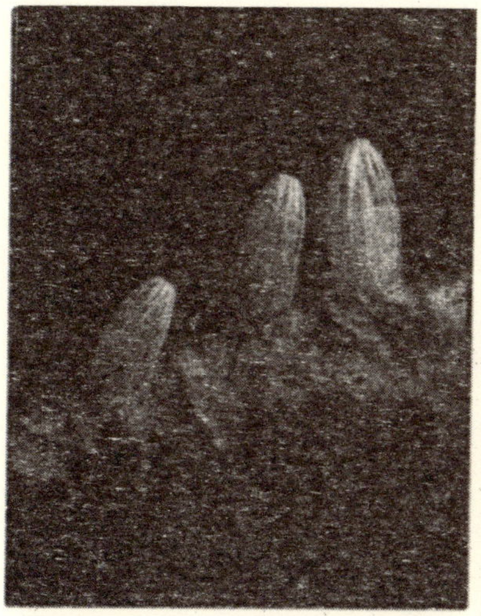

Eggs (magnified) of green-veined white

Larvae of the butterfly

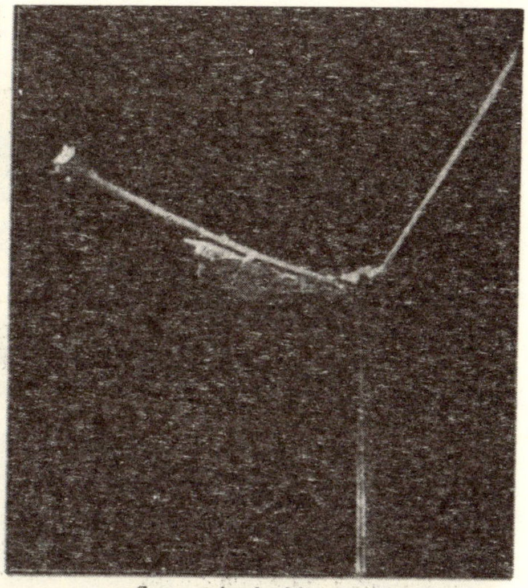

Green-veined white pupa

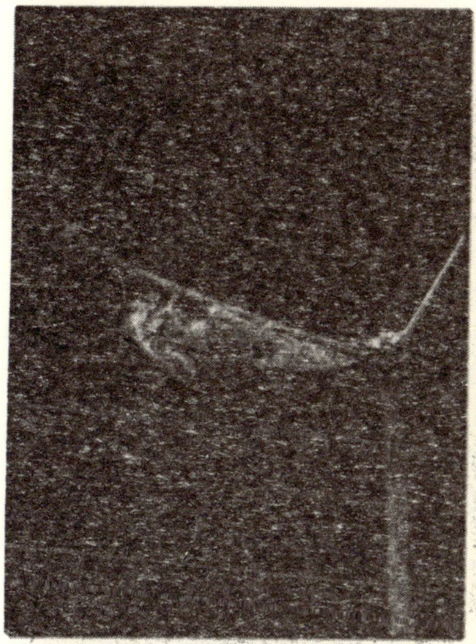

Butterfly emerges from chrysalis

Resting at the top of a stem

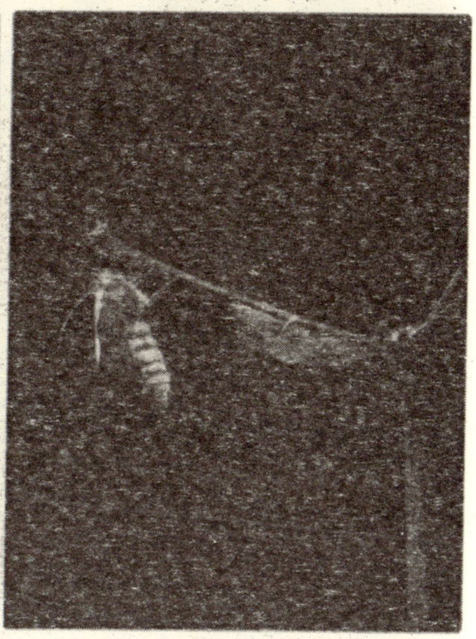

Wings beginning to unfold

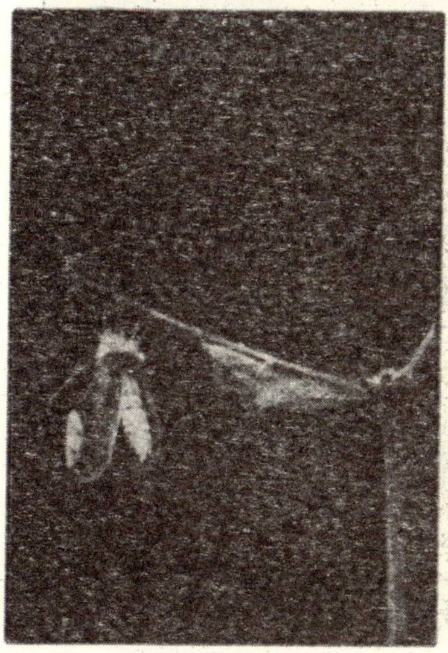

Wings go on opening

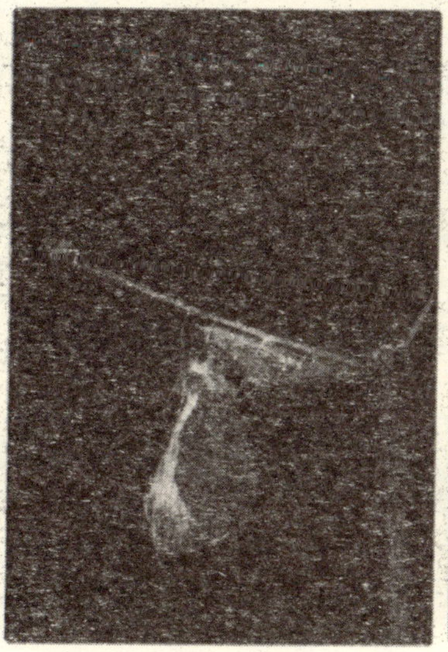

Wings fully extended

Butterfly ready for flight

A BUTTERFLY LIFE: GREEN-VEINED WHITE WHOSE LIFE-SPAN DEPENDS ON THE TIME OF BIRTH

The length of life of a green-veined white depends upon whether it is hatched from a first or second brood egg. From an egg laid in June a caterpillar appears which will become a butterfly in the same year, while from a second brood egg the caterpillar will not become mature until the following spring, remaining in the chrysalis stage through the winter. The adult lives of most butterflies can usually be measured by days, and not very many at that. Our photographs show the life-story of the green-veined white. Photos: J. J. Ward.

man it is shortened by social conditions, worry and the like. Life can be lengthened by the amelioration of these conditions and in a certain case it has been computed that such changes would increase the expectation of human life by 13 years. All human deaths are in reality tragedies, as premature and unnatural as those of the beasts of the field; whereas if life were prolonged through greater harmony between the body parts and between the living thing and its environment, its full potentialities could be attained; death would come only at its appointed time as the close of a symphony, and would be accepted just as instinctively and thankfully as we now accept sleep.

But these environmental changes are not all that influence the span of life, for longevity is a fixed thing for each living being. Professor Crew wittily remarks, "He who wishes to live long should choose long-lived ancestors." Is there any way whereby hereditary longevity may be prolonged? The answer is No eternal youth, the world would be overpopulated so that death would then be a necessity to be carried out by law or war. Indefinite reproduction and survival would be no use, and in Nature a thing of no use is discarded. But Nature has secured the survival of a sufficient number of the fittest in higher organisms by limiting longevity through restricting rejuvenescence of the cell. Natural death is ordained to come at a certain time and that time comes after the individual has contributed a sufficiency of the portions of the body to produce new individuals, and has given these offspring a good start in life.

The potential longevity of animals is rarely realized; in most animals it is cut short by enemies, hunger, cold, etc.; in

J. J. Ward

SPECIMENS OF A FAMILY WHOSE LARGEST MEMBERS LIVE THE LONGEST

Of the cuttlefish and octopus it seems to be true that the larger species live longer than the smaller ones. A giant octopus probably takes several decades to reach the end of its life, while the smaller specimens probably only survive for two or three years and the smallest only twelve months. The lower photograph is of an octopus and the upper of a sepia or cuttlefish.

Chapter CXXIX

Living Jewels of The Sea

By Henry Neal Milligan

Zoologist of the Horniman Museum

A PRAWN is not commonly regarded as a charming thing. It is opaque, and of rather a sickly colour; its rigid limbs stick out aggressively; and its dull eyes bulge and stare too much. When Charles Dickens wanted to give us a picture of the unprepossessing Major Joseph Bagstock (in "Dombey & Son"), the great humorist drew the poor Major with a complexion like a Stilton cheese, "and his eyes like a prawn's." Certainly, it is not usual to expect to find beauty in a prawn.

But this unfavourable opinion is based on experience with boiled prawns. He who has seen a living prawn knows better. Let us go to the aquarium and watch one of them, or, if possible, get one in a vessel of clear glass and hold the receptacle up to the light. The living prawn is a thing altogether different from the clod in the fishmonger's shop. It is astonishingly translucent, with brown stripes in the skin; its limbs are mobile, and in action graceful; and its alert eyes are bright. Let us take a candle after dark, and go again to see the prawn in its aquarium. If we hold the candle in the right way, between our eyes and the prawn's, we shall find that its eyes, reflecting the light, resemble two balls of coloured fire. During such a nocturnal examination it may happen that the eyes of the prawn are conspicuous from their brightness while the other parts of its body are almost invisible, and at such a time little is to be discerned except what seem to be two tiny glowing balls, moving, apparently of their own volition, through the water. Few visitors to an aquarium can see such things without expressing surprise and pleasure, and not infrequently they make apt comparisons, remarking that the prawn's eyes resemble fiery globes, or diamonds, or living jewels, or perhaps a cat's eyes, and so forth. And naturally the question then arises: are there other such surprises awaiting discovery amongst the living things of the sea? There are, indeed, very many smallish animals, unlikeable enough when seen dead, either on the beach or preserved in the jars of a museum, which are splendid creatures when alive. There are some which may fairly be compared with living jewels, whilst others resemble beautiful pieces of glasswork, or suggest objects made of porcelain. The purpose of the present article is to draw attention to some of the more interesting of such animals.

H. Shepstone

MARINE GEM MODELLED IN GLASS

Owing to the difficulty of preserving them and often because of their minute size, models are made of many brightly coloured sea creatures. Above is a glass model, many times life size, of dictiophimus. The animal is seen under the umbrella-shaped latticed structure.

THERE are, for example, certain kinds of marine creatures called Radiolarians. They belong to the lowest animal group (the Protozoa), and are mostly so small that they cannot be known properly without the aid of a microscope. They are specks of transparent jelly-like matter, with radiating strands. Many of them are very pretty, being of such bright yellow, blue, or red colours, and having such beautiful shells, that they have actually been called "gems of the ocean." It is given to very few of us to be able to see living radiolarians, but it is relatively easy to get a sight of their shells, which are often to be purchased, mounted on glass slides, ready for use with the microscope. In the absence of anything else, we can nearly always manage to see pictures, both of the animals and their shells.

Some four thousand kinds of radiolarians are known, and their shells, some of which are siliceous and others horny in composition, are of various forms. In one radiolarian the shell resembles a ball, in another a helmet, in this one it suggests a basket, in that one a ring, in another a disk, and in yet another it is simply a loose mass of "spicules," and so on. Heliosphaera has a shell which is a ball of lattice-work, whilst the shell of another

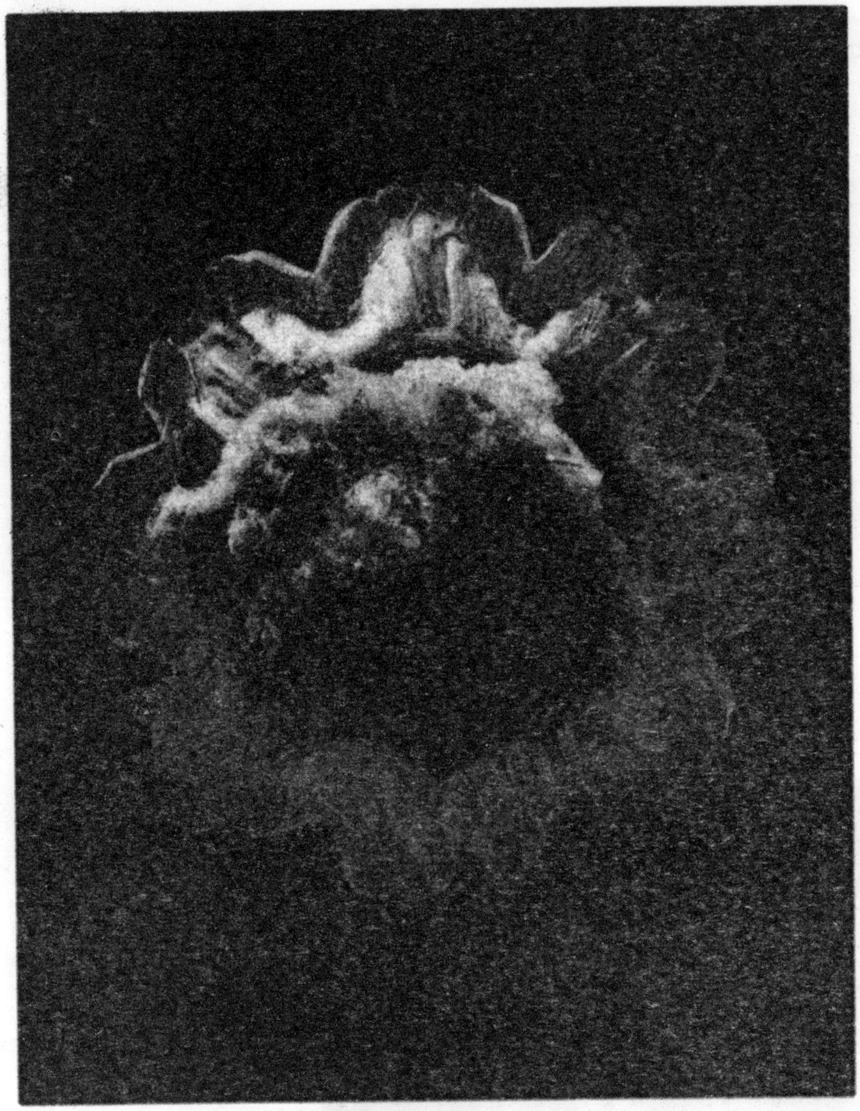

AMBER-TINTED YELLOW HAIR JELLY-FISH

Sometimes measuring three feet across, the big jelly-fish of the North Sea, called the yellow hair jelly-fish, is one of the most lovely things in the sea. The disc by which the creature swims is beautifully coloured and furnished with a curtain of tentacles. This specimen was photographed alive by F. Schensky of the Biological Institute, Heligoland.

species, called Actinomma, is composed of three lattice-work balls lying one inside the other and attached together by radiating bars. Eucyrtidium has a shell somewhat like a helmet pierced with holes. As some readers may like possibly to learn more about these interesting creatures it might be well to remark here that large-scale models of several species of radiolarians (including the three kinds last named) are on exhibition in the Coral Gallery of the Natural History Museum at South Kensington.

Amongst the Sponges there are many forms of great interest. One of them is that famous kind which has received the striking and picturesque name of Venus' flower-basket Where is the museum which does not show a Venus' flower-basket, and where is the visitor who, having seen the specimen, has failed to expatiate with enthusiasm on its exquisite beauty? But it is the skeleton of the sponge, not the complete sponge, whose beauty we see and admire. This statement may be found rather surprising, and so it should be explained that what is usually called a sponge (such as the bath-sponge) is really only the scaffolding, the skeleton, which supports the softish body of this rather lowly kind of animal, the soft enveloping parts being artificially removed before the sponge is sent into the market. It is about sponge-skeletons, then, we shall have to speak, for the sponges themselves, on the whole, are rather drab things. A bath-sponge, for instance, when alive and complete, is a blackish object, whose appearance would generally be thought to be not at all attractive. Now, one of the best examples of sponges which are not quite pleasing, but whose skeletons are very beautiful, is provided by that Venus' flower-basket with the mention of which we began our account.

This sponge is one of a number which are appropriately named Glass-Sponges, because their skeletons are composed of siliceous matter resembling glasswork. The skeleton of the Venus' flower-basket is a slightly curved tube, of a form which suggests a cornucopia, and is about a foot in length. The tube is of a gleaming silver colour, resembling in structure an extremely fine trellis-work, with platform-like projections running obliquely around it, and covered in a-top by a sieve-like plate. It suggests nothing so much as a large and very complex piece of glasswork, and, indeed, when it is looked at through the window of a museum-case, it might easily be supposed really to be made of strands of very fine spun glass. The scientific name of the genus of flower-baskets is Euplectella, the best known species, *Euplectella aspergillum*, being found off the Philippines. Semperella is another kind of glass-sponge with a beautiful skeleton. In yet another sort, the Japanese Periphragella, the skeleton forms a curved funnel from which numerous small tubes branch off. Farrea has a very beautiful skeleton of branching tubes.

Colony of polyps

Polyp colony

Portuguese man-of-war

Medusa

Group of Madrepore polyps

Medusa

SOME OF THE WONDERS OF THE SEA THAT ARE LIKE STRINGS OF PEARLS AND CLUSTERS OF GEMS

There are very many small creatures which gleam with beautiful colours when alive in their native sea although they may resemble bits of shrivelled jelly when found dead upon some beach. Preserving such organisms in the glass jars of a museum does not show us the wonderful brilliance of colouring. The colourings of polyps and of the jelly-fish seen here are cases in point. Only in life can their beauties be seen and so these specimens have been modelled in glass, science helping craftsmanship so that exact replicas are obtained. Photos by A. Ullyett.

Aphrocallistes is another splendid sort which should be mentioned. Carpenter's glass-sponge (*Pheronema*), first found in deep water off the north coast of Scotland, is goblet-shaped, with a mass of rope-like glassy fibres underneath. There are, too, many other species.

Various opinions are entertained about jelly-fishes, one of which, seemingly, is that they are little more than nasty messes occasionally to be found in a half dissolved state on the seashore. This, however, can hardly be the view of anybody who has ever sailed

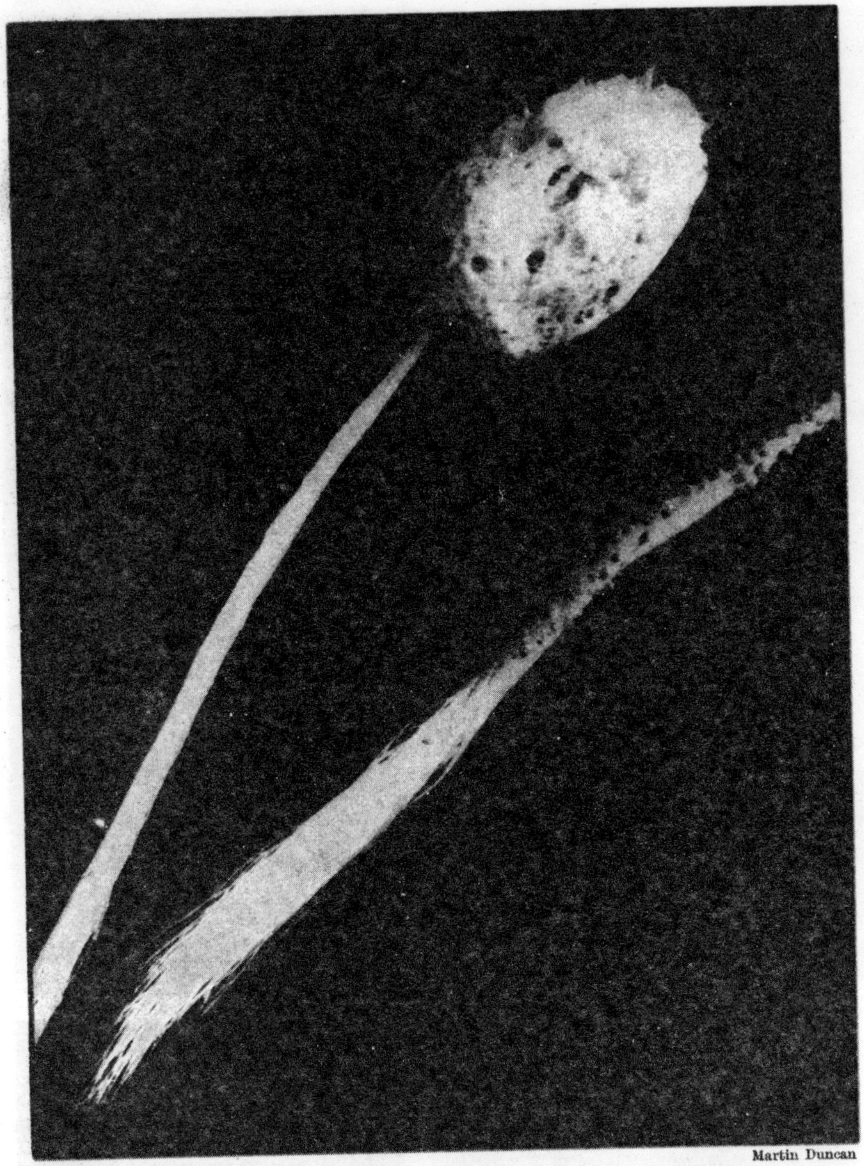

Martin Duncan

GLASS ROPE SPONGE OF JAPAN THAT SUPPORTS A STRANGE FAMILY

Among sponges there are many forms of particular beauty, but it is in their skeletons that their charm chiefly lies. The example seen here is a glass rope sponge and resembles a strand of intricately twisted glass. This is not a model that we see here but a photograph of the actual animal. Attached to it is a curious community of creatures called hydroids,

on a calm summer sea and taken a close look at them. Few sights, indeed, are so pleasing as a flock of these delicate transparent creatures gently pulsating in the blue water. One well known kind, practically world-wide in distribution and common enough in British waters during the warmer months, is that named scientifically *Aurelia aurita*. It is rather like a saucer in form and in size, with four large tentacles depending from around its mouth, which lies in the centre of its lower surface. Around the margin of its body is a fringe of little tentacles. It is composed of a glassy jelly-like substance, usually milk-blue in colour, and is very translucent, four puckered horseshoe-shaped organs of a beautiful violet hue being conspicuous near its centre. The colours of this jelly-fish, however, like the colours of other sorts of jelly-fishes, are not necessarily quite the same in every individual. Some specimens of Aurelia are rather greenish than milk-blue. The animal supports itself in the water by rhythmical contractions of the saucer-like part of its body. Occasionally a retreating tide leaves a healthy living specimen imprisoned in a sand-pool, and then, if we are fortunate enough to be present, we may take the opportunity to enjoy the sight of the full beauty of the Aurelia at our leisure.

ANOTHER sort of jelly-fish is *Pelagia noctiluca.* Its body is more like a bell than a saucer in shape. Usually it is tinged with rich rose-purple, streaked with reddish-brown, the rose-purple being deeper in hue on the tentacles. Another bell-shaped kind is *Rhizostoma pulmo*, creamy-white in colour with a blue, or sometimes purplish, edge to its bell, and yellowish organs showing through the translucent body. Its tentacles are daintily frilled and puckered, and blue and yellow in colour. It is often found in English waters, but is commoner in the Mediterranean, where it may reach as much as two feet in diameter, with a length, counting body and tentacles together, of perhaps four feet. For this exquisitely beautiful jelly-fish the author has a special affection, for he made his acquaintance with it, or rather his first acquaintance with it, when it was in a healthy living state, under peculiarly favourable conditions in that delightful aquarium belonging to the Naples Zoological Station, which stands, a conspicuous white building, in the gardens known to Neapolitans as La Villa. Rhizostoma, and other sorts of jelly-fishes, newly taken from the sea, could there be watched as they pulsated in the glass-fronted tanks.

A jelly-fish of a sort is that famous animal, commonly called the Portuguese man-of-war and scientifically named Physalia. It has a large oval air-bag with a puckered keel in its upper line and its two ends drawn out each into a point. The air-bag projects above the surface of the water, and serves the creature both as a float and a sail. From the part below the air-bag there hang, along with certain other organs, numerous sinuous tentacles, which are prey catchers. Physalia is really a more complex thing than an ordinary jelly-fish, and is usually regarded as being composed of a number of individuals which are in organic continuity, each performing some work useful to the whole "colony." One individual is the air-bag ; others are tentacles, others egg-producers, and so on. This creature is a fine sight as it floats, or drifts with the wind, at the surface of a warm sea, and many travellers have given descriptions of it. One observer explains that it shimmers with the most splendid colours, its air-bag seeming to be of molten silver, adorned with light blue, violet, and purple, the keel being marked with vivid carmine, and the tentacles are of a wonderful delicate ultramarine blue.

However, the man-of-war is a dangerous creature, for those beautiful trailing tentacles are studded with stings powerful enough to hurt or even disable a man. The kind of Physalia described above is the best-known species, common in the Mediterranean, but there are others closely related to it. Many other kinds of compound jelly-fishes are known in addition to the men-of-war, and all of them have beautiful forms or colours, or both. Physophora and Stephanomyia are two which may be named. The former is a very dainty species, from the Mediterranean, with a small air-bag at the top of a long central axis, and beneath the air-bag two rows of rowing bells, and below these again the tentacles. Some models of jelly-fishes, of the compound "colony" sort as well as of the more ordinary kinds, may be seen in the Museum at South Kensington, not far from the models of radiolarians to which we have already referred.

Like so many other smallish marine animals, the sorts just mentioned are phosphorescent. The bag of the man-of-war shines brightly at night. The Pelagia is a species noted for this peculiar property, as its name of noctiluca or night lantern suggests. It might here be mentioned that a kind of animal, called the Pyrosoma, superficially like a jelly-fish in appearance, though really of much higher rank, is

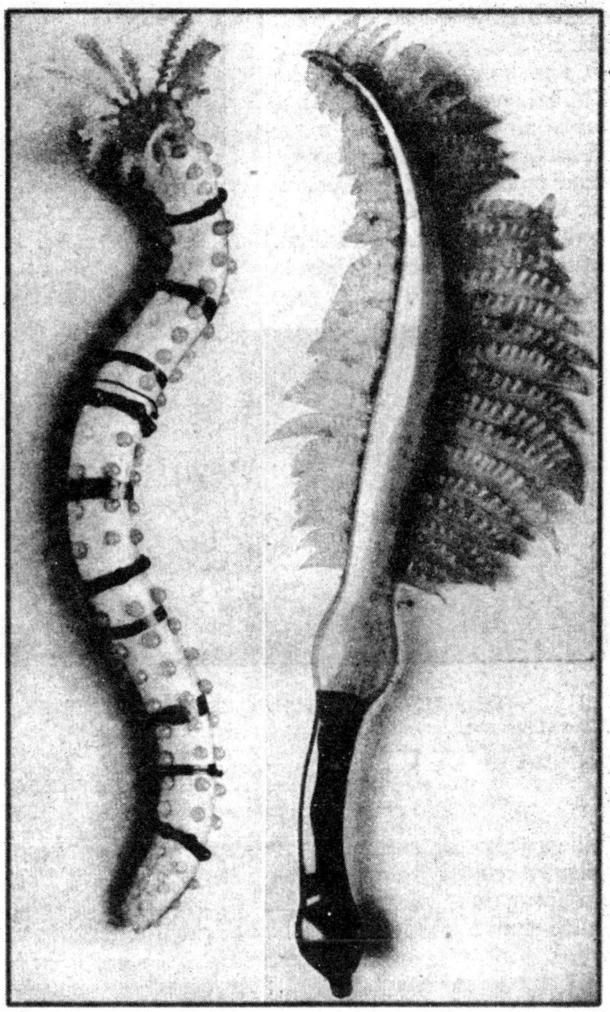

MODELS OF SEA-PEN AND SEA-WORM

Owing to its resemblance to a quill a certain family of corals common round the British coasts has received the name of sea-pen (right). Each so-called pen is really a colony of polyps. On the left we have a sea-worm.

A. Ullyett

SKIN OF A SEA-CUCUMBER

The sea-cucumbers, worm, or slug-like animals of the sea, are remarkable for having limy particles on the skin. Under a microscope these particles will be seen as little plates provided with tiny anchors for fastening the animal to its burrow in the sand.

remarkably phosphorescent. H. N. Moseley, in his interesting book on the voyage of the "Challenger," mentions that at night he wrote his name with his finger on a Pyrosoma, and presently his name came out in letters of fire.

There is a splendid animal, called the Venus' girdle (*Cestus veneris*), which is very like a jelly-fish, and, indeed, related, though not very closely related, to the jelly-fishes. It is strap-like in form, may reach a length of several feet, swims with sinuous motions of its body, and is transparent.

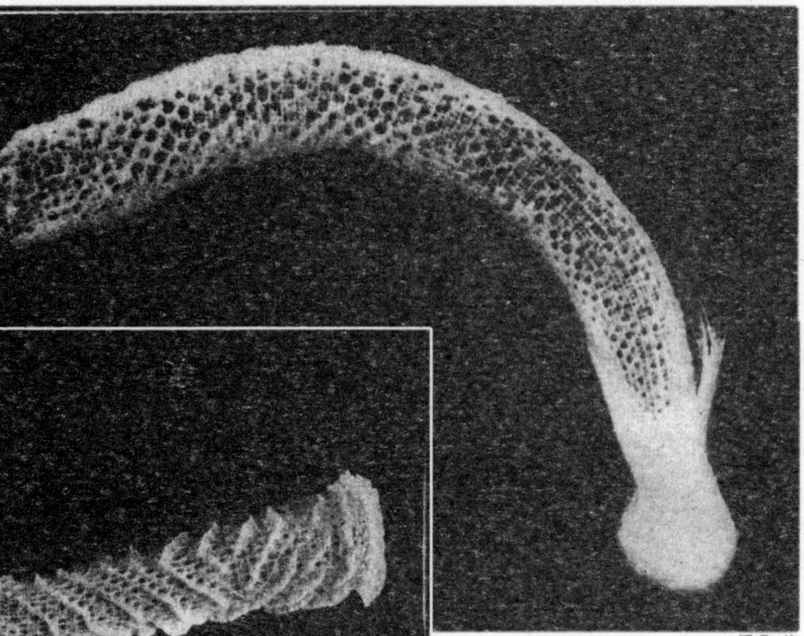

H. Bastin

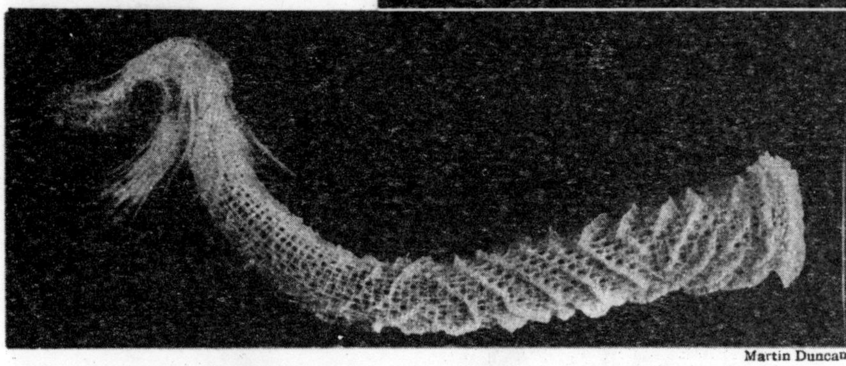

Martin Duncan

BEAUTIFUL SPONGE CALLED VENUS' FLOWER BASKET

One of the sponges outstanding for the decorative beauty of its design is the Venus' flower basket. In life this sponge is not very good to look at, but its skeleton, when properly preserved and displayed, is indeed a thing of beauty as its name suggests. The skeleton consists of a curved tube shaped like a cornucopia and made of a silicious, glass-like substance.

EVERYBODY has heard of the beautiful animals called sea-anemones. They were made the subject of a delightful book by one of the older school of naturalists, Philip Henry Gosse, and, notwithstanding that this work was published so long ago as 1860, it is still to be read with pleasure and profit by all who care for such matters, though naturally it is not altogether abreast of modern knowledge. No written description, however, could do justice to the sea-anemones, even when accompanied by such charming coloured plates as those which illustrated Gosse's book. It will, of course, be understood that sea-anemones are true animals, in spite of their name and the fact that they do in a way suggest what they have sometimes been called, namely, the "flowers of the sea." The best-known kind is the common sea-anemone (*Actinia equina*). Its body is a short column, fixed by a flat base to a rock, and it has numerous mobile tentacles in concentric rings on its upper surface or disk. Some individuals of this species are red, others green, others brown, and some in colour are so suggestive of strawberries that they are called strawberry anemones. Near the base of the outer ring of tentacles is a ring of pretty blue prominences.

Perhaps the most glorious of the British sea-anemones is the Plumose, which as a rule is pale cream in colour, with a tall column, and a curled disk on which stand the little translucent tentacles. The opelet is brownish, with long and sinuous tentacles of bright green. The gem, a smaller kind, only about an inch across the disk, is pinkish-brown with longitudinal white bands, the disk being grey, blue, and scarlet. The globehorn is still smaller, not much more than a quarter of an inch across, but is very dainty, having a red, green, and white disk.

Mention might here be made of two simple little gem-like corals, each only about half an inch in diameter of disk, which are found on the south coast of England. One, called the Devonshire cup coral, has a brown column and a chestnut and white disk, whilst the other, called the scarlet and gold coral, has a red column and bright yellow tentacles. A coral animal is essentially similar to a sea-anemone, but its basal parts are embedded in, and protected by, a limy cup of white coral.

A distant relation of the sea-anemones and corals is the creamy-white or delicate pinkish creature called dead man's fingers (*Alcyonium*). A dead specimen is not altogether an agreeable thing, for it is a soft fleshy mass of such a form and appearance as perhaps to justify its unpleasant popular name. In life, however, there may be seen, stretching from out the fleshy mass, numerous tiny little "polyps," each perhaps half an inch long, and each essentially similar in structure to a sea-anemone. The polyps are extremely dainty, being translucent and resembling creatures made of whitish glass. Allied to the dead man's fingers is the sea-pen (*Pennatula*). It suggests a fleshy feather, having a basal stem, by which it is anchored in sand, and from each side of the upper part of this stem there springs a row of plume-like appendages. Its colour is red

Chapter CXXX

Nature's Schools for Animals

By Sir William Beach Thomas

Author of "The English Year"

MOST animals live by what we often call "the light of nature." They move and feed and multiply and preserve themselves, and in some few cases play games without any sort of instruction from parent or school teacher. They do most of these things by what always used to be called instinct.

Lately men of science have split up instinct into two divisions, one of which they call tropism, the other instinct. By tropism they mean something that the animals do without being altogether conscious of what they are doing, certainly without any particular intention. They act like a sunflower which turns to the light or a creeper that circles round till it finds a support. Young eels or elvers, as soon as they arrive at our shores always swim up stream; and young spiders always climb upwards to the top of the nearest post or grass blade or bush or whatever it may be. We presume that they do not know why they do these things, though both the swimming up stream and the climbing up a post have distinct uses.

Many animals could not be taught because they never see their parents. The elvers, which are born in the Atlantic Ocean, set off westwards and never see their parents again. A very large number of insects, such as single bees, butterflies and moths, are born after their parents are dead; but the higher up the scale of life we go the more need have the young of parents' care and instruction. Insects have little groups of nerve-centres, scattered about their body, and these serve instead of brain and help them to live without any schooling. It is the higher animal such as birds or foxes that must go to school, because they have brains.

There are, however, a few exceptions. Several delightful stories have been written about "The school of the hives," describing how the young bees are instructed by their elder sisters in a variety of jobs, first inside the hive and afterwards in gathering pollen and honey from the flowers and in fetching water. The little bee was called "Maia" in a charming story written by an Austrian naturalist, and Mr. Rudyard Kipling called two of his heroines Sacherissa and Melissa. Both accounts, though written as stories and not meant to be taken quite literally, are more or less true.

AMONG ants and bees the work is divided out and is not a little complicated, and the workers seem to receive some sort of instruction in the particular work allotted to them. They seem able to inform one another of this thing and that by means of their antennae and by stirring them to imitation. The chief subject taught in their nurseries and schools is "division of labour." Sir John Lubbock, who was afterwards Lord Avebury, argued that ants were more intelligent than apes; but, even if this is truer than most of us think, they are not so open to teaching.

If we look for animal schools under the water we shall not find them among the fish, though some parent fish will defend their young with savage courage; and there is one species that teaches the young to swim for protection into the father's mouth! But we talk about "schools of porpoises." Now the porpoise is a mammal of the waters. It escapes from sharks and such enemies by its skill in swimming manoeuvres; and some of those who have watched schools of porpoises gambolling are convinced that the old porpoises teach the young the queer gambols that they indulge in, and so give them the secret of safety. Very likely it is so, but we must

F. W. Bond

PHALANGER TRAINING ITS YOUNG TO GLIDE

Here we see a short-headed phalanger with its young upon a tree stump. The animal is an expert glider, stretching out a membrane joining its fore and hind limbs. This one is teaching its young the trick, beginning with a moderate leap from a small height.

come to birds and land mammals before we can find quite obvious examples of what may be called school-teaching.

Birds are very clever animals. They have large brains and, as some professor said, could be much cleverer if they wanted to be ; and they use their brain for learning things. The first thing taught them is to be afraid, and the second not to be afraid. Here are some examples.

One of the most instructional of mothers in the kingdom of birds is the green plover. There was once a family which lived on a little island in the midst of a little stream. On the edge of the stream was a tree, and from behind it you could watch the family at school. One high, quick call meant food. Other calls of a softer, lower sort made the chicks behave in different ways, but the purpose of each was too difficult to decipher. If the watcher made any movement or tapped the tree trunk one quick and very high call uttered by the mother was immediately observed by every single bird. They all squatted down so low that they disappeared from sight. The sharpest pair of eyes could not notice that the small island held any population at all. The parent birds could tell the young to play this disappearing trick, even though they were a long way off, but the cry from a distance was different. It was more like a prolonged wail ; and so long as it lasted the young remained obediently quite still and as low as possible. A great many of the ground-nesting birds are taught the same lesson. It is wonderful to watch the little terns and oyster-catchers and plover which nest on the ground on the coast of Norfolk disappear from sight. The young birds —as the eggs—are coloured so much like the beach on which they build that you are in danger of treading on them from inability to see them. Both the biggest birds and the smallest spend a good deal of time in teaching simple lessons. The eagle and the tit are good examples that have been known and noticed for many hundred

F. W. Bond

MONKEY PARENTS THAT GIVE THEIR LITTLE ONES "LESSONS"

Simians, coming high up in the animal scale, develop slowly and have to go through a deal of schooling at their parents' hands. Anyone who has watched monkey parents, especially the mothers, will know that "spare the rod and spoil the child" is their motto all the time. Here are a Barbary ape (bottom) and a sacred baboon (top).

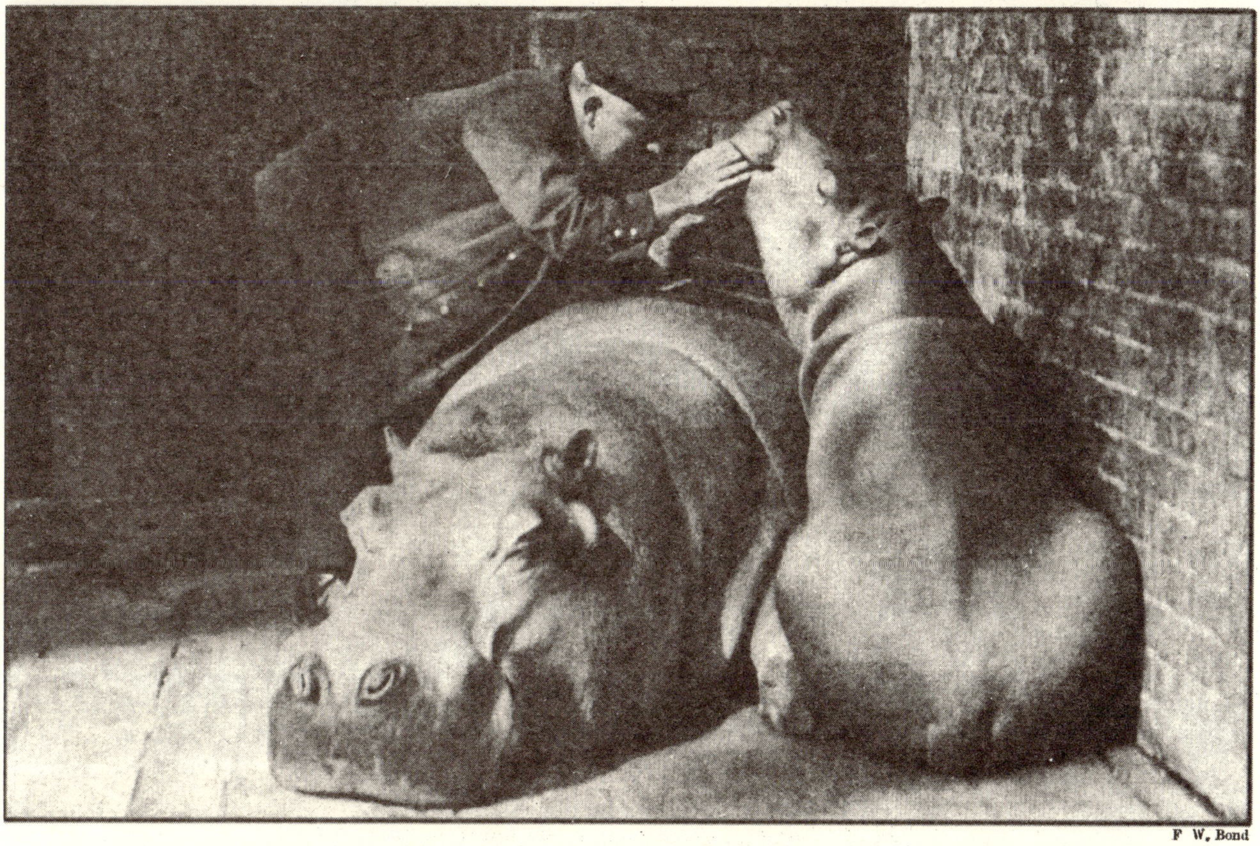

F. W. Bond

HIPPOPOTAMUS MOTHERS THAT HAVE TO GIVE THEIR LITTLE ONES SWIMMING INSTRUCTION

A hippopotamus, despite its ponderous frame, can be very active on land. But it can be positively agile in the water, diving and swimming beneath the surface or suddenly floating with only the nostrils exposed. All these things, on which life depends, have to be taught by the mother to her young, for it is not every little hippo that takes kindly to the river the first time it goes for a swimming lesson. Here we have a keeper playing with a new acquisition to a zoo and a mother hippopotamus standing guard over her little one.

F. W. Bond

KANGAROO PARENTHOOD AND A SEA-LION ADMONISHING ITS CUB

With the kangaroos, the period of training for the serious business of life does not start till the young are well on towards the stage when they can leave the marsupium or pouch in which the mother carries them. Young kangaroos are born in a very undeveloped state, unlike such mammals as deer, whose fawns can often stand a few hours after birth. In the lower photograph is a kangaroo feeding its young, while above we have a sea-lion and its cub. Sea-lion cubs have to practise swimming and landing on a surf-beaten beach, under parental tuition.

F. W. Bond

DORSAL HYRAX FROM EQUATORIAL AFRICAN FORESTS: A TREE PORCUPINE OF CANADA

As a general rule the smaller animals do not spend such a long time learning to hunt and avoid the particular dangers that will attend their life as the larger. By becoming proficient earlier, and also by producing more young at a birth the animals preyed on can keep abreast of the preying beasts in the struggle to live. Our photograph shows a dorsal hyrax and its progeny (bottom) and a Canadian tree porcupine imparting the silent but all-important lessons of feeding and concealment to its family (top).

wings effectively and flew down to the ground safely. Most young birds fly at once by the light of nature, but now and again you may see a young tit as timorous as this young eagle. It will perch on the edge of a nest while the parents lure it by all sorts of devices to make the great adventure. They too fly backwards and forwards, as if for instructional purposes, and on one occasion the mother was seen to dangle a caterpillar just out of reach.

Birds have to learn to feed themselves as well as to fly or swim. Among the best schoolmistresses are the neat little dabchicks, which are common on the Norfolk Broads. The young can swim—as can most animals—by the light of nature; but they have to learn to dive. Now a dabchick on the water teaches very much in the same way as a swallow in the air. The swallow advances by regular steps. First she feeds the young, even when

years. There is a wonderful passage in Deuteronomy which describes very accurately the teaching methods of the eagle—" as an eagle stirreth up her nest, fluttereth over her young, spreadeth abroad her wings, taketh them, beareth them on her wings—"

An observer in America said that he saw an eagle do all these things. One of the young was afraid to throw himself from the nest into the air, and no wonder, for the nest was built near the top of a high cliff. The timid youngster stood shivering on the very edge of the nest while the mother eagle flew past again and again, calling on her baby to fly. It clearly understood the orders, but could not quite pluck up courage. At last the eagle took sterner measures. She flew up, dived down at the nest and knocked the sticks away from under the eaglet which was launched into the air and began to tumble.

The mother then dived underneath it, let its feet rest for a moment on her back and then slipped away again. This time the learner managed to use its

F. W. Bond

SCHOLARS OF WOODLAND AND BURROW, YOUNG ELANDS AND BADGERS

Alert and sensitive are the eyes and ears of the mother eland (bottom) and she soon imparts her characteristics to her young. A very thorough mother, believing in a good all round training is the badger (top) and for anyone lucky enough to see it, a litter of badger cubs being put through their paces is a lesson in animal schooling indeed.

F. W. Bond

W. S. Berridge

CRESTED PORCUPINE AND A COW AND CALF OF THE VANISHING BISON OF EUROPE

Most characteristic of the porcupine is its instinct to defend itself with its quills. These quills are loosely attached to the skin and having penetrated the hide of the enemy are liable to work inwards, supplying a reminder to leave porcupines alone. This defensive method is instinctive, but the mother has to teach her young to hunt and hide (bottom). Above is one of the rare European bison and its calf. All animal teaching is concerned primarily with survival. But this calf is learning too late. Already the European bison is on the point of extinction

F. W. Bond

LEARNING THE LESSONS OF CAPTIVE LIFE IN A ZOOLOGICAL GARDEN: BACTRIAN CAMEL AND GIRAFFE

Imitation is the chief means by which young animals learn their lessons in Nature's wonderful school. Animals such as the camel and giraffe are very nervous and when young keep as close to the mother as possible. Thus all day they have, at their side, a pattern and example of what to do in this circumstance or that. If any lesson is not learnt adeptly or obedience is not instant, a bite or a kick serve to drive the lesson home. In zoological gardens, one of the first things that offspring realize from their parents is the attitude to be adopted, first of all towards the keeper and then to the members of the public. Brought up in a zoo an animal soon learns to take advantage of its position to gain the various tit-bits available.

they can fly, in the nest. Then she feeds them in the air; and a very pretty sight it is to watch the two joining beaks while on the wing. Lastly she drops food just in front of them in the air and so persuades them to catch it. In this way they learn to chase flies and midges themselves.

The dabchick teaches two lessons at the same time. She swims about in front of her brood, making little short dives for them to watch. Then she often does this with a fish in her mouth, in order, one must suppose, to induce them to follow. Often she will wound a fish and drop it, while still able to swim slowly, just in front of her children. Dabchicks and a good many other birds will carry their young on their backs, and there are some which go a step further and dive while holding on to their young, so forcing them to practise this difficult manoeuvre—and difficult it is. A quaint and quite common sight is the frantic effort of the young moorhen (not to be confused with the dabchick) to imitate its parent. It puts its head under the water but cannot make the fluffy body follow; and will thus swim along, thinking no doubt that it is diving splendidly.

F. W. Bond

PATAGONIAN CAVY: A RELATIVE OF THE GUINEA PIG

There are various species of cavy, all found in the continent of South America. Cavies are rodents and their domesticated brethren are familiar to all as guinea pigs. Above is a Patagonian cavy. In sandy parts the cavy lives in burrows; in marshy districts in thick vegetation. Lessons suitable to either state have to be learned.

Animals of many sorts carry their young about and so teach them in what used to be called in Greece "peripatetic schools": young bats cling to their parents in flight. Woodcock will carry a baby a long distance. Some diving ducks grip the chick between the beak and the neck and so dive with it. Most of the Australian animals—the marsupials—carry their young in pouches, but for most of the time the young are too little developed for learning. So do some squirrels, though the pouch is of a very different sort. The quaintest spectacle of all is a mother opossum with her tail stiffly arched over her back. Round this the several young on her back twist their tails and by the time the family have made a number of journeys the young can climb almost as well as their parents. The greatest of all the secrets of education is imitation.

It is a general rule that the bigger animals, whether birds or mammals, take longer to grow up than the smaller. The albatross and eagle, for example, are among the slowest of birds; and the more slowly they grow up the more they require teaching. Few birds have been watched more successfully than the golden eagle; and a number of observers have seen it teaching the young bird how to tear up its food. Like the swallows they first put the food into the young bird's mouth, but when they have nearly reached the flying stage they bring the rabbit, or part of a rabbit, to the nest, tear it up in full view and eat a part themselves by way of example.

In one case a young eagle was heard to cry for food though the leg of a rabbit lay on the nest. The old bird refused to feed the youngster, but coming back at its cry broke up the leg and ate most of it. The next day a whole rabbit was left and the youngster did its own tearing. It had seen how to do it; and seeing is the most permanent form of learning. Wordsworth said of the young of the chief of the animals (as we think ourselves) that it behaves

> As if his whole vocation
> Were endless imitation

and this is even truer of animals that cannot talk much and cannot read at all. We are not so very different in some ways. With some birds the parents, which spend infinite pains in feeding the young and educating the young, compel them to leave home the very moment their education is complete. The English robin is probably the most remarkable example: but many birds drive away their fully educated young. Even the domestic hen is in this list.

It is possible, though perhaps not very probable, that birds teach their young certain simple sanitary

ZEBRA MOTHER WITH HER GROWING YOUNG ONE IN A ZOO

Zebra meat is a favourite diet of lions and the utmost alertness and fleetness of foot are the conditions on which life depends in the African veldt. It is to be wondered how much of this knowledge is imparted from parent to offspring when both are safe in a zoo. If taken thence and let loose in Africa it is probable that the accumulated nervousness of generations would be too strong to be influenced much by captivity and the animals, parent and young one, would be fully alive to hitherto unencountered dangers.

precautions. Small birds, especially warblers and some finches, are very careful indeed to remove all dirt from the nest and spend a good deal of energy on this ; but at a certain stage the young learn to avoid fouling the nest, almost as if they had been taught to save their parents trouble or had learned the first lessons in hygiene.

The most notable essays in instruction most of us have seen—some in zoological gardens, some in the field of nature—are concerned with the mammals who live by hunting. They resemble in this the bigger birds of prey. The merriest and most instructive of sights is a vixen giving lessons to her cubs. She knocks them over like ninepins, bites them, forces them to struggle with her ; and will proceed in this way all round the family circle. Now and again in the riding or cleared space of a wood one is vouchsafed a view of this attractive lesson in physical drill. The vixen is careful of her cubs but she gives them a good rough-and-tumble, designed, without question, to make them hardy and active, against the time when they must forage for themselves or run to assure their own safety. The young enter into the spirit of the thing, though now and again a cub will lose its temper and

F. W. Bond

YOUNG MALAYAN TAPIR AND ITS MOTHER TEACHER: GREVY'S ZEBRA AND FOAL

Animals that are pursued seem to undergo rather less rigorous and detailed training than those that pursue. In the lower view is a Malayan tapir, to be distinguished from its Brazilian cousin by the white band around its body. The tapirs form one of the interesting links between Malaya and South America and are one of the oldest existing types of mammal. In the upper illustration a Grevy's zebra is suckling its young one. These four-legged creatures have the lesson to learn of extreme caution and quick self-effacement.

E N.A.

as to teach them the necessary arts. The practice of a family sliding down a bank and diving one after the other in a catch-as-catch-can frolic has been often described. Only a youngster most carefully trained in diving, swimming and hunting can catch fish, and the training is most thoroughly given.

It is a little surprising that games of sorts are not included in the teaching of bird or mammal parents. Quite a large number of young birds, especially wagtails and warblers, and a good many young mammals gambol and play something very like games with one another. One naturalist, who gave an admirable description of the amusements of some young warblers, remarked that most of them were played in the absence of their schoolmasters. A fox cub will play games by itself, as

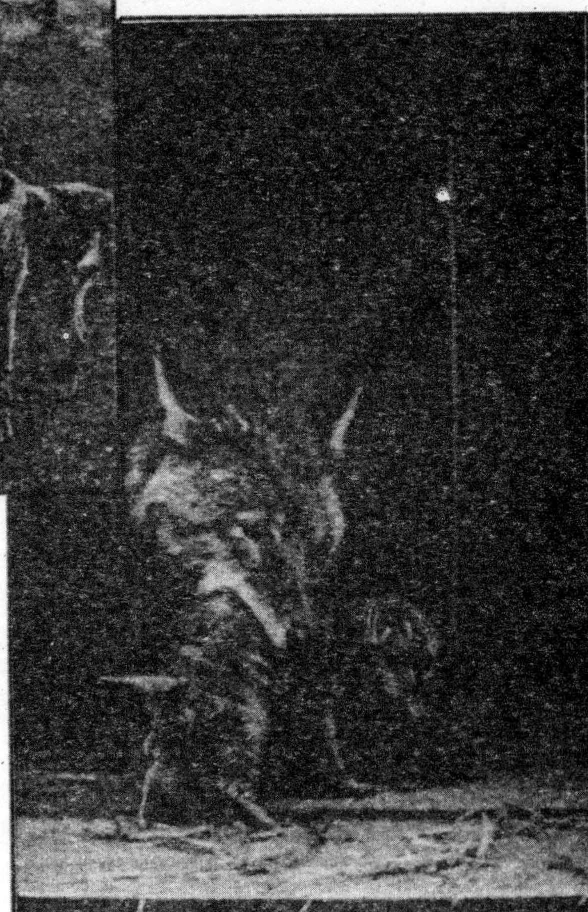

W. S. Berridge

MOTHER TRAINING FOR WOLF AND BEAR

Predatory animals put their cubs through an intensive training. Here we have a prairie wolf (bottom) attending to her cub. Above are three black bear cubs up a tree where they have fled from some dogs. They have already learnt a useful lesson.

bite back a little too hard. In just the same way young tigers and lions in the zoos delight in being instructed. Some of the keepers will take out young tigers into an open space and play a rough-and-tumble with them to the obvious delight of the cub and doubtless to the good of its health.

No one quite knows what instructive means. What is sure is that the cleverer animals do instruct. It does not much matter how far they consciously reason.

Some say that no animal more thoroughly instructs its young, especially in the art of hunting, than the lion. Parent and child go out together on a hunt and the cub crouches and races and creeps furtively in exact imitation of the bigger beast; and at last no doubt sees how to spring as well as how to follow and trail. But it can hardly excel the otter which is certainly the most thorough instructor among English animals. It has invented games, just as Colonel Campbell invented them in the War, which are designed to keep the young cheerful as well

Arthur Brook

BIRDS THAT ARE BUSY TEACHERS OF THEIR FLEDGLINGS: PHEASANT AND BUZZARD

Birds are most industrious instructors of their young. Sometimes the fledglings, on developing the flight feathers, are very unwilling to leave the nest and go flying. The age-old struggle to conquer the air and, first of all, the fear of it, has to be gone over again. All sorts of tricks are used to get over the difficulty—sometimes the parent will pitch its young one into space so that it has just got to fly whether it cares to or not. Below is a pheasant with a chick on her back. Above we have a pair of buzzards at their nest.

will dogs and cats, throwing up bits of wood or other playthings into the air. There is certainly an element of play in the vixen's lessons; but for the most part the other animals give instruction that is definitely and directly concerned with the business of life, with the acts of hunting or being hunted.

It is very difficult in watching animals at school or elsewhere to be sure what is done by mere instinct, what by the lessons of experience acting in co-operation with instinct. Birds and most insects, except ants and bees, make nests without any teaching whatever, and sing songs without any teaching. If you take a young thrush out of the nest and keep it in an aviary it will when the time comes, if you give it the chance of collecting materials, make a nest just like the parent nest, will draw the bents through mud and water and line the nest with mud. The male will also sing very much the same song as its father sang, though he was almost silent and certainly did no teaching when the young bird was

F. W. Bond

BRED TO DANGER: GNU AND BARBARY SHEEP

Generally found in open country in company with zebras the brindled gnu or wildebeest of Africa (bottom) is far better able to defend itself than any zebra. The horns are curved in the most formidable way, so as to come into play for a thrust at the end of a charge. Above is a Barbary sheep and two lambs.

under his care. The young geometric spider will make a perfect geometric nest with the same radii and the same sticky threads as its mother used in her design, though it has never had experience of such a web, much less learned to make it. Only the higher animals must go to school if they would learn the business of life. The nearer they approach to reason the more necessity is there for instruction.

What the higher, or school-going animals are, is not always easy to say. Lord Avebury, as we have seen, thought the ant was more intellectual than the ape; but in general you may decide by the size of the brain. The chief difficulty comes in comparing birds with mammals, for birds have a good brain for their size, are very bright and intelligent and can certainly learn readily. Very many of them are mimics. It is not only the parrots and minahs and starlings that can learn a sort of speech.

The hippopotamus teaches its young to swim very much as the duck, which forcibly carries its ducklings under the water; and the one animal is as clever as the other at both the teaching and the learning.

The question is: Is the next generation a little wiser than the last?

Chapter CXXXI

Shell-Life of Pond and Stream

By Edward Step

Author of "Shell Life"

WHEREVER there is a natural depression in the ground surface, or one that has been left by man after digging out clay or gravel, falling rain, surface drainage or a neighbouring marsh or spring will fill it with fresh water. Not many months after it has been converted thus into a pond, a little exploration will show us that the hollow has become tenanted already by many forms of life—vegetable as well as animal, for the former is a necessary basis for the latter. This rapid population of these isolated bodies of still water, large and small, has often occasioned surprise and speculation; but repeated observations have shown that the principal agents in the introduction of water-weeds and snails are the feet of aquatic birds.

At first, invisible spores of low green algae drop from the atmosphere, and these, germinating quickly, give off much oxygen, which makes the water habitable for air-breathers. Then a mallard, flying across from water perhaps miles away, drops in to investigate this new resort. To the webs of his feet are still clinging a few plants of duckweed, or a scrap of one of the larger pondweeds that can propagate itself by throwing out new shoots. On these there will be, almost surely, a few eggs or young of the water-snail. Insects come on the wing and deposit the eggs of their aquatic larvae; newts and frogs come afoot.

The fresh-water molluscs, like those of the land, had their origin from those of the sea; and though, thus stated, it appears to have been a violent change from salt-water to fresh-water conditions, there is every reason to believe that it was effected gradually.

We may form an idea of the transition by observing present-day molluscs of the upper sea-shore and the estuary. The limpets and several of the top-shells and winkles spend hours between the tides each day, on the rocks well out of the water which is probably the way in which the original land-snails became accustomed to a new mode of life. In a like manner, some of the fresh-water forms may have arisen from those we find in the higher rock-pools that, except at spring-tides, receive water only from the clouds. The rough winkle, for example, is in the air for a greater part of the day than it is in the water; and the long interval appears to be essential for its comfort, as though it were preparing itself for a terrestrial future.

OTHERS, we know, like the pretty fresh-water nerite, found their way inland via the estuaries, at first into brackish and then into fresh water, ascending far up the big rivers, thence into the streams. In flood-time when the streams and brooks overflow, some of the molluscs would be carried into the ponds, and left there when the surplus waters drained back into their old and proper channels once more.

H. Bastin

PRODUCING PEARLS IN PONDS

One of the so-called water mussels, *Unio tumidus*, illustrated above, produces individuals that sometimes form pearls within their shells. This particular species is found in ponds and lakes as well as in the running water of rivers.

In the change over from marine to fresh-water conditions of existence, the difficulties must have been great. In all probability only a few forms surmounted them and were able to transmit their modified organization to other generations: for the species now found in our ponds and streams represent only a few of the naturalists' "families."

The structural organization of many of the pond-snails is somewhat simpler in character than we find in the land-snails. A detailed comparison would be out of place here; but it may be pointed out that the members of certain groups have only one pair of tentacles or "horns," and these have their eyes at the base instead of at the tips of these organs. Though the individual is both male and female like the land-snails, the sexual apertures are apart, permitting union with two other snails at the same time. Like land-snails, they are air-breathers; and to permit of their

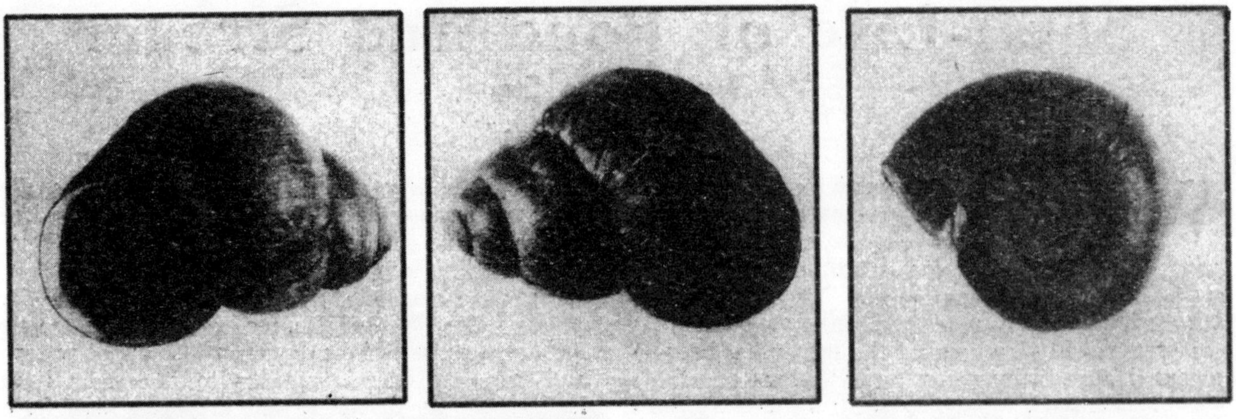

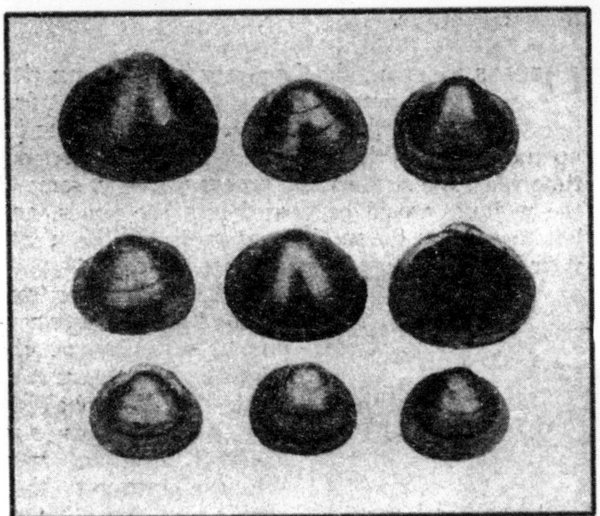

E. Step

VARIED SHELLS FORMED IN FRESH WATER

Below is a specimen of a fresh-water bivalve *Sphaerium corneum* with a handsome brown shell. Above are (left and centre) views of *Vivapora* showing the opening of the shell and the reverse side and (right) a fresh-water snail, *Planorbis cornea.*

remaining under water without drowning, a fold of the mantle serves as an air-chamber, which has to be re-charged by frequent visits to the surface of the pond

The mouth is furnished with cutting jaws, and with the hook-studded ribbon-tongue which rasps the food, as in land-snails and sea-snails. As a rule, the pond-snails are vegetarians, subsisting upon the abundant water-weeds and confervae. For this reason, in Victorian days when aquarium-keeping was a society fad, they were allowed to share a vessel with the goldfish, in order to keep down the growth of algae on the glass. They did more ; their eggs and young often enabled the starved fishes to live. For there is a curious but widespread belief that goldfish do not need food. The truth is they can fast a long time, but not indefinitely. Thus the pond-snails were useful to both fish and owner.

If we allowed a little imagination—regardless of facts—to play in this matter, we might see the little blue-rayed limpet of the olive seaweeds making its way up the river and becoming changed into the tiny fresh-water limpet of our streams. The collector of shells who knew nothing of the animals would have no hesitation in putting this next to the marine species; and even the great Linnaeus was sufficiently misled by the similarity of form to put it near the common limpet. The animal shows no affinity with the real limpets, but comes close to the snails of the pond.

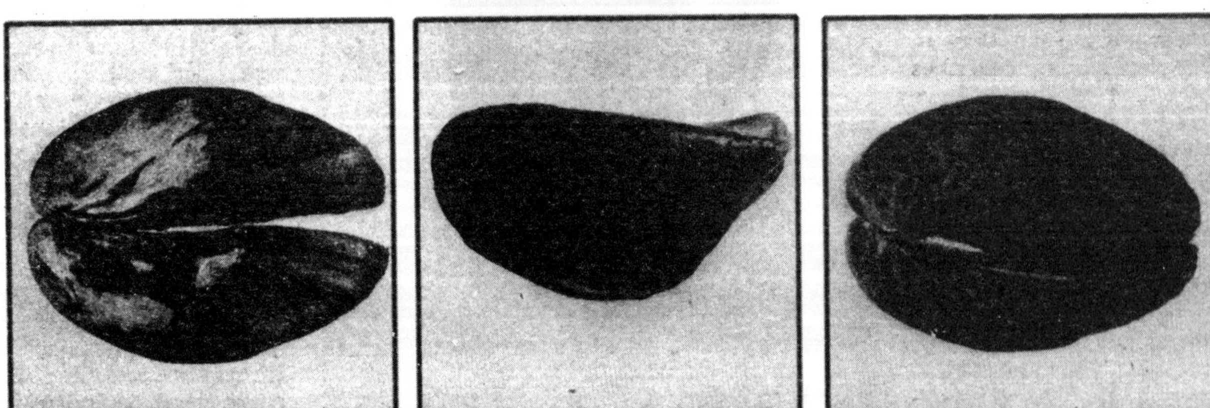

H. Bastin

HANDSOME SHELL ACCIDENTALLY INTRODUCED INTO ENGLISH RIVERS

This yellow or green-brown shell marked with bands of purple and deep brown was fortuitously introduced into England during the nineteenth century. First located in the Surrey Docks, whither it had probably journeyed upon imported timber, it has since spread into most counties by way of river and canal. Its real home is in the rivers and streams of Asia, which flow into the Aral and Caspian Seas. The photographs show (left) the shell slightly open, (centre) one valve from the side and (right) the valves closed.

Anodonta cygnea opened to show anatomy

Unio margaritifer (outside)

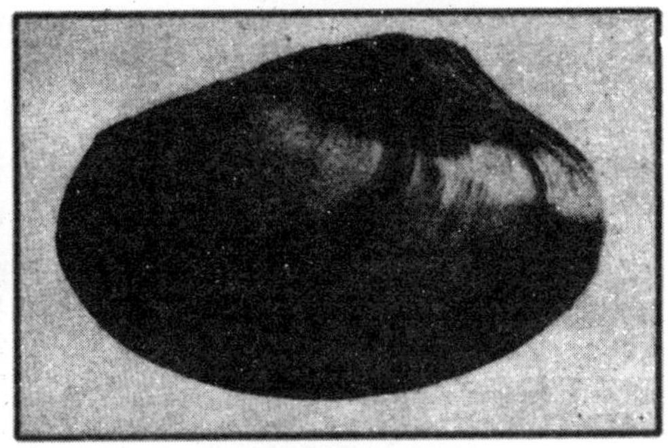

Anodonta anatina

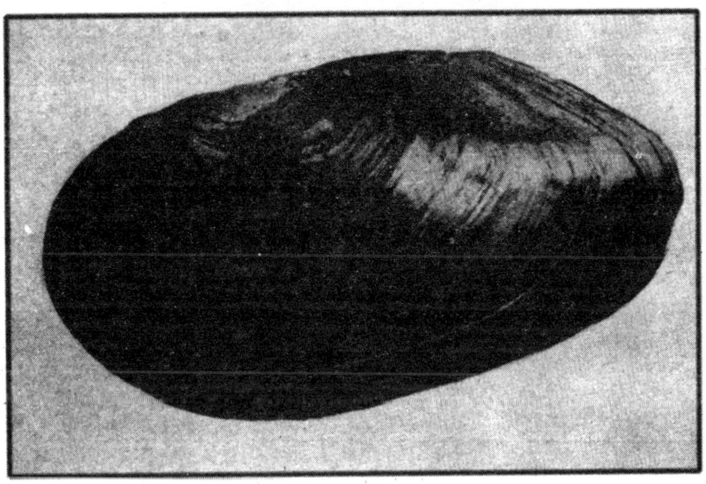

Outside of Anodonta cygnea

Unio margaritifer (inside)

FRESH-WATER MOLLUSCS FROM SLOW AND FAST RIVERS OF BRITAIN

The upper and lower photographs on the left are of the fresh-water mussel *Anodonta cygnea*. Below is the shell from the outside and above we have the valves opened to show the animal inside. It is found in slow or stagnant water, such as that of canals. It measures in some cases eight or nine inches long. *Anodonta anatina* (right centre) is a smaller member of the same family with a more glossy shell. *Unio margaritifer* (right bottom and top) is another fresh-water mussel but it lives in fast water. Photos E. Step & H. Bastin.

This fresh-water limpet is a small creature with an oval, limpet-like shell of yellow-grey tint, not more than a third of an inch long, its spire curled slightly to the rear with an inclination to the right side. This form of shell is fitted for the life it leads in swift-flowing streams, where it glides over stones at the bottom, cropping the weeds and aquatic moss (*Fontinalis*), or clustering on the rocks of a cascade.

A smaller species, known as the lake limpet, prefers the quieter life afforded by the slower rivers, canals, lakes and ponds ; but it is not of such general occurrence as its larger relation. The shell is more oblong than oval, flatter, and the slight spire turns to the left : points by which the two species may be determined readily.

But we have at least one fully verified example of the progression of marine snails from the estuaries until they become inhabitants of purely fresh water also. This is Jenkins's spire-shell, a diminutive snail less than a quarter of an inch in the height of its shell. By the middle of last century it had made its way through the brackish waters of the lower Thames

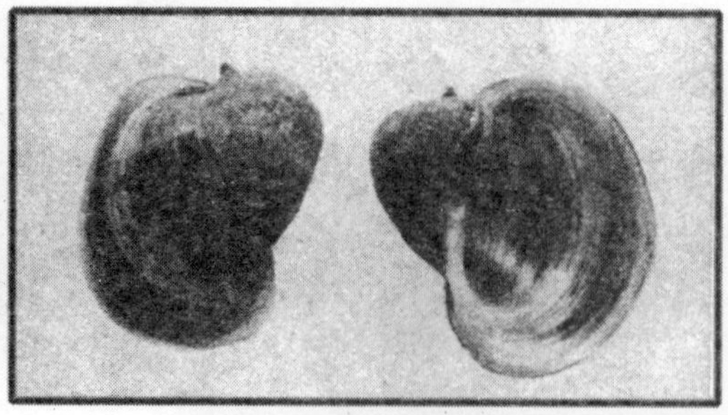

as far as Gravesend. By the nineties it had pushed up to Greenwich; to-day it may be found in the streams and rivers of the central parts of Britain; though on the Continent of Europe it still appears to be restricted to the estuaries. This interesting little mollusc belongs to the group that have four tentacles and the mouth of the shell closed by an operculum attached to the tail—the latter character causing them to be classed as Operculates. Jenkins's spire-shell is unique in the fact that no male specimen has been found so far; yet the race is kept up by the unaided efforts of the female!

The fresh-water nerite has a small but solid shell of obliquely oval shape, varying from yellow to black in its ground colour, splashed or chequered with white or purple. The half-round mouth is closed by a stony plate of the same shape. The animal is yellow, spotted with black, and its black head is extended into a snout like that of the sea-shore Tops. It is found in rivers and canals in England and Ireland.

THE largest and most striking of these snails that can retire behind closed doors is the river snail, though the door here is only of thick, horny substance. The form of the shell is that of an exaggerated periwinkle which has lost its stoniness. It is about an inch and a half high, with a blunt spire, and the ground colour is a pale dirty green over which run spirally three dull brown bands; the mouth is oval, and the door fits it with accuracy. The dark grey or brownish animal is spotted with yellow, has a broad foot and a distinct snout. The male may be known by the right tentacle being shorter than the left, and somewhat clubbed: the sexual organ is pouched in it. The female retains her eggs until they have hatched. The very young shells are hairy, and bear three spiny ridges, which are replaced later by the brown bands. It is found in the slow waters of rivers and canals of England as far north as Yorkshire; in Wales, and rarely in Ireland. The related Lister's river snail is very similar but slightly larger, with a more glossy and thinner shell, which has a sharper spire and a more circular mouth. It is found under similar conditions to those of the last-named, but only in England.

H. Bastin

FRESH-WATER SNAILS THAT ARE A BOON IN AN AQUARIUM

For those who have an aquarium the fresh-water snails of the family *Limnaea* are extremely useful. Their chief food consists of decomposing matter, both vegetable and animal, and by consuming this they help to keep the water clean. Below we see *L. stagnalis*, while above are (left) *L. peregra* and (right) *L. auricularia*.

Two other snails of flowing water and of similar type to, but much smaller than, these river snails may be mentioned: they are the common bithynia and Leach's bithynia. They are more conical in outline, with sharper spire, and the mouth is closed by a thick chalky door. The common bithynia is found in sluggish streams, ditches and ponds, but its northward distribution extends only to southern Scotland. The dark brown or blackish animal has thread-like tentacles, and its eyes are not stalked. Its eggs, united in a gelatinous band, are attached to stones and weeds. The pale brown shell is only about half an inch high, of which the body-whorl accounts for more than half, conical in general shape with an oval mouth. Leach's bithynia is not half the size of the other, and is a more local shell in parts of England and Ireland, but does not occur in Scotland. It is much thinner and paler, and the mouth is nearly round.

Three other snails of this group found in slow waters and ponds are the very small valve-shells of similar structure to the bithynias, but they wave a respiratory plume outside the shell as they glide in companies over the weeds. The common valve-shell is brownish-yellow, rather globular, with a lower spire than in bithynia, and the round mouth is closed by a thin horny door. The yellow-grey animal is almost transparent. The flat valve-shell is not only smaller and thinner, but has no raised spire, the coils taking the form of a disk. At first sight, it might be overlooked as one of the trumpet-snails (dealt with later), but the door to the mouth shows the difference at once. The valve-shell animals are hermaphrodite.

More familiar to the observant rambler are what we may call the pond-snails, of the genus Limnaea, the general form of their thin yellow or brown shells recalling that of the whelk—and we have heard the great pond-snail referred to as the fresh-water whelk, and the early naturalists so classed it. There is a large body-whorl above which the smaller whorls form a tall, slender and sharp spire; the mouth is a long oval. Large specimens are two inches high.

The yellow-grey animal has large flat tentacles with a broad base tapering to sharp tips. It is very

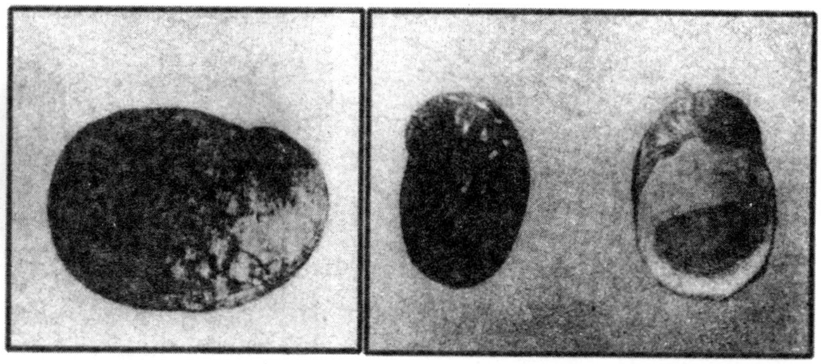

H. Bastin

SHELLS TINTED IN YELLOW, BROWN AND GREY
There is only one species of the mollusc family *Neritidae* in Britain, and its name is *Neritina fluviatalis*. Below we see it natural size and above two views which are both considerably enlarged. It attaches itself to stones on the beds of streams.

active, and does not restrict itself to vegetable food: it has been known to kill and eat young newts, and we have seen scores of them feeding upon a drowned dog; a newspaper cast upon the pond by an untidy tripper will be covered and eaten by the snails. Full-size examples of this snail will be found only in large bodies of water.

The marsh-snail, which is very like the last-named, is only half the size, with the body-whorl less expanded and the mouth, consequently, much narrower. The colour is brown. It is found in shallow pools, marshes, and often where there is no free water, among the wet vegetation of bogs. But the dwarfed marsh-snail, which looks like a half-grown and paler marsh-snail, inhabiting similar situations, is more likely to be found out of water. This amphibious habit is often very costly to the sheep-farmer, for this snail is an intermediate host for the liver-fluke which causes "rot" in sheep. When the flock is turned out to graze a marshy pasture, the snails are eaten with the grass, and the parasite makes its way to the sheep's liver.

Another member of this group is the smooth pond-snail, which is more cylindrical in the shape of its glossy shell, which has a narrower, pear-shaped mouth. It inhabits ponds and ditches, but is of only local occurrence, and more plentiful in the North of England than elsewhere. The most ubiquitous species, however, is the wandering snail, to be found in slow and stagnant waters everywhere, and getting its name from its habit of journeying through the wet grass in search for new worlds when its fecundity has caused over-population of its birthplace. It has a thin yellow or brown shell, about three-quarters of an inch high, which is nearly all body-whorl, the spire being usually quite small. The oval mouth is very large and almost as broad as the body-whorl. It is, however, a very variable species, and the proportions differ according to the water content of the ponds in which they are found. Even more extravagant in the mouth opening of the shell is the ear pond-snail, whose body-whorl is almost as wide as the height of the shell and its aperture shaped much like the human ear. Owing to the great breadth of the body-whorl in adult examples the spire looks ridiculously small. The black and white dotted brown animal is rather sluggish, and when walking carries its shell across its back. It is found in large ponds, canals and slow streams, but is quite local in its distribution.

The two species of bladder snails are more inhabitants of ditches and sluggish streams than of established ponds, though they may make a temporary visit to these. The fountain bladder-snail is the more familiar species, and its empty shell may be mistaken for one of the varieties of the wandering snail; but the material is much thinner and it will be found that the wide opening is on the reverse side of the shell.

When the dark grey animal is in possession and gliding along with jerky motion, there is no mistaking it for any other; the mantle extends far outside the shell and its finger-like lobes wrap the shell, almost covering it. The head bears a pair of very long, slender tentacles turning outwards, and between them at the base are the eyes. The moss bladder-snail has a longer, more slender shell with a narrow mouth. It is not at all covered by the mantle; and the blackish animal has much shorter tentacles. Both species resemble some of the slugs in spinning mucus threads from water-weeds to the surface-film, on which they glide up and down.

Fresh-water Shells

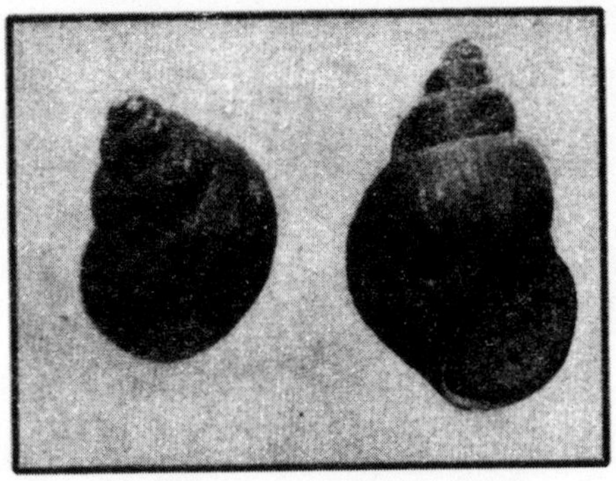

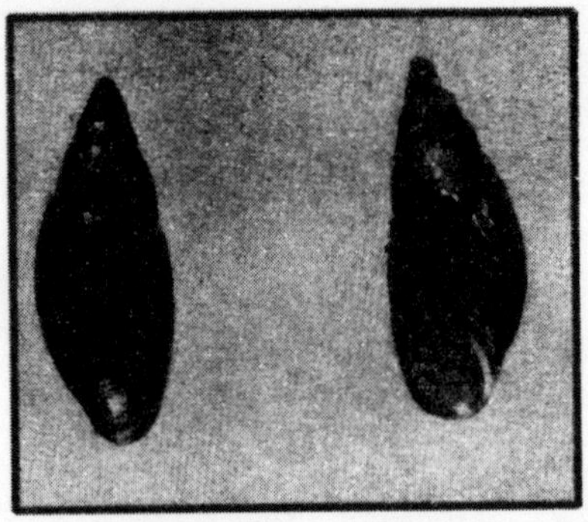

Then there are about twelve snails whose shells are coiled in one plane, with the mouth to the left side, as in the bladder-snails. They are known usually as trumpet-snails. Most of them are quite thin disks, from a quarter to less than an eighth of an inch in diameter; but one of them is nearly half an inch thick and more than an inch across. This is the ram's-horn or great trumpet-snail, which is reddish-brown or olive in colour, paler above than below; there is also a variety with a yellowish white shell. The mouth of the shell would be circular but for the bulge of the next whorl. The dark brown animal, which is very small in relation to its housing accommodation, has a short head with a pair of long, slender tentacles, with the eyes between them at the base. A lobe of the mantle on the left side acts as a gill; it has red blood. Although local, it is a widely distributed species, except that in Scotland it is found only in the south. Its habitats are ponds, streams and canals.

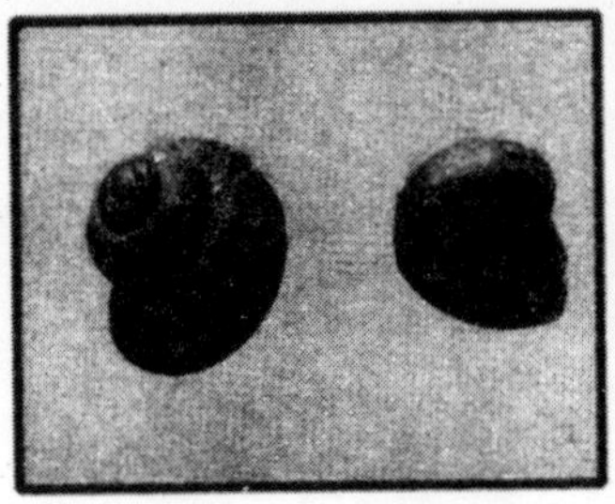

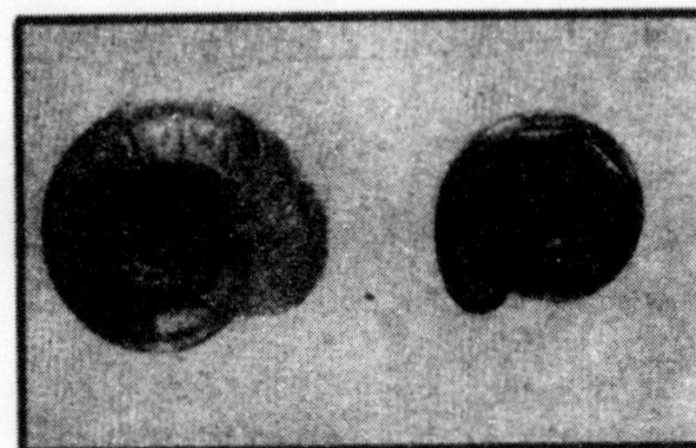

H Bastin

ENLARGED VIEWS OF LITTLE SHELLS OF DITCH AND POND

A curious feature of the little shell, which is widely distributed in Great Britain and called *Valvata piscinalis* (bottom left) is that the central spire is so flattened that the shell is almost a disk. Next to this we have (bottom right) ***Segmentaria nitida.*** Above are *Bithynia tentaculata* (left) and ***Apleiba hypnorum.***

It remains to make brief mention of a few of the bivalve molluscs that find a living in the ponds and streams. They are known as fresh-water mussels and cockles, but though they have considerable resemblance to the marine molluscs with the same popular names, it must not be assumed that the relationship is very close. The structure of bivalves has been dealt with already, in the article on sea-shells, and will apply to those of the fresh waters. By far the most striking of these British bivalves is the swan mussel, found partly buried in the mud of lakes, large ponds, canals and rivers, the finest example, occurring in two forms—which some regard as distinct species. Its dissimilarity to the edible mussel of the seashore is evident when we compare the relative positions of the " beaks " of the two animals. That of the mussel is at one end of the greatest measurement and the true length of the shell. In the swan mussel the breadth of the shell is greater than its true length, which is, of course, from the beak to the opposite margin. The thin shell is greenish yellow with concentric lines of brown, in some forms with green lines radiating from the beak; the inside, however, is white.

The animal has a large yellow foot, by the aid of which it buries itself partly in the mud. The hinder extremity of the shell is left in the open water, and through a fringed space in the mantle a current of water is drawn in. This passes over the gill-plates, and microscopic food contained in it is collected and passed on to the mouth. Large numbers will be found crowded together, average specimens measuring five or six inches, but older ones may be nine inches. The eggs—about 300,000—are retained in a pouch until they hatch in a larval stage with a temporary shell. These pass into the outgoing current of water, and their shells being furnished with hooks, they attach themselves to the fins of fishes and so get themselves carried to a distance from their birth-place, when they drop into the mud and develop permanent shells.

Three other freshwater mussels are distinct, from the lower edge of the broad shell being almost straight. One of these is the pearl mussel, for which there was formerly a sort of " fishery " in the north, a very small percentage of the old mussels containing pearls of various colours. Another species is known as the painter's mussel, owing to the fact that artists' colours were sold formerly in these shells, as artists' gold is supplied still. The third species is the river mussel, whose shell is of thicker material and the valves more inflated. The shells of all three—which are elongated ovals in shape—show an advance upon the swan mussel in having a few hinge-teeth, which the latter has not.

Another fresh-water mussel is very similar in appearance to the true mussel of the seashore, and, like it, spins a byssus as a holdfast. This is the zebra mussel, so called because its yellow-brown shell is marked with wavy lines of a darker tint. There is geological evidence that it is an ancient member of the British fauna; but in recent times it was unknown in the living state until early in the last century, when it appeared in the Thames, journeying, it is believed, on vessels from the Baltic ports.

Chapter CXXXII

Creatures that Love the Dark

By F. Martin Duncan

Librarian to the Zoological Society of London

"CREATURES that love the dark" naturally suggests to our minds the owls, the bats and the moles, who shun the honest light of day and so have gained a bad reputation. Then there are the nocturnal beasts of prey that skulk in their lairs when the sun is in the sky and steal forth under cover of darkness seeking whom they may devour. But none of these creatures, although they love darkness, lives altogether in the dark. One can never be quite certain that a beast of prey may not be wandering about in the daytime.

Owls hawk over the countryside in the full light of the moon; bats leave their hollow trees or ivy-covered towers in the twilight; and even the mole will emerge from his underground fortress in the evening or the early hours of the morning in order to drink at the nearest pool or stream.

Strange and varied are the ways of many of the creatures living in this world of ours, and truly amazing, at least to the human mind, is the extraordinary existence led by some of the lesser and little known inhabitants of the animal kingdom. Of all those who dwell in the strange places of the earth few are, perhaps, more remarkable than the "cave animals." They are veritable "children of darkness," for they pass their whole lives in a state of perpetual night; entombed in deep subterranean caverns far below the surface of the earth, where no ray of light can penetrate.

In both the Old and New Worlds, especially in the caves of Austria and in the famous caves of Kentucky, living creatures belonging to many different types of animals are found leading this strange unnatural existence. They are the descendants of those who once, ever so many years ago, lived above ground in the ordinary way in cavernous regions, and who were accidentally carried down to the world below; or, peradventure, having wandered into one of the numerous entrances that lead to these caves, lost their way in the vast, dark labyrinths into which they had incautiously strayed and so were unable to return to the light.

Most of the bold adventurers probably perished, but those who survived adapted themselves to their new environment and became the founders of the strange races of animals that inhabit the underworld to-day.

W. S. Berridge

AMERICAN BURROWING OWL

Found in both North and South America the burrowing owls are rather strange birds. They make their homes away from the sunlight down the burrow of a prairie dog or other tunnelling animal.

Naturally the majority of these cave dwellers are small creatures such as insects, spiders, and myriapods. They are mostly blind, or nearly so, their eyes in the course of generations having degenerated from disuse and the absence of the necessary light stimulus. But this is not invariably the case; insects with well-developed eyes occur in many of the caves, and these presumably are forms which have not been long incarcerated; while in certain species of beetles the females only have lost their sight.

OWING to their sojourn in the realms of darkness, where from year's end to year's end there is no variation in temperature, no night or day, no winter or summer, few enemies to contend with, and very little in the way of food, other changes and modifications in the structure and appearance of these troglodytes have, through successive generations, been gradually brought about. Absence of light has resulted in loss of pigment, consequently they are mostly white or very pale in colour. Lack of nourishment has caused a general depauperation and a diminution in size, so cave insects are as a rule considerably smaller than their relations of the outer world and often mere skeletons; while their limbs and feelers have become longer and are extremely attenuated. On the other hand, in compensation for the loss of eyesight the senses of smell and touch are in most cases remarkably acute in these cave dwellers; the slightest vibration in the air seems to affect them and put them on their guard against possible danger.

Many cave animals, in spite of their sightless condition, are surprisingly sensitive to light. The flash of a torch will send crowds of tiny beetles scurrying to hide themselves in the nearest available cracks and crevices. Indeed, from the way some of these little creatures run briskly about, exploring the ground as they seek for food, it is difficult to realize that they are totally blind—they behave, in fact, in exactly the same way as their allies that live above ground in the daylight and have eyes.

The least known cave insects are the Adelops and Anophthalmus beetles. The adelops are related to the sturdy burying-beetles (noted for their habit of interring any small animal they happen to find lying dead upon the ground). The species found in the celebrated Mammoth Cave of Kentucky is a minute, colourless insect, absolutely blind—only the rudiments of the outer eye having survived the long years spent by successive generations in perpetual darkness.

DEEP in the earth, where never a ray pierces the stygian gloom, the little adelops live and move and have their being, and reproduce their kind true to type. Blind from birth, for no trace of visual organs has been discovered in the larval form, they appear to suffer but little inconvenience from their sightless condition. They are wonderfully active and wary, instantly detect the approach of danger, and run so quickly that it is by no means easy for the explorer to capture one of these little creatures.

The Anophthalmus belong to the same family as the fierce, brilliantly coloured tiger beetles that spend their active hours running about and hunting for small defenceless insects, or other soft helpless creatures, in order to devour them. These blind Carabidae are found in the caves of Austria as well as in Kentucky, while other species, with very small eyes live under large stones, or in deep fissures in the soil in various parts of the world. The latter are very minute and extremely sluggish in their ways. But the totally blind, subterranean representatives of the family are said to be as quick and agile as the predaceous tiger beetles, and behave exactly as if they possessed eyes and were able to see in the dark.

Then there are several subterranean grasshoppers and crickets (whose progenitors, ignoring the famous proverb, " Look before you leap," once leaped too far and disappeared for good and all in the deep

J. J. Ward

LONG-EARED BAT

Discovered in its hiding-place, the hated light of day was let in upon this lover of darkness so that it might be photographed. Above we see it entering a hollow tree, where it can spend the day in its favourite gloom until dusk comes to set it free.

recesses of the earth) that drag out a strange and unnatural existence, shut out from the sun in whose rays their more fortunate relations chirp so cheerily. Some of the crickets in the smaller caves still possess eyes, although these organs can be of little use to them. They spend their time clinging to the damp walls and jump about with great alacrity when they are disturbed, waving their long feelers in the most ridiculous manner. Others are totally blind, and in the Mammoth Cave lives a weird, aberrant grasshopper having neither eyes nor wings ; a mere skeleton of an insect with extraordinarily attenuated legs, and thread-like antennae of prodigious length.

J. J. Ward

LONG-TAILED FIELD MOUSE THAT PREFERS DARK TO DAY

Disliking the glow of day the long-tailed field mouse spends the waking hours of ordinary folk asleep, only bestirring itself at twilight. In the lower photograph we see one of these little creatures starting for home after a food hunt. Above the mouse is hurrying back to rest having stayed out a little later than usual.

What all these insects feed upon is a puzzle, as no plant life, with the exception of a very few fungi, can exist in the deeper caves owing to the complete lack of light. The adelops beetles and other scavengers in the Kentucky Caves congregate in greatest numbers in places where exploring parties are in the habit of picnicking, and doubtless live fairly well upon the crumbs and fragments left by the visitors. Cave centipedes probably manage to eke out a meagre existence by feeding on decayed wood and rare fungus growths. Numbers of them have often been seen feasting on the hardened drops of tallow which had fallen on the beaten tracks of the cave from the candles carried by tourists ; but the now more general use of the electric torch has robbed these little troglodytes of one of their chief sources of sustenance.

How the blind, carnivorous beetles continue to sustain life is a mystery. It is presumed that, guided by sound and their keen sense of smell, they seek out and devour the larvae of their own, and other, species of beetles, besides killing and eating any spiders, mites, etc., that they encounter in their peregrinations. In any case their food supply must be extremely scanty, and this condition of things is probably one of the chief causes of their reduced size and general emaciation.

Several species of spiders and their long-legged relatives popularly called harvestmen have exchanged an out-of-door life for a hermit-like existence in subterranean caves, where they lurk under stones or in deep crevices. They are, for the most part, weak, diminutive creatures, more or less blind ; though certain species, living in "twilight caves," differ very little from their allies in the upper world.

Some of the most aberrant spiders found in the deeper caves still retain their ancestral habits to a certain degree. A few still spin weak, irregular webs, although this proceeding is quite useless in their changed environment ; indeed, it is an unsolved problem how these sedentary spiders live, unless they subsist upon mites and other minute creatures that may occasionally wander within their reach. Other spiders continue to weave silken cocoons round their eggs, though such a protection is no longer necessary in a situation where climatic conditions never vary. In the Mammoth Cave tiny, oval cocoons, measuring no more than the eighth of an inch across, containing from two to five eggs, are not infrequently found tucked away under large stones. They are the work of the Anthrobia, a delicate white spider, faintly tinged with pink, in which all traces of eyes have disappeared.

In the great Mammoth Cave, which covers an area some 8,000 square miles in extent, are many still, dark lakes and deep, silent pools ; while through the maze of chambers, grottoes, pits, avenues and labyrinths of which the cave is composed several streams

STRIPED OWL AND WINKING OWL: HUNTERS OF THE EVENING AND THE DIM NIGHT HOURS

To say that owls are lovers of darkness is not enough. These birds, for the most part, certainly prefer night to day for the pursuance of their activities and nearly always avoid moving about in bright sunlight if they possibly can. Yet owls will be very busy under a brilliant moon which is shedding so much light that the night cannot by any means be called dark. This preference for night time means that the creatures preyed would also be night lovers. An owl has been observed hovering at nightfall about a wheat-stack which was inhabited by rats. The colony of rodents, no doubt, fancied itself snug among the straw when dusk came, but the owl flew close to the sides of the stack, occasionally shooting out a claw and grabbing some luckless rat.

and rivers wind their way. Naturally one would not expect these subterranean waters (which bear such appropriate names as the "Dead Sea," "River Styx," "Lethe Lake," "Devil's Cooking Tub," etc.) to be highly populated, but they are by no means altogether devoid of life. White, eyeless worms wriggle about among the pebbles at the bottom of the streams, a few phantom-like fishes and minute, glassy-looking crustaceans move silently about in the dark waters. The food supply of these creatures must be scanty to the last degree, and, unless they devour one another, they must depend chiefly upon the animal and vegetable débris washed down from above; as the waters in these caves are very clear and practically free from organic matter.

All the aquatic, subterranean animals are white, or almost colourless, and more or less transparent, and nearly all are blind. The few exceptions to the rule do not, in most cases, belong to the true, old-established cave dwellers, but are casual visitors that have been carried down the "sink holes," or inlets, by which the water enters the caverns from the upper world. Curiously enough, many of the aquatic animals appear to be more closely allied to marine than to fresh-water forms, and are believed originally to have found their way underground through submarine fissures.

ONE of the most interesting of these "denizens of the deep" is the blind crayfish (*Cambarus pellucidus*) of the Mammoth streams and rivers. It is a delicate little creature, hardly two inches long, with slender legs and claws. As its name implies, it is very transparent, and although usually colourless it is occasionally a pale greyish hue.

When in its natural habitat the crayfish appears to live chiefly upon smaller species of crustacea; although it will seize anything in the way of food that comes within reach of its claws. Its cautious behaviour when, in captivity, it encounters anything unusual has been amusingly described by Professor Putman, who has kept specimens of *Cambarus pellucidus* in his aquarium.

He says, "As soon as the food is dropped into the water the blind crayfish darts backward and then extends its antennae and stands as if on the alert for danger. After a long while, sometimes from fifteen to thirty minutes, it will cautiously crawl about with its antennae extended as if using them for the purpose of detecting danger ahead. On approaching the piece of meat, and, *before touching* it, the animal gives a powerful backward jump and remains quiet for a while. It then cautiously approaches again, and sometimes will go through the performance three or four times before it concludes to touch the article, and when it does touch it, the result is another backward jump." Finally, after advancing and retiring in this manner several times, the crayfish timidly feels the morsel of food with its antennae, and when quite satisfied that the thing is not dangerous it takes it in its claws and carries it to its mouth.

The tenants of the dark waters appear to be engaged in an endless game of "blind man's buff," a grim game, in which all the players are blind, and those who are "caught" usually pay forfeit with their lives. Thus, while groping with his sensitive antennae for slender blind prawns, shrimps, and lesser crustaceans, the blind crayfish not infrequently itself falls a victim to a hungry blind fish!

The blind fish (*Amblyopsis spelaea*) haunts the River Styx of the Mammoth Cave as well as other subterranean streams east of the Mississippi. It is a small, colourless fish, never exceeding five inches in length, with sightless eyes, which are mere vestiges, completely hidden under the skin. To enable it to find its way about the fish has a large number of "touch organs" provided with delicate, highly nervous filaments, arranged in a series of transverse ridges on each side of its head.

LIKE most cave dwellers the *Amblyopsis* are very timid. They spend most of their time hidden under rocks and stones at the bottom of the water, though now and again they rise to the surface "like white aquatic ghosts" and swim about in search of food. But they are ever on the alert, and at the least unusual disturbance in the water they dart away, disappearing into the inky depths below. Some naturalists assert that these blind fishes have very accurate hearing and take alarm at the softest whisper. Others say that they are not sensitive to sound, but are immediately affected by the slightest vibration.

The *Amblyopsis* is popularly called the "big blind fish" to distinguish it from the "little blind fish," a smaller species, rejoicing in the scientific name of *Typhlichtys subterraneus*, often found in the same situation. Another interesting cave dweller is the blind fish of Cuba (*Lucifuga dentares*) that although living in fresh-water subterranean streams is closely allied to certain small fishes in the tropical Atlantic and Indian Oceans. This little fish is covered with minute scales and is provided with tactile organs, in the shape of small raised tubercles bearing sensitive hairs, with which to feel its way about in the dark.

Two famous subterranean dwellers are the cave salamanders—the Old World proteus, or olm, and the blind salamander of Texas. The "olm," to give this peculiar creature its most popular name, is found only in Carniola, Carinthia, and Dalmatia, where it lives deep down below the surface of the earth in the underground waters that flow through dark caverns and enormous stalactite grottoes, few of which have ever been thoroughly explored; and it is only at flood time, when the waters are at their greatest height, that this strange archaic animal is to be seen.

THE olm has a snake-like body about a foot long, with a long, narrow head and muzzle, the latter being abruptly truncated at the tip. The small, inadequate limbs are set widely apart and are most unsatisfactory from a locomotory point of view. But this is of little consequence to the olm, which is one of the most sluggish of creatures, and spends most of its

Fox Photos

J. T. Roberts

LITTLE OWL AT HOME AND A FIERCE "TAME" OWL

The ways of animals are very varied and a little owl is one of the more curious variations among birds. It shares the characteristics of both day and night fliers. In daylight it suffers considerably if it shows itself too much, for the small birds in the immediate vicinity of the spot where it has chosen to perch are very liable to gather together for the purpose of mobbing the owl. But at night it makes its power felt, killing roosting birds and pouncing on field mice. The upper photograph shows an owl biting its keeper's finger.

life lying motionless upon a rocky ledge, or amongst the stones at the bottom of the water. With the exception of the bright red gill-tufts on each side of its neck this salamander is perfectly white from nose to tail, but if brought up to the surface and exposed to the light it will gradually darken and ultimately turn jet-black. The eyes of the creature have degenerated and are completely hidden beneath the opaque skin covering the head, and, judging from its behaviour when kept in an aquarium, it appears to be guided towards its prey by the movements in the water, and possibly by its sense of smell.

But although the olm in its natural home in the deep places of the earth probably snaps up any small creature carried by the water within its reach, it is unlikely that it troubles to wander far in search of food; for this strange animal, apparently, can exist for years without eating anything at all—certainly specimens of the olm kept in confinement have been known to do so. But this peculiarity is not confined to the olm, as blind fish when kept in tanks will often refuse to feed, and seem to be none the worse for it.

W. S. Berridge

INDIAN SAND SNAKE, A NIGHT HUNTER

Living in open sandy places and hiding under rocks by day, the sand snakes of India come out at night in search of lizards, small mammals, and even worms. They are harmless to man and when alarmed can burrow rapidly into the sand. After a successful night's hunting they retire once more to the shelter of a boulder and sleep away the hours of daylight.

Although most salamanders are listless, secretive creatures, spending the best part of their lives concealed under stones at the bottom of the water, in holes in the damp earth (if they are terrestrial species), or buried deep in the mud, like the so-called "mud eel," the olm was for a long time believed to be the only representative of its kind leading a subterranean existence. But at the beginning of the century the boring of an artesian well 188 feet deep near San Marcos, Texas, brought to light another troglodyte salamander that, in company with several bleached and blind crustaceans and aquatic worms, was shot up from the nether regions by the sudden gush of water. *Typhlomolge rathbuni*, as the newly discovered cave dweller was named, measures from three to four-and-a-half inches in length. It is a remarkable looking little creature with a large, flat head terminating in a square mouth and a flattened tail with a fin like that of an eel. Its vividly scarlet gills stand out in striking contrast to the white skin which clothes the entire body; the eyes are completely hidden, and as it creeps along over the ground it swings its little legs in irregular circles at each step.

Like the olm, in captivity the Texas salamanders appear to be able to exist quite comfortably without food for long periods. All efforts to induce them to eat have so far failed, although they speedily adapt themselves to life in an aquarium, swim about and climb on the rocks with much activity, what time they are not hidden in some dark corner.

One would hardly expect a bird of the air to be numbered among the cave dwellers. Nevertheless in certain deep, dark caves in the coastal cliffs or mountains of South America the curious guacharo, or oil-bird, makes its home, only quitting its gloomy retreat at dusk, when it flies considerable distances in search of its food, which consists chiefly, if not entirely, of the fruit of the nectandra tree. The bird's flight is swift and noiseless, like that of the owls and the night-jar. It plucks the fruits from the tips of the slender boughs with its powerful, hooked beak without pausing in its flight, and occasionally ascends to a considerable height in the air.

Naturally this cave-loving bird is seldom seen, and when first discovered by naturalists in 1799 was believed to be confined to Venezuela; but it is now known to breed in Columbia, Ecuador, Peru, Guiana and Trinidad. It is about the size of a crow, with a similar hooked and notched beak. The general tone of its plumage is soft chocolate brown and grey, ornamented with large white spots, while on each side of its mouth are twelve long, stiff, whisker-like bristles, which no doubt are highly sensitive and help the bird to find its way about easily in its dark and dreary haunts.

Unfortunately for the oil-birds the ugly nestlings are considered a great delicacy by the native Indians—in spite of their strong odour that is said to be reminiscent of cockroaches—while the older birds, when dead, are of value for the abundance of oil they yield. At certain seasons of the year the natives enter the caves and systematically kill large numbers of

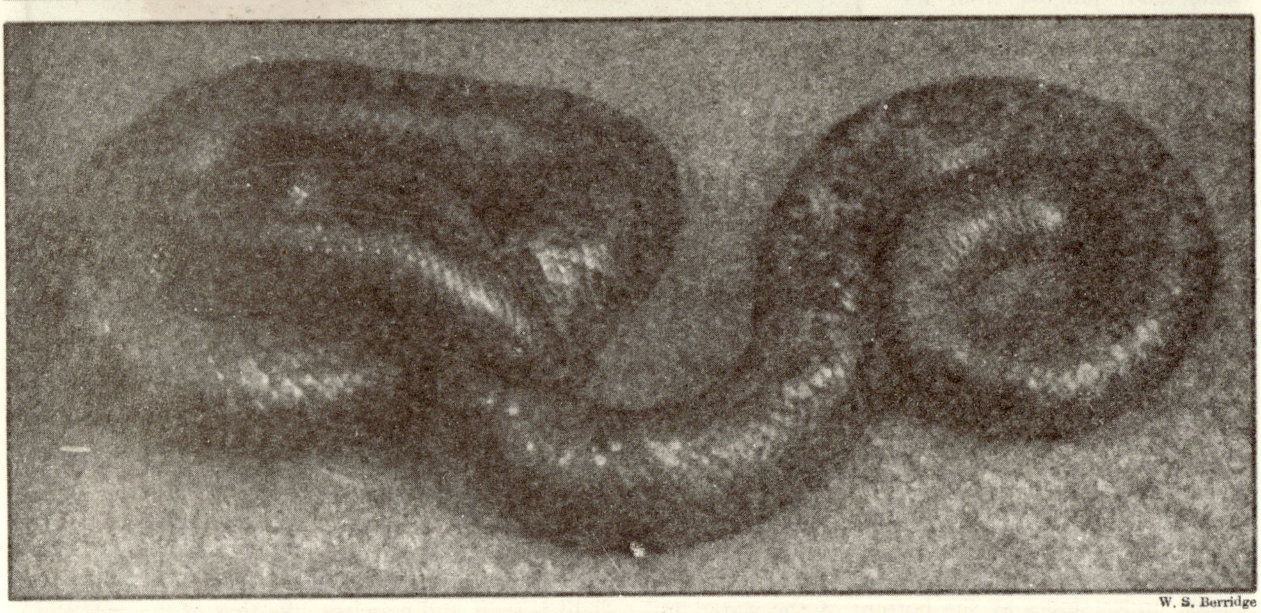

W. S. Berridge

BURROWING AND SHUNNING THE LIGHT: CALABAR AND SHIELD-TAIL SNAKES AND SCORPIONS

A number of different kinds of snake live under the ground, preferring the darkness to daylight. In the centre photograph is a burrowing calabar snake from Africa, while above is a spotted shield-tail. The shield-tails are confined to Southern India and Ceylon. They live at a depth of three feet or so beneath the surface, and seem to feed exclusively on earth worms. But like the scorpions (bottom) at any cost they avoid light. They burrow, strange to say, with their blunt tails.

W. S. Berridge

WEIRD SUBTERRANEAN LIZARD AND A BURROWING SNAKE OF AFRICA

Modified in a most interesting way for an entirely subterranean life the amphisbaena lizards of South America can progress with equal facility either forward or backward. They make narrow galleries in the soil and often take up residence in an ant's nest, feeding on the inhabitants. They also devour worms. Their eyes are hidden beneath the skin and there are no ears. It is as though these creatures had discarded everything not of immediate use in a life of darkness. Above is a burrowing snake of the Gold Coast.

E. J. Manly

H. Bastin

NIGHT FLYING HAWK MOTH AND A SALAMANDER THAT HIDES IN THE MUD

At dusk of a July day a moth, whose body is striped in red and white and black and has greyish wings, may be seen hovering in front of such flowers as those of the tobacco plant, petunia and geranium. It feeds on the wing, inserting its very long proboscis into the heart of the blossom. It continues its operations till well into the night, hiding during the bright hours of day. The upper illustration is of a salamander called the mud puppy which lives buried in the mud. It is officially known as *Siren lacertina* and comes from U.S.A.

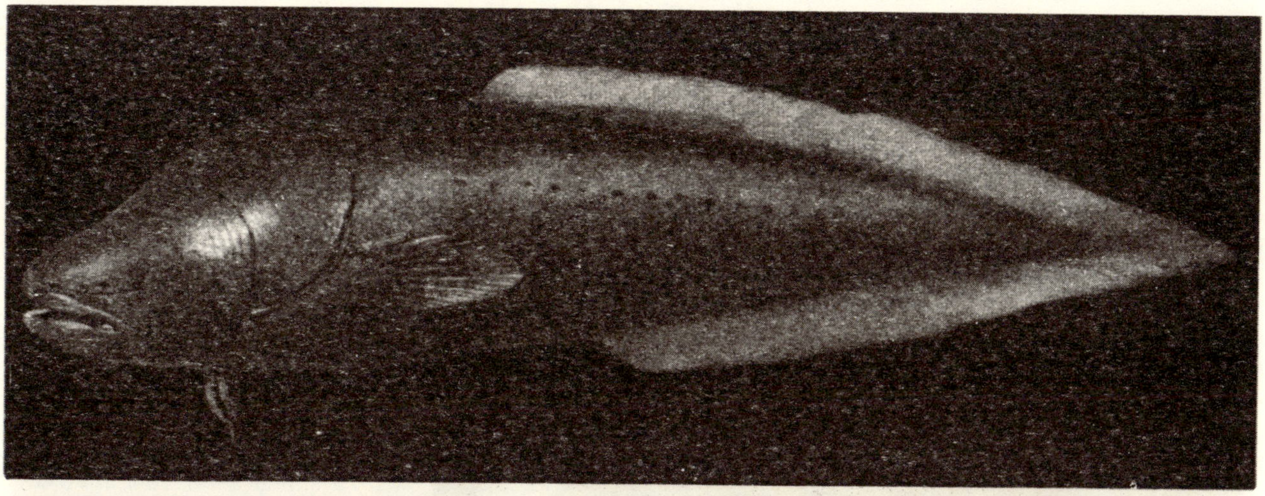

W. S. Berridge

J. J. Ward

TOAD THAT PREFERS TWILIGHT; FISH WITHOUT EYES THAT SWIM IN SUNLESS STREAMS

In the bottom photograph we find a toad coming out of its dark, cool hiding place to find a meal after the sun has gone down. Above (centre) is an amblyopsis or blind fish which is found in one of the sunless rivers of the Mammoth Cave and in some other underground rivers east of the Mississippi. It is blind and quite white but has a number of very sensitive filaments on its head which serve to guide it. The top illustration is of the Cuban blind fish. This also has sensitive organs with which to feel its way in its perpetual darkness.

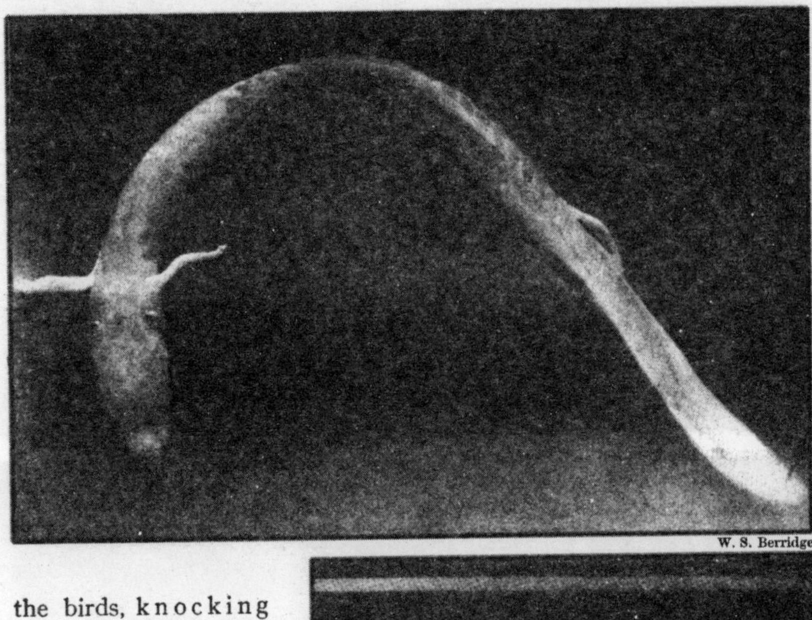
W. S. Berridge

Naturally no warm-blooded animal is found living altogether in the depths of the earth. No mammal is a cave animal in the strict sense of the word, though there are many which burrow in the earth and make their homes in caves, in rocks, or in the hillsides, while rats, of course, are ubiquitous, and penetrate into many of the great subterranean caves in all parts of the world. The fossil bones of several prehistoric mammals have been found in deep caverns, but these animals did not lead a subterranean life; they became entombed by some upheaval or subsidence in the earth.

the birds, knocking them down with long poles, and in consequence of this persecution they nest in the most inaccessible places—on ledges jutting out from the roof and in holes and crevices high up on the walls of the caverns. The nests are flat, circular masses composed of a clay-like substance and look like huge cheeses. Each one contains from two to four eggs, which are at first white, but soon become quite dull and dingy-looking.

To explore one of the breeding caves of these oil-birds is a somewhat eerie experience. The birds, startled by the flickering light of the natives' torches, circle round the intruders with loud croaks and harsh, rasping cries. The air seems filled with the rush and beat of wings, while from the brooding birds, reluctant to leave their nests, plaintive wailing cries, as of unseen spirits of the night, arise on every side high up in the gloom of the cavern.

Natural History, N.Y.

OLM OF THE DARK MYSTERIOUS CAVE RIVERS OF DALMATIA

With a snake-like body, some twelve inches long, the olm is a queer creature found only in Carniola, Carinthia and Dalmatia. It lives in rivers flowing far below the earth's surface, through grottoes and stalactite caves. Only at times of flood, when the waters are far above the normal level, is the olm ever seen. It has four feeble legs, and spends most of its time motionless at the bottom.